The Railroad-What It Is, What It Does

The Introduction to Railroading

by
John H. Armstrong

REVISED EDITION

Simmons-Boardman Publishing Corporation
1809 Capitol Avenue Omaha, NE 68102

The information presented in this book is in no way intended
to supersede or negate any rules or regulations of government
bodies, the AAR, or individual carriers. Further, it is not intended to conflict with any currently effective manufacturers
operating, application, or maintenance instructions and/or
specifications. The publisher is not responsible for any
technical errors which might appear.

First Edition, First Printing, May 1978
Second Printing, January 1979
Second Edition, First Printing, March 1982

Acknowledgement

We wish to thank the following people for their valuable technical assistance: J.A. Pinkepank, Burlington Northern Railroad Company; and W.J. Nail, Union Pacific Railroad.

We are grateful to the following companies for their help in providing illustrations used in this text:

Burlington Northern, Inc.
Pullman Standard
Union Pacific Railroad
WABCO Railway Products Group
Trailer Train Corporation

TABLE OF CONTENTS

LIST OF ILLUSTRATIONS

1

RAILROAD TECHNOLOGY-- THE TOOLS OF THE TRADE

A railroad consists of two steel rails which are held a fixed distance apart upon a roadbed. Vehicles, guided and supported by flanged steel wheels, and connected into trains, are propelled as a means of transportation.

Key Inventions and Evolutions

Within that definition there is a host of variations in forms of propulsion, details of track structure, train make-up or "consist", dominant class of traffic and so on which fall within the meaning of the term "railroad." But those are its essential features, and there are good reasons why each is important.

Arguing whether the rail, the flanged wheel or the train is the most basic invention is as futile as trying to decide which leg of a three-legged stool is most important. It is also unimportant whether the true ancestor of the railroad was grooved pavement on the island of Malta dating from the time of the Roman Empire, a medieval German mine tramway, or one of the cast-iron "plateways" operating in South Wales in the 18th century. The *system* which evolved from these beginnings, however, was the first phase of the most important transportation advance in all history, the application of heat energy from a machine to transcend the limitations of animal power. Therefore, it's worth taking a minute or two to see what's distinctive about it, as an introduction to a closer look at its principal parts as they exist today.

The Cheap, Low-Friction Guideway

The railroad concept, in the first third of the 19th century, combined three critical factors:

1. It *reduced friction* to an extent that let the heavy steam engine not only move itself across the land but have enough power left over to move a good load at an unprecedented speed.
2. It *reduced the cost of a low-friction roadway,* making it possible for the railroad to penetrate any area of the country where raw materials were found or people lived and worked.
3. It provided a *guideway,* removing the limitation of transporting everything in single vehicles. This spread the cost of motive power and crew over a practical number of loads.

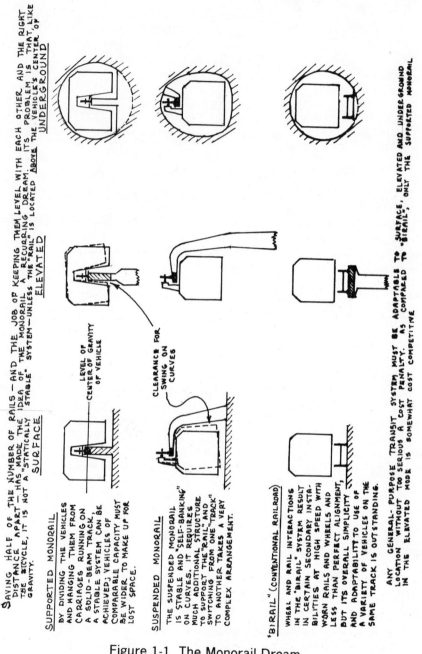

SAVING HALF OF THE NUMBER OF RAILS — AND THE JOB OF KEEPING THEM LEVEL WITH EACH OTHER AND THE RIGHT DISTANCE APART — HAS "MADE THE IDEA OF THE MONORAIL A RECURRING DREAM. ITS PROBLEM IS THAT, LIKE THE BICYCLE, IT IS NOT A "STATICALLY STABLE" SYSTEM — UNLESS THE "RAIL" IS LOCATED ABOVE THE VEHICLE'S CENTER OF GRAVITY.

<u>UNDERGROUND</u>

<u>ELEVATED</u>

<u>SURFACE</u>

LEVEL OF CENTER OF GRAVITY OF VEHICLE

CLEARANCE FOR SWING ON CURVES

SUPPORTED MONORAIL

BY DIVIDING THE VEHICLES AND HANGING THEM FROM CARRIAGES RUNNING ON A SOLID-BEAM TRACK, A STABLE SYSTEM CAN BE ACHIEVED; VEHICLES OF COMPARABLE CAPACITY MUST BE WIDER TO MAKE UP FOR LOST SPACE.

SUSPENDED MONORAIL

THE SUSPENDED MONORAIL IS STABLE AND "SELF-BANKING" ON CURVES. IT REQUIRES MUCH ADDITIONAL STRUCTURE TO SUPPORT THE "RAIL" AND SWITCHING FROM ONE "TRACK" TO ANOTHER TAKES A VERY COMPLEX ARRANGEMENT.

"BIRAIL" (CONVENTIONAL RAILROAD)

WHEEL AND RAIL INTERACTIONS IN THE "BIRAIL" SYSTEM RESULT IN CERTAIN SECONDARY INSTA- BILITIES AT HIGH SPEED WITH WORN RAILS AND WHEELS AND LESS THAN PERFECT ALIGNMENT, BUT ITS OVERALL SIMPLICITY AND ADAPTABILITY TO USE OF A VARIETY OF VEHICLES ON THE SAME TRACK IS OUTSTANDING.

ANY GENERAL-PURPOSE TRANSIT SYSTEM MUST BE ADAPTABLE TO SURFACE, ELEVATED AND UNDERGROUND LOCATION WITHOUT TOO SERIOUS A COST PENALTY. AS COMPARED TO "BIRAIL," ONLY THE SUPPORTED MONORAIL IN THE ELEVATED MODE IS SOMEWHAT COST COMPETITIVE.

Figure 1-1 The Monorail Dream

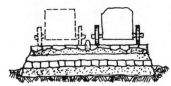

IN ROMAN TIMES, A MAJOR IMPROVEMENT IN ROLLING RESISTANCE AND A CORRESPONDING INCREASE IN LOAD CARRIED (PARTICULARLY IN BAD WEATHER) WAS ACHIEVED BY BUILDING A STONE-PAVED ROAD ON A DEEP FOUNDATION FOR HARD-WHEELED CARTS & CHARIOTS. THE PAVING HAD TO BE MORE THAN TWICE THE WIDTH OF THE VEHICLES AND WAS VERY LABORIOUS & EXPENSIVE TO CONSTRUCT.

SOME MEDIEVAL MINERS HAD TO PUSH HEAVY LOADS THROUGH TUNNELS — EXTRA WIDTH WAS COSTLY, SO CARTS GUIDED BY PULLEY-LIKE WHEELS RAN ON A TRACK OF WOOD STRINGERS NAILED TO CROSSMEMBERS — THUS "PAVING" ONLY THE ESSENTIAL STRIPS OF THE ROADWAY. TRACKS LATER WERE EXTENDED OUTSIDE THE MINES.

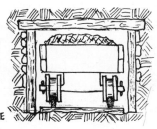

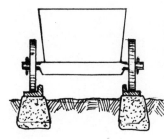

EIGHTEENTH-CENTURY SOUTH WALES TRAMWAYS USED A SINGLE FLANGE ON THE "PLATEWAY"— SHORT SEGMENTS OF CAST IRON, USUALLY MOUNTED ON STONE BLOCKS.— TO KEEP PLAIN-WHEELED CARTS ON THE TRACK. SOME OF THESE PLATEWAYS WERE 20 MILES LONG; TRACKWORKERS IN BRITAIN ARE STILL CALLED "PLATELAYERS". A MAJOR PROBLEM WAS KEEPING THE TRACK CLEAR OF DEBRIS.

SINGLE-FLANGED IRON WHEELS RUNNING ON THE HEAD OF "I" OR "T"-SECTION IRON RAILS HELD IN GAUGE BY WOODEN CROSSTIES RAPIDLY PROVED TO BE A MORE SATISFACTORY SYSTEM — SELF-CLEANING, READILY CROSSED BY ROADWAYS, RELATIVELY INEXPENSIVE, CUSHIONED SLIGHTLY BY THE WOOD'S FLEXIBILITY.

IT WAS SOON FOUND THAT MOUNTING THE WHEELS RIGIDLY ON A ROTATING AXLE KEPT THEM IN GAUGE BETTER, MADE EFFICIENT BEARINGS AND LUBRICATION POSSIBLE.

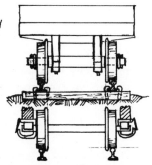

Figure 1-2 Evolution of the Flanged Wheel and Rim

How Many Rails?

As in the development of any system depending on and combining several separate inventions, there were many basic decisions to be made. There were many false starts, misconceptions and side issues that were resolved by time and experience. Even such a fundamental question as the "right" number of rails re-emerges periodically, to the extent that some recent studies of alternatives for urban transportation have used the term "bi-rail" to disguise the fact that re-inventing the railroad turned out to be the best technical answer to the requirements. Fig. 1-1 discusses the reasons why the monorail remains a dream, useful only under extremely limited circumstances.

Where Does the Flange Belong?

Fig. 1-2 shows: a) the way the *rail*road made reduced friction affordable, and b) how the best way to keep the cars on the rails evolved. Almost from the first flanged metal wheels, one inch became the "standard" flange height, and no reason for any substantial change has ever been found. Fig. 1-3 shows why the flange was found to belong on the inner edge of the wheel tread.

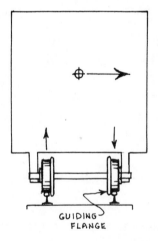

FLANGES ON OUTSIDE OF TREAD

FLANGES ON INSIDE OF TREAD

LATERAL DISTURBING FORCE

GUIDING FLANGE

GUIDING FLANGE

DISTURBING FORCE TENDS
TO LIFT GUIDING FLANGE FROM
RAIL

DISTURBING FORCE TENDS
TO HOLD GUIDING FLANGE DOWN
ON RAIL

Figure 1-3 Where Should the Flange Be?

APART FROM COST SAVINGS FROM HAVING ONE OPERATOR CONTROLLING A LARGER AMOUNT OF TRANSPORTATION CAPACITY, HOOKING VEHICLES TOGETHER INTO TRAINS GREATLY INCREASES THE CAPABILITY OF A SINGLE "LANE" OF SPACE TO HANDLE, SAFELY, LARGE AMOUNTS OF TRAFFIC AT ANY REQUIRED MAXIMUM SPEED.

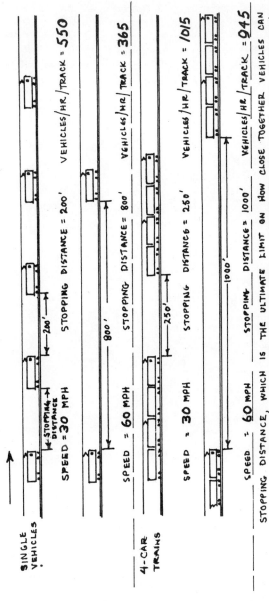

STOPPING DISTANCE, WHICH IS THE ULTIMATE LIMIT ON HOW CLOSE TOGETHER VEHICLES CAN SAFELY TRAVEL, VARIES WITH THE SQUARE OF THE SPEED; INCREASING THE SPEED WITH VEHICLES TRAVELING SINGLY REDUCES THE NUMBER OF VEHICLES WHICH ONE TRACK CAN CARRY PER HOUR. EVEN 4-CAR TRAINS MORE THAN DOUBLE THE CAPACITY OF A SINGLE TRACK TO HANDLE TRAFFIC AT 60 MPH, ALLOWING FOR SOMEWHAT LONGER BRAKING DISTANCE WITH A TRAIN (LOWER WIND RESISTANCE, SOME DELAY IN BRAKING ACTION).

FOR FREIGHT-LENGTH TRAINS, CAPACITY IS MUCH GREATER, EVEN THOUGH THE LENGTH OF THE TRAIN ITSELF BECOMES THE LARGER PART OF THE "TRACK OCCUPANCY TIME". 1000' TRAINS OF 80 CARS EACH, WITH 3000 FT. STOPPING DISTANCE, GIVE A TRAFFIC CAPACITY OF 2535 CARS/HR AT 60 M.P.H.

Figure 1-4 Why Trains?

Why Trains?

Once there is a guideway, it becomes feasible to hook cars together into trains, with important savings in cost. One-car trains, as exemplifed by the electric interurban railway and the street car, proved relatively short-lived variations of the theme, with the latter making its comeback (under the alias "LRV" or Light Rail Vehicle) in the form of 2- or 3-car units. Fig. 1-4 shows why combining the vehicles into trains is important in increasing the *capacity* of a narrow transportation corridor, particularly important in providing needed mobility without wasting vast areas of real estate.

2

THE ROUTE SYSTEM-- HOW RAILROAD NETWORKS EVOLVED

In the early part of the 19th century, the big question was whether or not the railroad idea would work. Cast iron rails sometimes broke under the first impact from the weight of the new steam locomotive. Boilers blew up, and huge costs were predicted for tunnels, in the belief that trains could climb only the gentlest of grades.

However, within a few years, tough wrought iron rails became available. The timber crosstie proved not only cheaper than the massive stone blocks originally planned as "permanent" supports for the rails, but did a far better job of keeping the rails the right distance apart. Experience proved that useful loads could be hauled over mountain ranges on grades of more than 100 feet of rise per mile of track. The "pilot truck" guided the locomotive around sharp curves, and workable designs were developed for the many auxiliary devices. Track switches, headlights and whistles were designed to make the railroad a complete commercial enterprise.

It became clear that a railroad could be built to go just about anywhere. With this wide-open choice, the real question became one of economics; railroads should be built where there was, or reasonably could be expected to be, enough demand for transportation to support the line and pay back the cost of building it. Prosperity and people usually *followed* rather than preceded the coming of the railroad, so faith and luck were important, too.

The North American Rail Network

In practice, developing a logical system of railroad trackage wasn't straightforward. Useful transportation is a matter of moving something from where it is produced, to where it is needed. Population affects both ends of the trip.

The first railroads had stictly limited objectives; they headed inland from established port cities to sources of raw materials and agricultural products. Unless there was water power or a good harbor to determine its location, a small village had little chance to grow. The Baltimore and Ohio Railroad changed this concept. They proposed to connect the ocean with the natural waterway of the Ohio river and offset New York's water-level Erie Canal. The B & O demonstrated that goods could now be carried across the mountains at a competitive price. And all year too!

The railroad network then began to grow on its own. Once a line was in operation, population grew more rapidly along it than elsewhere. Chicago became *the* metropolis of the Midwest because it was a major railroad junction. A new generation of cities such as Atlanta appeared, communities whose location was due solely to the fact that railroad lines crossed or terminated at that particular point. Other towns with equally good geographic locations withered on the vine or perhaps had to move a few miles, if main-line rail routes passed them by for some reason or other.

On the basis of purely technical reasons, locating a railroad line so that it can provide useful transportation at minimum cost is a complicated business, as we shall see. That's not the end of it, though. Competitive, political and even such emotional factors as civic pride, sheer optimism and especially greed have often completely overwhelmed engineering considerations. Parallel lines were built which really were not needed. In other cases, the anticipated growth of the area served never materialized or the mineral wealth proved to be more limited than expected. Conversely, some lines that were shaky affairs at the start served to keep unpromising areas in business until new developments or discoveries let them blossom into prosperous, stable communities.

Traffic Density

With all these historical factors and uncertainties; plus the effects of governmental regulation, the rail system of the North American continent evolved into and remains as a largely interconnected network which can move goods in quantity from anywhere to anywhere via a reasonably direct route or routes.

Table 1 provides overall figures on the mileage of line and track in the United States, Canada and Mexico at the present time and an indication of the general classes of ownership represented by the organizations operating segments of this network. Because of the common "standard" gauge, the numerous connections across international borders, and standardized agreements on such essentials as equipment design and maintenance, rentals, and customs administration the railroads of the three nations function as a unified system.

While there has been a continuing trend to merge private railroad companies into larger and larger systems and the bulk of the network and its traffic is accounted for by a smaller and smaller number of corporations, there is also a continuing trend toward the establishment of short-line railroad companies operating light-density branches connecting with main lines. Under various forms of private or public ownership and support, these lines serve communities and industries which, for various reasons, cannot provide traffic which can be handled profitably under the operating conditions to which mainline railroads forming the basic network are committed. Thus, while the total number of railroad companies is far smaller than it once was (there were over 1300 operating in 1910), it has remained relatively stable in recent years.

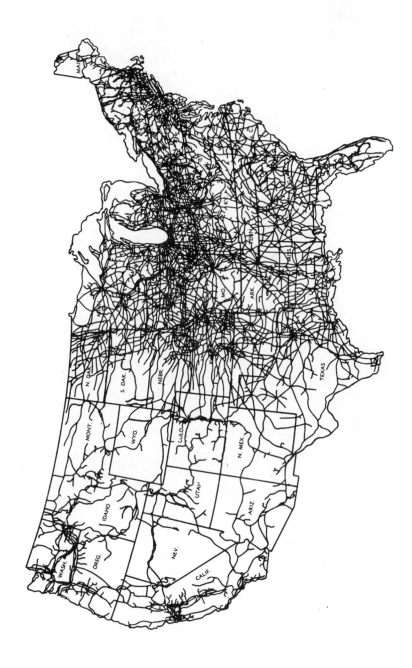

Figure 2-1 Network of Rail Lines in the United States

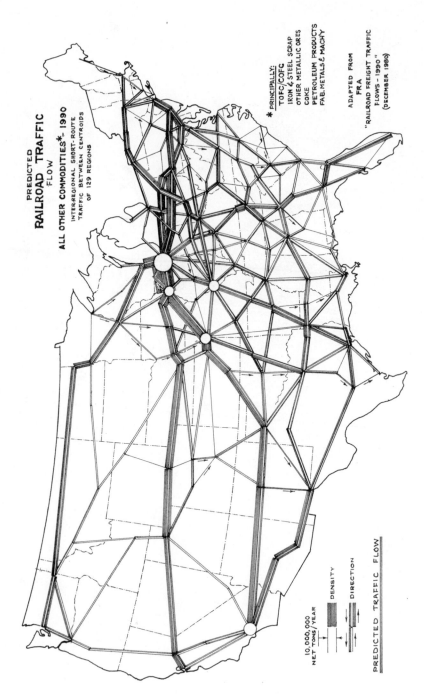

Figure 2-2 Railroad Traffic Flow — All Other Commodities

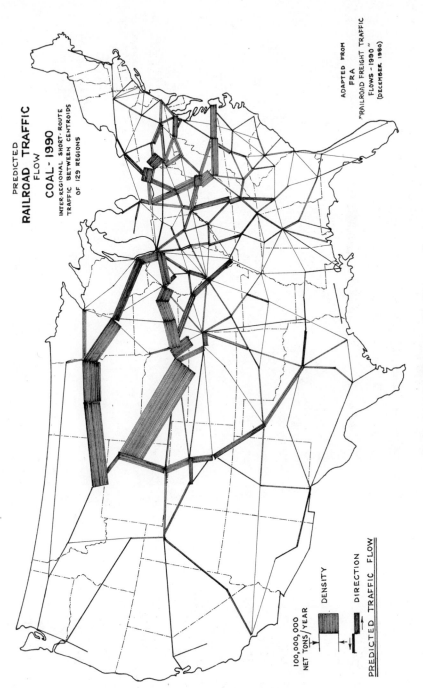

Figure 2-3 Railroad Traffic Flow — Coal

TABLE I
THE NORTH AMERICAN RAIL NETWORK
(1976—FRA AND OTHER ESTIMATES)

	CANADA	MEXICO	UNITED STATES	TOTAL
MILES OF LINE				
"FIRST-TRACK" ONLY, EXCLUDING RAPID-TRANSIT, SWITCHING AND TERMINAL COMPANIES, ETC. TRACK OVER WHICH MORE THAN ONE COMPANY OPERATES COUNTED ONLY ONCE. COMMON-CARRIER ONLY.				
STANDARD GAUGE (4' 8½" OR 1435 MM)	45,100	11,950	193,500	250,550
NARROW GAUGE (3' 6" OR 1067 MM)	725	—	—	725
(3' 0" OR 914 MM)	100	450	10	560
TOTAL	49,925	12,400	193,510	251,835
MILES OF TRACK				
INCLUDING SECOND, THIRD AND FOURTH TRACKS; SWITCHING AND TERMINAL COMPANIES, SIDINGS AND YARD TRACKS OPERATED BY COMMON-CARRIER R.R. COMPANIES.				
TOTAL	64,000	15,100	311,500	390,600
OWNERSHIP - MILES OF LINE				
PRIVATE COMPANIES	18,595	—	191,880	
NATIONAL (GOV'T CORPORATIONS)	24,550	15,100	1,250	
PROVINCIAL, STATE, MUNICIPAL	1,860	—	380	
COMBINATION	920	—	—	
NO. OF COMPANIES				
TOTAL	22	10	520	

Fig. 2-1 shows the United States network of rail lines operating in the 1970's time frame, with equal line width whether a particular route is an *A Mainline* (under a categorization undertaken at the direction of Congress in the early 1970's, a line carrying at least 20,000,000 gross tons per year), a *B Mainline* in the 5,000,000 to 20,000,000 gross ton range, an *A branchline* carrying 1,000,000 to 5,000,000 tons, or a *light-traffic* line (branch) which doesn't reach the 1,000,000-ton mark (an average of 28 cars in each direction each business day). On the average in the United States, gross ton mileage per year per mile of line amounts to about 8,000,000.

To give a better picture of the distribution of traffic, Figs. 2-2 and 2-3 show the predicted density of rail traffic in 1990 for two commodity groups:

All Other Commodities, which includes intermodal "piggyback" trailer/container on flat car (TOFC/COFC) traffic of increasing importance, is typical of the general merchandise freight traffic which is a basic part of the traffic carried by main lines throughout the country and reflects to a considerable degree the location of major manufacturing and processing industries and the population concentrations that support or patronize them.

Coal, the largest single commodity hauled by rail, reflecting traffic between producing areas and the three major consumers — electric power generating plants, metallurgical industries, and ports handling coal shipments for overseas consumption.

Class I Railroads

Railroad *companies* are classified by the Interstate Commerce Commission (U.S.) on the basis of gross revenue; since 1978, Class I status has required $50,000,000 per year or above (up from $10,000,000 previously), reducing the number of such railroads to about 40.

Branch Lines

Light-traffic lines make up over a quarter of the routes in the United States but handle less than one percent of the ton-miles. The extent to which they are a cost burden on the system is extremely difficult to determine, since traffic originating or terminating on these lines contributes to the profitability of the main-line trains in which it may eventually travel. Communities served by branch lines often have a high degree of importance to the industrial life of an area and a correspondingly high degree of political visibility.

Consolidation

The greatest amount of railroad track in the United States was reached in 1916. Since that time, although freight ton-miles have more than doubled, total miles of line have decreased about 24 percent. This was accomplished by consolidation of traffic and the abandonment of parallel and branch lines. Much additional trackage has been downgraded from through-line to secondary status. Since the railroad only works at full efficiency as a "wholesale" transportation machine, this concentration of traffic has played a major part in keeping the system as a whole in business. Deciding where to locate a new line or how to handle traffic over the existing network with maximum overall efficiency is now a matter for the most elaborate forms of computerized "operations research analysis" and completely beyond the scope of this text. Nevertheless, looking at just one piece of this puzzle with real numbers conveys how the railroad operates to use (and conserve) energy to move the largest part (about 38%) of the nation's intercity freight traffic.

A Look at a Single Railroad System

As an example, we will use the "East-West Railroad," a simplified, make-believe system typical of any fairly large line which has been formed by the gradual merger, lease and purchase of dozens of smaller railroads over many decades. Like real railroads in both the eastern and western parts of the continent, it has at least one major mountain range to overcome, and the location of its lines is greatly influenced by the presence of river valleys and the irregularities of the coast line. The system map (Fig. 2-4) is not drawn to scale, but the distance from A to J along the East-West's main line is about a thousand miles.

Connections and Competitors

Other railroads in the same area as the E-W include the Northwest and Northeast (NW & NE) which taps territory generally north of the E-W and also reaches the ports at the metropolis of J and the industrial city of O; its main line goes to the port city of AA, which the E-W does not reach. The Southwest and AA (SW & AA) extends from an inland area south of the E-W's western terminals to AA, crossing the E-W at several points in the process. The Southeastern RR and the Peninsular Ry. are shorter lines which serve areas south of F and J, respectively, which are separated by an arm of the ocean.

Coming in from the Far West are the so-called "transcontinental" railroads, not truly coast-to-coast, but extending two-thirds of the way and connecting at gateway cities such as B and HH with the Eastern roads. Even on this simplified map, two points are clear:

- There are many routes from almost any point to any other.
- The larger rail systems are *connections* with each other for traffic originating or terminating in their own territory and *competitors* for through traffic.

From point KK on the STU railroad, for example, a shipment to AA could go south on the STU to the SW & AA connection and then directly to AA, involving only one interchange, or it could be routed STU to B, E-W to G, SW & AA to destination, a shorter route but with two interchanges. The routing STU to B, E-W to T, NW & NE to destination is longer, but does not take it up and over the mountain range between E and F.

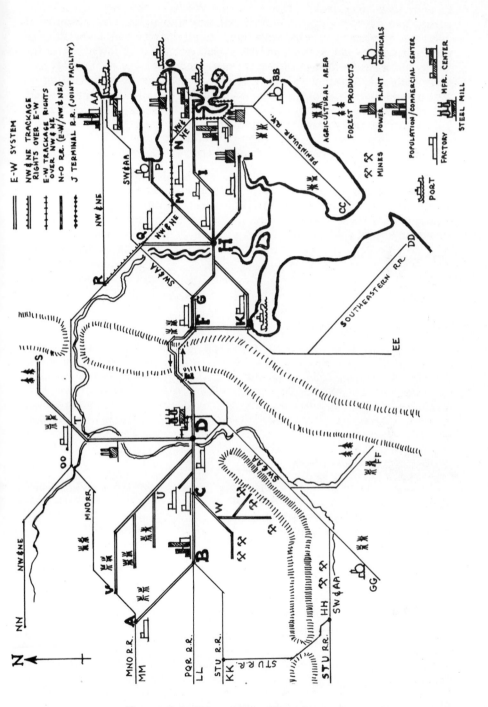

Figure 2-4 Map of East-West System

Pulling the Map Together

For many commodities, the principal competition in recent decades is from other modes of transportation, common-carrier and unregulated contract trucks using the interstate highway system, barge traffic on open waterways and those made navigable by the Army Corps of Engineers, and pipelines. A more subtle form of competition is *decentralization*. Corporations manufacturing and distributing products have the choice, over a period of time, of arranging their plants and distribution centers so as to reduce the amount of transportation involved in the whole process. The extra cost of producing goods in smaller plants may be more than balanced by reduced transportation costs from being closer to more customers.

Wherever possible, therefore, the individual railroad companies will combine, coordinate or connect their tracks and other facilities to hold down overall costs. Several examples of this, common throughout the country, are found here.

Paired Tracks Both the E-W & AA built their single-track lines through the only practical pass through the mountain range. The two lines are now "paired" between E and F; eastbound trains of both railroads use the SW & AA track, while all westbound trains go via the E-W line. Thus each road gets the advantages of double track while maintaining only a single line.

Trackage Rights From R to Q, the NW & NE runs its trains over the E-W's track by paying a specified "toll," often referred to as a "wheelage" charge because of its being based on the number of cars involved. From M to N, the arrangement is the reverse. Trackage rights arrangements vary with circumstances. Usually, the owning line does not grant rights to its tenant line to receive or deliver freight to on-line customers.

Joint Facilities Between N and O, both E-W and NE & NW trains run over the N-O RR, a jointly-owned company which is responsible for the operation of the line. In the metropolitan area of J and its port, both lines connect with the Peninsular Ry. and reach many industries, terminals and docks by way of the J Terminal RR., which is owned jointly by the line-haul railroads involved.

Detouring All roads in the territory have standard detouring agreements with each other, so that in an emergency the trouble spot may be bypassed by the best available route.

Interline Terminology In the United States, about 75 percent of all rail shipments involve at least two different railroads, so interchange of freight cars and the establishment of interline rates is an integral part of the business. Some of the terminology is illustrated in Fig. 2-5, and the side-effects will show up throughout further discussions of tracks and trains.

Which way is Best?

What is the "best" route for hauling coal between D and H (en route from the mines in the W area to the huge power plant at L)? Assume that

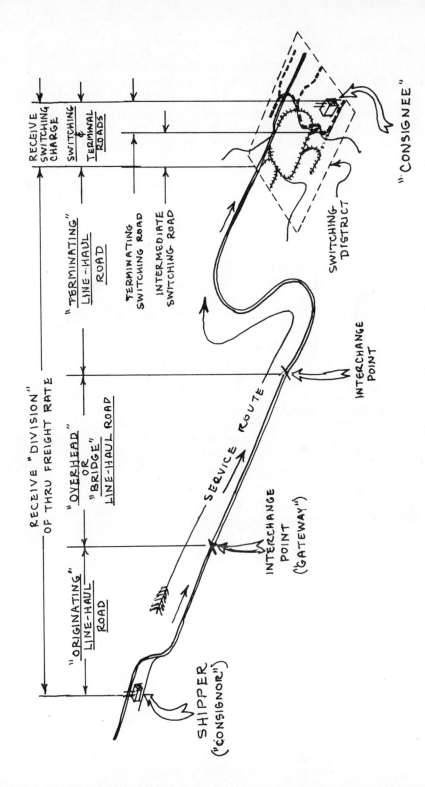

Figure 2-5 Freight Movement Terms

the route which takes the *least total energy* to do the job is best. (This is not the whole story by any means, but energy is a major influence when hauling freight.)

The Alternate Routes Fig. 2-6 shows the routes available. The direct route D-E-F-G-H via the E-W's main line is the shortest, but it takes you up 4,000 feet and back down again. The alternate D-T-R-Q-H route, aside from using "foreign" trackage from T to R, is downhill all the way for the coal, but 250 miles longer. Which is more important?

<u>Train Resistance</u> Train resistance may be divided into two main elements, *rolling resistance* (including the resistance to wheels rolling on the rail, friction in the journal (axle) bearings on the cars, and wind resistance) and *grade resistance*. The first is all friction, and once the

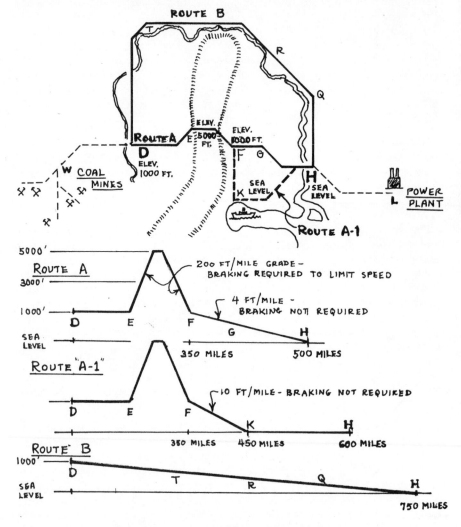

Figure 2-6 Three Ways to H with Coal

energy is expended it is gone forever. Grade resistance results from the energy you must put into the train to lift it vertically. The energy is returned without loss when the train comes back down again.

On a gentle grade, one-third of one percent or less, all this energy can be recovered by letting the train roll along without applying the brakes; the locomotive has correspondingly less work to do in keeping the train moving at the desired speed. However, on a mountain grade (for example, two percent, or about 100 ft. to the mile) almost all of this energy must be dissipated as heat using the brakes to keep the train from exceeding the speed limit. A great deal of the energy put into reaching the top of the mountain is lost.*

Fig. 2-7 gives typical values for the rolling friction of cars of a type likely to be used to move trainloads of coal to a power plant, 100-ton capacity alloy-steel or aluminum-body gondolas weighing 25 tons empty. Rolling resistance varies with the weight of car, being considerably more for a ton of empty than for a ton of load. It also increases gradually as the speed increases. We will use typical running speeds of 35 mph for the loaded train and 45 mph for returning the empties. The formula usually used for estimating train resistance (Davis) gives 4.2 lb. per ton for the loaded car, and almost three times as much *per ton* for the empty. The following graph (Fig. 2-8) fully illustrates this principle.

Grade resistance per ton is 20 pounds for every percent (one foot rise in 100 ft. of forward travel) of grade and doesn't vary with car weight or train speed. The energy it takes to lift a ton to the top of the mountain is entirely a matter of how high it is.

Adding Up the Horsepower-hours

The mechanical energy or work we're concerned about here is the product of a *force* acting through a distance. The *rate* of applying energy to a job is *power*, pulling twice as hard at the same speed or moving twice as fast while pulling with the same force represents twice the power. James Watt chose "horsepower" as the unit for rating his 18th century steam pumping engines and defined it as 33,000 ft-lb of work (lifting pounds of water to a height in feet, for example) per minute; he chose a value somewhat above what any horse alive could keep on doing, presumably to avoid complaints. Today, power is often expressed in the unit named after James himself, the *watt,* and we pay our electric bills on the basis of kilowatt-hours of energy. Since locomotives are still rated in horsepower, we'll stick with this unit; 746 watts (or three-quarters of a kilowatt) equals one horsepower.

Fig 2-7 proceeds to calculate the energy in horsepower-hours it takes to roll an empty and a loaded car one mile on level track and to lift it 100 ft. in elevation. The *energy* it takes to overcome a given difference in elevation is the same if you do it via a 0.05 percent grade or straight up in an elevator. As we'll see in studying locomotive performance later on, grade *does* make a huge difference in the tractive force needed. Now we're ready to see which route uses the least total energy in moving a 100-ton car of coal from D to H and bringing the empty back for another load.

*Except in electric traction with "regenerative braking" not currently in use in the U.S.

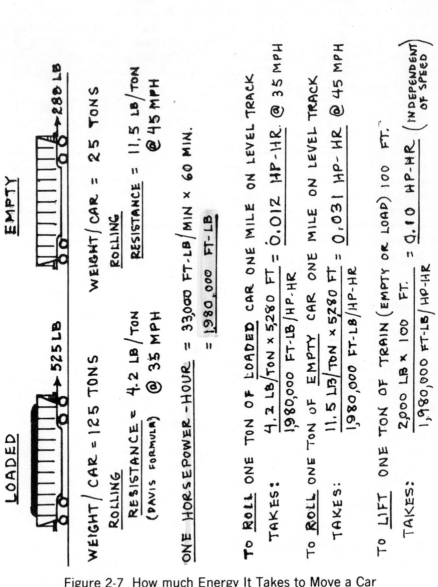

20

Figure 2-7 How much Energy It Takes to Move a Car

LOADED

EMPTY

525 LB

288 LB

WEIGHT/CAR = 125 TONS

WEIGHT/CAR = 25 TONS

ROLLING

ROLLING

RESISTANCE = 4.2 LB/TON
(DAVIS FORMULA)   @ 35 MPH

RESISTANCE = 11.5 LB/TON
@ 45 MPH

ONE HORSEPOWER-HOUR = 33,000 FT-LB/MIN × 60 MIN.

= 1,980,000 FT-LB

TO ROLL ONE TON OF LOADED CAR ONE MILE ON LEVEL TRACK

TAKES: $\dfrac{4.2 \text{ LB/TON} \times 5,280 \text{ FT}}{1,980,000 \text{ FT-LB/HP-HR}} = 0.012 \text{ HP-HR} @ 35 \text{ MPH}$

TO ROLL ONE TON OF EMPTY CAR ONE MILE ON LEVEL TRACK

TAKES: $\dfrac{11.5 \text{ LB/TON} \times 5,280 \text{ FT}}{1,980,000 \text{ FT-LB/HP-HR}} = 0.031 \text{ HP-HR} @ 45 \text{ MPH}$

TO LIFT ONE TON OF TRAIN (EMPTY OR LOAD) 100 FT.

TAKES: $\dfrac{2,000 \text{ LB} \times 100 \text{ FT.}}{1,980,000 \text{ FT-LB/HP-HR}} = 0.10 \text{ HP-HR} \left(\begin{array}{c}\text{INDEPENDENT}\\\text{OF SPEED}\end{array}\right)$

Route A Fig. 2-9 adds up the two classes of resistance for loaded and empty trips by each route. Route A, over the mountains, uses 750 hp-hr to lift the car the 4,000 ft. summit. Practically all this energy is lost because the train must descend the steep eastern slope under careful control of the brakes, converting the energy into heat. From F to H (Fig. 10), no brakes are needed on the gentle grade, and we have a net *input* of 125 hp-hr to boost the car up 5,000 ft., none of which we can get back on this trip. Total=1,638 hp-hr per car, or 16.38 hp-hr per net ton of coal hauled.

Route B The entire 750 miles of gently descending water-grade can be run without using the brakes, so 125 hp-hr needed to overcome 750 miles of rolling friction is provided by the change in elevation. We have to put some of that energy back in returning the empties: the total for Route B works out to 1,605 hp-hr, about two percent less than for Route A, in exchange for an extra 500 miles of wear on wheels and roller bearings.

Route BA We notice that while Route B was the overall winner, Route A used less energy in getting the empties back (513 to 605 hp-hr). This is because of the greater effect of rolling friction over the longer route on the relatively hard-pulling empties. This suggests looking at a circle route, with the loads going east along the river and the empties coming back over the mountain, Route BA. Sure enough, this does the job for 1,513 hp-hr, six percent less than Route B. This would be a very practical routing mechanically, since the same locomotives hauling the heavy

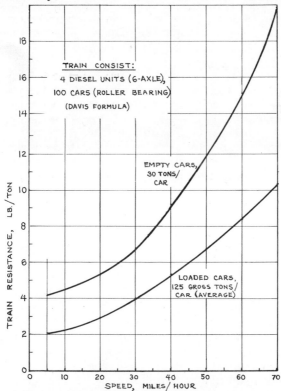

Figure 2-8 Train Resistance

loads east could probably get the empties over the mountain without a helper on the steep grade. From an overall operating basis, it might be more costly because such one-way movement over long distances results in a lot of "deadhead" costs in getting the train crews back for their next trip.

Route A-1 The idea of hauling those cars all the way back empty suggests another look at Fig. 2-6. Suppose there is import iron ore which could come into the port at K and be hauled to the mills at D -- this would mean an extra 100 miles in a side-trip from H to F via K, but it's physically practical since the dense iron ore can be hauled as a partial load in the big coal cars (the reverse, of course, won't work). It turns out that the total energy *charged to the coal movement* is only 1,241 hp-hr. Energy used to lift the weight of the cars back up from K to the summit of the pass is part of the cost of the ore movement, which still has a favorable situation because the coal movement is taking care of getting the empties to the ore dock. The coal movement is now taking 23 percent less energy than via Route B. Again, whether this is the best arrangement depends on other factors. The car utilization may not be nearly as good if, for example, ore-ship arrival is irregular. And extra car-days cost money, just as does diesel fuel.

Route BA-1 Finally, the lowest-energy routing turns out to be the "circle route" via the river eastbound with return through K to pick up the ore. A total of 1,116 hp-hr, or 32 percent less energy is expended then on Route A at a cost of a 35 percent increase in mileage, and with loaded car-miles 81 percent instead of 50. Quite an incentive to the railroad to do whatever it can to develop the K-D ore traffic!

Train Performance Analysis

This single-factor analysis omits many refinements and details which would have to be included in any real-life assessment, such as the effects of track curvature, the capacity of the various lines to handle the traffic without delaying other trains, and so on. Today, it is practical for a computer, using grade, curve and consist data to calculate train performance with great precision. The results of individual train performance simulations can then be programmed into the computer, which will determine the performance of each line of a network in moving traffic as a whole. With this information, the effects of enough different overall traffic patterns can be compared to get a good handle on the effects of such alternatives as track or signaling improvements, line relocations, train lengths and so on. *Train performance analysis* of this magnitude is becoming an increasingly important railroading tool, as its accuracy is demonstrated by comparing predictions with over-the-road performance.

General Performance Factors

To give a little better feel for the ways speed, grade, curvature and "stop and go" affect railroading, Fig. 2-10 puts these different factors on one chart, based on cars loaded to 80 tons each (a typical average for the mix of loads and empties likely to be found in service). By looking at this graph, we can get some idea of just how easily the cars roll; later on these matters will show up in the way tracks are laid out and locomotives are designed.

		EASTBOUND (LOADED)	WESTBOUND (EMPTY)	TOTAL ENERGY (HP-HR)	ROUND-TRIP DISTANCE (MILES)
		(TONS × HP-HR × DIST. OR HGT.)			
ROUTE A: (OVER THE MOUNTAIN)	ROLLING	125 × .012 × 500 = 750	25 × .031 × 500 = 388		
	LIFTING	+ 125 × .10 × 40 = 500	25 × .10 × 50 = 125		
		- 125 × .10 × 10 = -125			
		1,125	513	**1,638**	1,000
ROUTE B: (ALONG THE RIVER)	ROLLING	125 × .012 × 750 = 1,125	25 × .031 × 750 = 580		
	LIFTING	- 125 × .10 × 10 = -125	25 × .10 × 10 = 25		
		1,000	605	**1,605**	1,500
ROUTE BA: (CIRCLE ROUTE)		EASTBOUND ROUTE B (ALONG THE RIVER) 1,000	WESTBOUND ROUTE A (OVER THE MOUNTAIN) 513	**1,513**	1,250
ROUTE A-1: (SIDE TRIP TO PICK UP ORE LOAD)	ROLLING	125 × .012 × 500 = 750	25 × .031 × 150 = 116		
	LIFTING	+ 125 × .10 × 40 = 500	(H TO K ONLY-K TO D WITH ORE LOAD)		
		- 125 × .10 × 10 = -125			
		1,125	116	**1,241**	1,100
ROUTE BA-1: (CIRCLE ROUTE WITH ORE LOAD ON RETURN)		EASTBOUND ROUTE B 1,000 (ALONG THE RIVER)	WESTBOUND ROUTE A-1 116 (VIA K, TO PICK UP ORE LOAD)	**1,116**	1,350

Figure 2-9 Comparing the Energy it Takes to Deliver the Goods

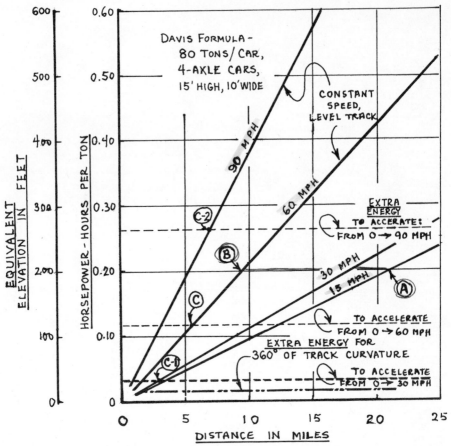

Figure 2-10 How Easily the Trains Roll

Grades and Power vs. Distance Considering the curve on the chart for 15 mph, for example, we see that the extra energy it takes to lift the train upgrade to an elevation of 200 ft. would move it about *21 miles* at that speed if it were on level track (Point A). No wonder that trains can move the goods with little energy input and need good brakes on even the gentlest grades. The second set of figures on the vertical axis puts the same thing in terms of horsepower-hours per ton. Two-tenths of a horsepower-hour (running your lawnmover for four minutes) would move that ton of train the 21 miles!

Power vs. Speed That same 0.20 hp-hr that moved the ton 21 miles at 15 mph would only take it about 9.5 miles at 60 mph (Point B), but at 30 mph it would make 18 miles. This shows that there is little to be gained by running a freight train on level at less than 30 to 35 mph, but that at 60 mph the extra resistance (primarily wind resistance) has begun to require significantly more energy.

Track Curvature Some extra friction occurs in hauling trains around curves, but the extra energy involved may not necessarily be large. As the line near the bottom of the graph shows, it adds about 0.014 hp-hr per ton (the equivalent of lifting the weight 14 ft.) to go around curves which are equivalent to a full 360° circle. Since a railroad following a river in hilly country may have the equivalent of several complete circles, curves *can* show up in the fuel bill. Wear on wheels and rails is a more expensive result.

Stop and Go Point C shows that the energy it takes to get a train up to 60 mph from a stop is equal to what it would take to roll it about 5.5 miles on the level at that same speed. The energy equivalent at 30 mph is about three miles (C-1) and seven miles at 90 mph (C-2). This shows that stops and slowdowns take significant energy; a 60 mph train stopping every 10 miles will use about as much energy in accelerating as it will in covering the distance. Since it takes only one third as much energy to go from 0 to 30 as it does from 30 to 60, a series of 30 mph speed restrictions is almost as much of a handicap.

3

THE TRACK: ALIGNMENT AND STRUCTURE

A four-unit, 12,000-hp diesel locomotive consist weighing 750 tons roaring around a curve at 70 mph is being guided and supported by 260 ft. of track which is made up of:

- 11.5 tons of steel rail, held in place by
- 600 lb. of spikes, and resting on
- 3.1 tons of steel tie plates, resting on
- 16.7 tons of treated wood crossties, resting in
- 130 tons of crushed rock ballast,

which in turn is supported by the sub-grade and the right of way.

With those tremendous weights and forces at work, it's easy to see that every item in the track has to be designed and maintained to do its part through rain, cold, heat, vandalism and the encroachment of weeds and brush. While railroad track seems massive in terms of weight, in comparison to the loads it must sustain, it is a relatively delicate, precisely balanced system.

Track Alignment

Although there are stretches of tangent (without curves) track in the United States as long as 78.66 miles, most trains are required to make numerous changes of direction, both vertical and horizontal. The effects of *grade* show up primarily in the locomotives it takes to overcome them (they will be considered in the next section). In hilly or mountainous territory, a reasonable grade *and* a practical cost of construction requires curving the line to follow the shape of the land.

Tangent and Curves Railroad civil engineers refer to straight track as "tangent", and use as much of it as possible because it is much easier to build and maintain. In the U.S. the sharpness of curved track is not measured by radius, (it would take an awfully long string to lay out the typical main-line curve,) but by "degrees," as illustrated in Fig. 3-1. Typical maximum speeds for some curves are also indicated. Wherever practical, main lines will get where they're going with curves of one or two degrees. But in mountain crossings it is often necessary to have at least a few curves in the 5 to 10 degree or sharper range to minimize grades. These curves add significant drag to the train, which helps the brakes going downhill but must be set for going uphill. Where curves and grades occur together, a common practice is to *compensate* for curvature by reducing the grade on the curved track so that the combined resistance is the same for both tangent and curved segments of the grade.

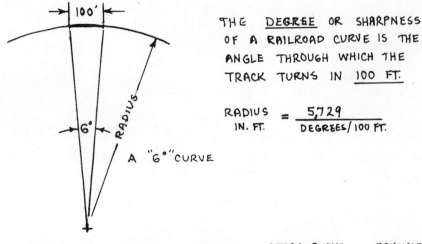

THE <u>DEGREE</u> OR SHARPNESS OF A RAILROAD CURVE IS THE ANGLE THROUGH WHICH THE TRACK TURNS IN <u>100 FT.</u>

$$\text{RADIUS IN FT.} = \frac{5,729}{\text{DEGREES}/100 \text{ FT.}}$$

A "6°" CURVE

DEGREE OF CURVE	RADIUS, FEET	TYPICAL MAX. SPEED	EXTRA CURVE RESISTANCE, LB/TON	EQUIVALENT INCREASE IN GRADE, %
1°	5,729	100 MPH	0.8	0.04
5°	1,146	50 MPH	4.0	0.20
10°	573	30 MPH	8.0	0.40
15°	383	25 MPH	12.0	0.60

Figure 3-1 Track Curvature

Superelevation To compensate for the effect of centrifugal force, the outer rail on a curve may be raised (super-elevated) to tip the cars inward. The maximum superelevation or "banking" ordinarily used on a standard-gauge line carrying general traffic (the difference in elevation between the two rails, also referred to as "cross-level") is six inches.

Six inches of superelevation fully compensates for centrifugal force (Fig. 3-2) at 95 mph on a one-degree curve or at about 45 mph on a five-degree curve. By long experience embodied in current Federal Railroad Administration (FRA) regulations, operation at speeds resulting in an outward force beyond that compensated for by the "cant" (tilt or superelevation) equivalent to three inches may be allowed; this is the maximum "cant deficiency" that is permitted in setting speed limits without a waiver covering a specific situation. Under most freight-traffic situations railroads will limit cant deficiency to a lower figure.

If heavy trains run curves regularly at much *less* than the speed for which they are superelevated, the wheel flanges will ride the *inner* rail and wear it rapidly. Therefore, the maximum and minimum speeds on a given track cannot be too far apart on lines where there are many curves.

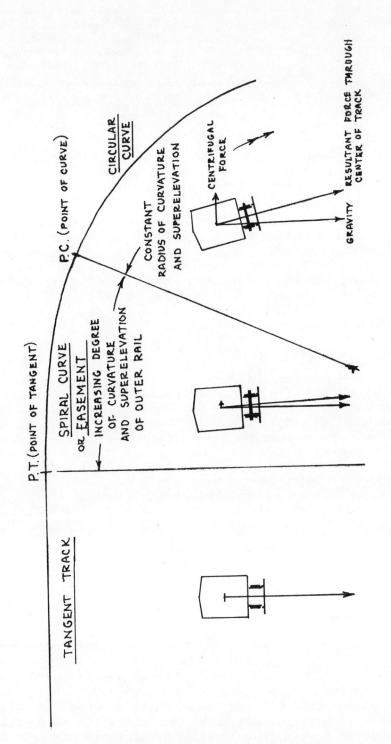

Figure 3-2 From Tangent to Curve — Smoothly

Spiraling   To attain the superelevation gradually so that the car suspensions can adjust to the change in "cross-level" of the track, a "spiral" or "easement" of gradually increasing curvature is used between each tangent and curved section of main-line trackage, as shown in Fig. 3-2. The length of the spiral depends on the allowable speed and the amount of superelevation, and may be more than 600 ft. in high-speed territory.

Track Gauge

The most basic characteristic of track forming the North American rail network is its common "standard gauge" of 4 ft., 8½ in., which allows freight cars to freely roll from the Arctic to Central America and from coast to coast. Fig. 3-3 shows how gauge is measured.

The actual measurement between railheads on a standard gauge railroad varies intentionally from this nominal dimension, and, of course, it changes somewhat with wear in service. There is a nominal clearance between the wheel flanges and the rail heads of about 3/4 inch. On some systems, such as rapid transit lines where it is possible to maintain track to higher than normal standards of accuracy, a nominal gauge of 4 ft., 8¼ in. can be used with the same wheel gauge. This tends to result in smoother running by reducing side-play.

Why Such An Odd Gauge?

The peculiar "standard" of about 4 ft., 9 in. was common on English tramways before the invention of the steam locomotive. Additionally, there is some basis for tracing this back from cartwheel spacing to the five-foot width of Roman stone gateways. George Stephenson and his son Robert, who were prominent promoters and engineers of railroad *systems* on an international basis, adopted 4 ft., 8½ in. as their standard. It is used throughout Europe (except in Spain, Portugal, Ireland, Finland and the U.S.S.R.); it was adopted as recently as 1955 by Japan in starting construction of its new high-speed passenger rail system.

Initially in North America there were many different gauges. It was not until 1863, when President Lincoln designated 4 ft., 8½ in. as the gauge for the railroad to be built to the Pacific coast, that it became clear that all the railroads of the United States would eventually be of this width. Railroads south of the Potomac and Ohio rivers were mostly of 5 ft. gauge until 1887, when several thousand miles of track was changed to standard over a single week-end. It then became possible to do away with transferring loads or switching car trucks at "break-of-gauge" points.

Is It the Right Width?

The uniformity of gauge is more important than the exact width chosen as a standard. "Wide gauge" systems such as those in India (5 ft., 6 in.) and the Soviet Union (5 ft.) use rolling stock of about the same size as that in North America, while heavy-duty railroading is carried on in South Africa, parts of Australia, East Africa, Japan and Newfoundland on tracks of 3 ft., 6 in. and meter (3 ft., 3 5/8 in.) gauge. Though there are

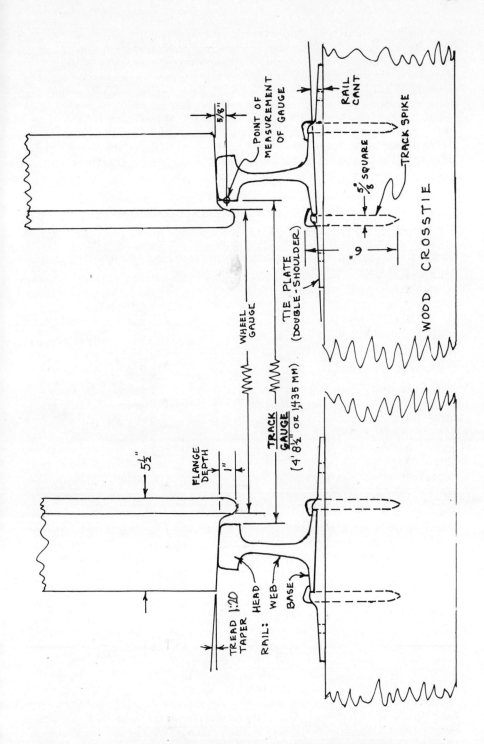

Figure 3-3 Track-Wheel Relationships. Dimensions shown are nominal.

situations in which a wider gauge could be advantageous, it appears that for general service, taking all cost factors into consideration, the present gauge is not far from optimum.

The Track Structure

The track structure's function is to transform the intense load of the wheel on the head of the rail to a moderate, distributed pressure which the earth underneath can sustain under all weather conditions without settling. Figs. 3-3 and 3-4 show the main elements of typical present-day track structure on a heavy-duty main line.

All of the major components have undergone continual change and strengthening. Perhaps, the newest wrinkle in track construction is the concept of roadbed stabilization fabrics. These synthetic fabrics, which are placed between ballast and subgrade, may prove to reduce ballast maintenance by improving drainage and preventing "fines" from pumping up from the subgrade and fouling the ballast.

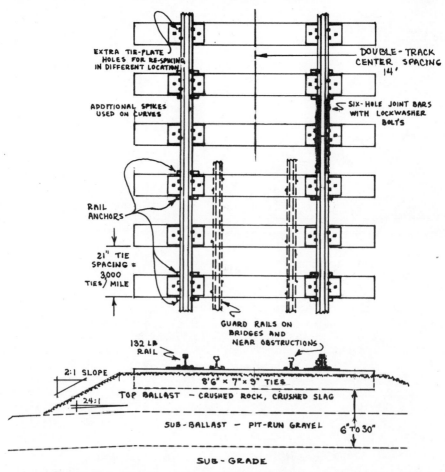

Figure 3-4 The Track Structure — Typical Mainline Track

Exploratory efforts continue to develop a radically different track structure (such as a continuous concrete-slab foundation) which will remain smoother, cost less and require less attention while withstanding heavier loads traveling at higher speeds. However, the same basic rail-tie-ballast system has continued to be used to date, as it represents the most practical compromise among the conflicting requirements for high performance, minimal maintenance and overall low cost.

Many minor aspects of track design have come about only through long experience. For example, it is standard practice to put the head-end of the bolts of a rail joint alternately on the inside and outside of the rail. This prevents a derailed wheel from knocking off *all* the bolts in a joint and allowing it to separate completely under the rest of the train, a "one in a million" possibility, but one that's considered worth avoiding. Now, let's look briefly at the main parts of the track structure to see how each has developed to pull its own weight in the total job of guiding and supporting the trains.

Rail

Iron alloys represent the only metals abundant and cheap enough to serve as the basic material for a *rail*road, and it's indeed fortunate that steel also has the most suitable combination of hardness, strength and stiffness of any engineering material. Early rails were made either of high-carbon cast iron (hard but too brittle) or wrought iron (tough but too soft). The mid-19th century inventions of the Bessemer and open-hearth processes for economically converting iron to steel reduced steel's cost by about 80 percent and were an indispensable factor in continuing development of railroads.

Rail Sections Rail is rolled from high quality steel containing 0.7 to 0.8 percent carbon and very limited amounts of the impurities sulfur and phosphorous. In cross section, rail is an inverted "T", and every dimension and radius is in accordance with designs (usually A.R.E.A., American Railway Engineering Association, standards) developed over many years, to get the best fit with new and worn wheels and the best combination of stiffness and freedom from points of high stress under all types of top and side loading.

Rail now being rolled weighs from 112 to 145 lb. per yard (56 to 72 kilograms per meter) and stands from six to eight inches high. New rail is laid originally on main lines, where under favorable conditions in tangent track it may be expected to carry up to 600,000,000 gross tons of traffic (a 10,000 ton train every hour for seven years, for example) before being removed for head wear or metal fatigue. Yard, branch and secondary tracks are commonly laid with "relay" rail which has served its time on the main line. On sharp curves the wear pattern differs between the "high" and "low" rails and wear is much more rapid than on tangent track; it is common practice to *transpose* rail from one side or location to another to equalize wear and make the best overall use of the steel. Total rail life before scrapping may be as long as 60 years.

Rail Defects and Developments Over the decades it was found that a certain small percentage of rails would develop "transverse fissures," fatigue cracks starting inside the rail head and growing gradually until the rail broke under a train. For a long time, the principal defense against these failures was keeping a record of the location of all rails rolled from each "heat" (or batch) of steel and removing them from the track if any of the heat developed such defects.

In 1926 the Sperry detector car was developed; it uses a magnetic (now supplemented with ultrasonic) nondestructive test process to detect and pin-point flaws as it passes over the rails. In the 1930's, it was established that a controlled-cooling process following rolling of the rails could virtually eliminate the "shatter cracks" in the rail steel which lead to transverse fissures, and all rail rolled since then has been so produced. Because of the extremely long life of rail, however, not all of the earlier steel is out of service. The increase in rail stress associated with the general use of 100-ton freight cars and higher speeds since the 1960's causes metal fatigue and its associated increase in the possibility of rail fracture to become a factor which, along with wear, may determine the useful life of rail in main-line service.

An important item in reducing rail (and wheel flange) wear on curves is the automatic rail lubricator, a device which applies a film of grease to each flange as the train approaches sharp curves; these have been in use for many years. Heat-treated (hardened) rail and changes in alloy content have been used to produce special rail for service in curve territory, with indications that the extra cost is well repaid.

Bolted and Continuous Welded Rail

For the last 50 years the standard rail length has been 39 ft. (for ready transportation in 40 ft. cars). Bolted joint-bars (Fig. 3-4), arranged to allow some lengthwise motion of the rails, connect the rail lengths. A gap, regulated to suit the temperature when the rail is laid so that it will just close on the hottest day, causes the rhythmic clickety-clack as a train moves along the track. Despite a great deal of design research, the joint is always less rigid than the rest of the rail and deflects enough to allow gradual wear and battering of the rail ends. This can be corrected by building up the rail surface with weld metal and grinding it to its original contour.

The reduced stiffness at the joint also causes greater load on the ballast and sub-ballast, resulting in "low joints" and resonant "rock and roll" of certain freight cars as well as rough riding unless overcome by frequent bolt tightening and tamping of the ballast.

The perfection of techniques for welding rail into continuous strings, transporting them to the site, and fastening them in place so as to overcome the effects of expansion and contraction (Fig. 3-5) has resulted in the present standard practice of minimizing joints in main line track. Lengths of rail, either new or relay, are welded into lengths (usually about 1,500 ft.) in a central facility. Loaded on racks on a permanently-coupled "rail train," they bend easily around curves as they are hauled to the point of installation. There, the train is pulled out from under each pair of rails, which descend to the roadbed, ready to be substituted for the old rail. The remaining joints can be eliminated by in-place welding with portable equipment. The laying of rail is restricted to a narrow range of temperatures near the upper limit of the expected range at the location (heating the rail if necessary to lay it in cooler periods) and care must be taken not to reduce the lateral stability of the track by working on ties or ballast at times when high longitudinal stresses may be present. Quality control in "field" welds (made in place on the track) is important to avoid "pull-aparts" at low temperatures.

As of 1980, over 80,000 miles of track in the United States was laid with continuous welded rail.

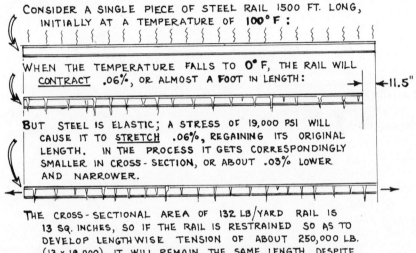

CONSIDER A SINGLE PIECE OF STEEL RAIL 1500 FT. LONG, INITIALLY AT A TEMPERATURE OF 100° F :

WHEN THE TEMPERATURE FALLS TO 0° F, THE RAIL WILL CONTRACT .06%, OR ALMOST A FOOT IN LENGTH : ←11.5"

BUT STEEL IS ELASTIC; A STRESS OF 19,000 PSI WILL CAUSE IT TO STRETCH .06%, REGAINING ITS ORIGINAL LENGTH. IN THE PROCESS IT GETS CORRESPONDINGLY SMALLER IN CROSS-SECTION, OR ABOUT .03% LOWER AND NARROWER.

THE CROSS-SECTIONAL AREA OF 132 LB/YARD RAIL IS 13 SQ. INCHES, SO IF THE RAIL IS RESTRAINED SO AS TO DEVELOP LENGTHWISE TENSION OF ABOUT 250,000 LB. (13 × 19,000), IT WILL REMAIN THE SAME LENGTH DESPITE THE 100° TEMPERATURE CHANGE. IN EFFECT, THE SHRINK-AGE IS FORCED TO OCCUR IN THE CROSS-SECTION RATHER THAN IN THE LENGTH; IT AMOUNTS TO ABOUT .002" IN A RAIL 6" WIDE.

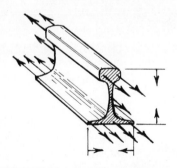

SINCE RAIL STEEL CAN WITHSTAND AT LEAST 75,000 PSI WITHOUT PERMANENT DEFORMATION, ALL NORMAL TEMPERATURE VARIATIONS CAN BE ACCOMMODATED WITHIN ITS ELASTIC RANGE. IF LAID AT A TEMPERATURE NEAR THE UPPER END OF THE ANNUAL RANGE IN THE AREA, THE RAILS WILL BE IN TENSION (TENDING TO STRAIGHTEN RATHER THAN BUCKLE THE TRACK) AT ALL TIMES WHEN THE TEMPERATURE IS LOWER.

Figure 3-5 How Can Continuous Welded Rail Be Practical?

Crossties

In an effort to create a truly "permanent way," some of the earliest railroads mounted their rails on stone blocks bedded firmly in the ground. This construction was impressively expensive in comparison to the practice of spiking rails to wooden crossmembers or "ties" laid on the surface, but it turned out to be a lot less satisfactory. The lack of any cushioning between rail and stone resulted in a jarring ride that damaged both rail and vehicle, and shifting of the blocks threw the track out of gauge.

On the other hand, the wooden tie turned out to have a combination of near-ideal properties. Hardwood is strong in tension (to hold the rails in gauge), in bending (to distribute the load to the ballast uniformly), and in compression (to support the rail) while providing enough flexibility to cushion impacts of wheels on rail. And, it is "nailable", so that the very simplest method of fastening rail to tie can be used.

Two major modifications have been made over the years to extend tie life. Steel *tie plates*, as long as 18 in. for the heaviest traffic, spread the load of the rail over a large enough area to prevent local crushing and cutting of the wood.

Pressure impregnation in which as much as 25 lb. of preservative is forced into a 200 lb. tie prevents decay. With these and other refinements, such as pre-drilled spike holes (which reduce fiber damage and improve the grip of tie on spike), the service life of first-quality ties has been extended to the range of 25 to 30 or more years.

Wood Substitutes

Reinforced concrete ties of many different designs are in widespread use throughout the world in areas where timber is in short supply and where axle loads are, in general, lower than in North American practice. In addition to test sections in several locations, production quantities of concrete ties are in service on the Northeast Corridor (Washington-Boston) high-speed line, in highly-curved heavy-traffic territory on the Canadian National, and on the Florida East Coast.

Concrete ties are highly uniform but necessarily used in a considerably different overall track system; deficiencies of concrete in tensile and bending strength and in resilience are offset by pre-tensioned steel reinforcement, and cushioning pads between rail and tie, with spring clips mating with cast-in-place metal inserts to clamp the rails in place. Under traffic, dynamic action is primarily between tie and ballast, rather than between rail and tieplate as in wood-tie track. Concrete-tie track tends to be more stable, primarily because of the greater weight of the ties (about 700 lb. vs. 225 lb. each) although they are usually spaced about 25% farther apart to take advantage of their uniformity. The overall relative economy of the two types of track will depend mostly on how long ties actually remain serviceable in practice.

Rail Fasteners

Track stays together primarily because of its geometry. The rail remains upright and in place not because the spike heads prevent it from overturning, but because the wheel forces acting on it (even on curves) are mostly downward rather than sideward and actually tend to keep the rail from turning over. Tightly-spiked rail, or rail secured by one of the numerous systems of elastic spring-clip or flexible-spike rail-tie restraints, avoids some of the wear that results from movement between the track parts as the passing wheels slam the rail and tie plates down against the tie. But the principal job of the fastening system is to keep the rail from shifting sideways. Therefore, the standard practice in strengthening track on curves to withstand heavy traffic is to use additional spikes (in the tie-plate holes provided) to hold the tie plates more firmly in place. The tie plate shoulders then hold the rail in place.

Creep

Rail also tries to move lengthwise or "creep," forcing ties and switches out of line and developing stresses tending to make the track buckle sideways. Therefore, all heavy-duty track is equipped with *rail anchors* or *anti-creepers*. These are spring clips (Fig. 3-4) which snap onto the base of the rail and come up against the tie to restrain motion. As many as four per tie may be required in places where heavy train braking, temperature, gradient combined with traffic or prevailing direction of loaded traffic tends to make the rail "run."

Ballast and Substructure

As you can see by watching wheels closely as they roll along the rail, even the heaviest, best-maintained track is not absolutely rigid; there is a "wave of deflection" moving along under each axle. This deflection amounts to about 1/50 of an inch for an empty freight car on the stiffest track, 1/10 inch for a loaded 100-ton car on the same track structure, and as much as 1/2 inch for the loaded car on relatively "soft" track, with correspondingly more deflection at the joints in bolted-rail track. As long as this deflection is uniform along the track, the ride can still be perfectly smooth. The more rigid the track, however, the less movement and wear there is between the rails, fastenings and ties.

The major job of the ballast is to hold the ties in place, prevent lateral deflections and spread out the load, which averages about 100 psi underneath the tie, to a pressure lower than the "endurance limit" of the subgrade. This accounts for the modern ballast section standards which cover the tie ends with a shoulder, sometimes 12 to 18 inches from the end of tie. The endurance limit is the pressure which a soil can withstand repeatedly without further settling; it may be as high as 50 psi for some sand-gravel soils, or it may be much lower. In problem areas such as swampy ground, it may be necessary to drive wood piles or even use concrete slabs to spread the load and provide a stable enough foundation to support the ballast and sub-ballast (Fig. 3-4).

Ballast Materials

More than 80 percent of the weight of the track (above the sub-grade) consists of ballast, so a primary requirement for ballast material is availability within a reasonable hauling distance. Crushed rock (granite, trap rock or certain hard sandstones), hard crushed furnace slags, and some forms of dense lava make the best ballast; washed gravel with enough crushed particles to make it interlock into a rigid mass may be almost as good. For lighter duty, limestone, pit-run gravel, cinders, oyster shell and even coarse sand have been used; today's prevalance of 100-ton freight cars on what would have been considered secondary trackage is resulting in a shift toward higher-grade ballasting.

In service, the ability of the ballast to resist degradation from the effects of tie motion (generating "fines" which may "cement" into an impervious mass) and continue to perform its most important function of draining rainwater freely is vital in achieving a low-maintenance, stable track structure. Soggy ballast also freezes in winter, causing higher stresses in the rail and tie system from rough-riding equipment and track heaving when it thaws in the spring.

Overall, good track drainage is of paramount importance. In level country, track is usually laid on a low embankment with side ditches. Where sub-soil conditions are good, ballast may be laid directly on the subgrade; otherwise a sub-ballast of pit-run gravel or a carefully-chosen roadbed-stabilization fabric may be essential in further spreading the load and maintaining clean ballast by blocking the migration of subgrade dirt.

Turnouts, Crossings and Trackwork

Another key "invention" in railroad technology is the "turnout," which diverts the train from one track to another. This relatively simple arrangement (Fig. 3-6), only two moving parts, is built in various lengths to suit the speed required in operating through the diverging (curved) route. Turnout sharpness is designated by the angle of its "frog," the assembly which lets the flanged wheels cross over the opposite rail. The longest turnout in common use is the No. 20 (some railroads go up to a No. 24), which is 152 ft. long from points to frog and will allow a train to enter a passing track or branch line at speeds as high as 50 mph. "Equilateral" turnout arrangements which "split the difference" and divide the curvature between the two tracks allow speeds in excess of 50 mph at important junctions or in entering and leaving a section of double track.

To the operating department of the railroad, a turnout is always a "switch," presumably because the only moving parts are the points which divert the wheels from one set of rails to the other. Fig. 3-6 also defines some of the other parts of the turnout assembly.

Crossovers and Crossings

Other important items of "trackwork" are the crossing, crossover, double-slip or "puzzle" switch and ladder, illustrated in Fig. 3-7. The most severe impacts on wheels and track elements occur at the frogs in turnouts and crossings. Designing items to accommodate both new and worn wheels as smoothly as possible has been a major challenge. Special features, such as high-manganese, work-hardening steel inserts in turnout and crossing frogs and stout rail braces to withstand the side thrust at switch points, are necessary to reduce wear and keep the rails in line without continual adjustment.

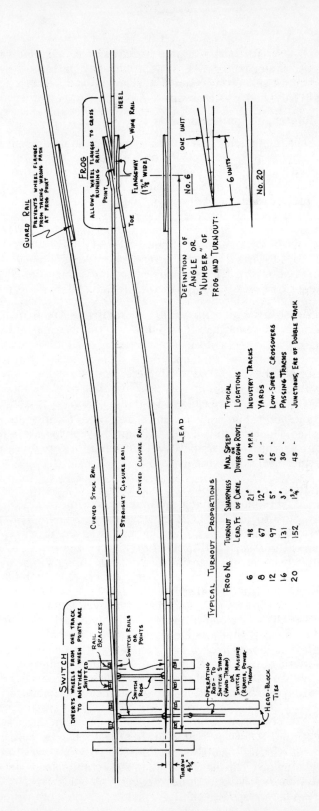

Figure 3-6 The Turnout (Left-Hand No. 6 Shown)

Nevertheless, it is this·simple and versatile system which can be designed to direct trains and cars through any pattern of trackage that made what we call "conventional" railroads so much more flexible and practical than their predecessors.

Track Maintenance and Standards

One of the important characteristics of track in its present form is that all its components -- except for the sub-grade itself, which tends to improve with age as it becomes thoroughly settled -- wear out and can be replaced on an individual basis without much interruption to traffic. The renewal process does not vary in principle from that of a hundred years ago -- worn rail is taken up and replaced; bad ties are singled out, removed and new ones are slid into place; new ballast is added. After a period of time the entire track consists of new material, but at no time has it been out of service for more than the interval between trains. On branch lines and short-line railroads, the entire process can be handled by a small, well-trained track crew, equipped with relatively simple tools.

The process by which virtually all main-line track maintenance is accomplished, however, has changed completely because of the necessity to mechanize all aspects of the job to keep labor costs within reason. Laying of continuous rail and major tie replacements are handled on a production-line basis, and seriously deteriorated roadbed is now likely to be renovated by a "sledding" process. A series of massive machines lift the entire track structure clear of the ballast, scrape up and clean all the ballast, add additional ballast, and return, realign and tamp the track to its new bed. Such an upgrading will not only put the line in shape for handling trains at competitive speeds but reduce subsequent maintenance costs dramatically.

In addition to a spectrum of machines which perform virtually all operations, from spike-driving and anchor-placing to shifting the track superstructure to put the rails into the desired alignment horizontally and vertically and tamping the ballast to keep it there, an overall measurement of track condition is provided by the *track geometry car*, a relatively recent development now in almost universal use by individual railroads and as part of the FRA inspection responsibility discussed below. Auxiliary wheels and sensors measure the position, curvature and smoothness of the two rails and the cross-level, gauge and alignment of the track as the car, a self-propelled or locomotive-hauled unit about as complex (and expensive) as a locomotive, travels rapidly over the line. Instrumentation aboard generates an analog plot which can be used directly in evaluating and correcting deviations from standard and also digital data which can be used in statistical analyses as a basis for longer-term, system-wide scheduling and planning of track maintenance.

FRA Standards

The Railroad Safety Act of 1970 for the first time gave the Federal government (through the Federal Railroad Administration) jurisdiction over track quality. This has resulted in the establishment of "minimum" safety standards for inspections, roadbed and track structure, geometry and corresponding speed limits. Six classes of track are defined, ranging

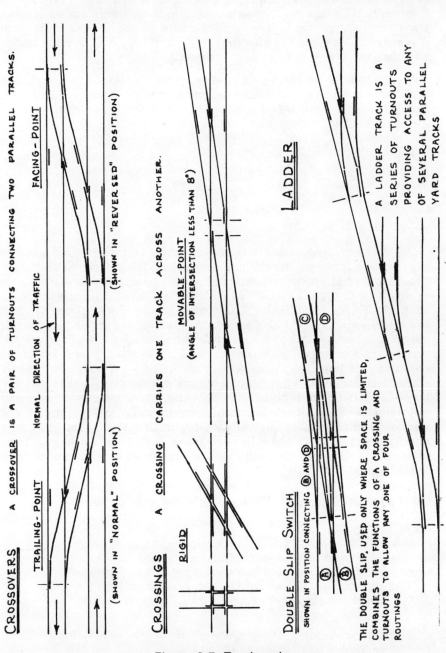

CROSSOVERS A CROSSOVER IS A PAIR OF TURNOUTS CONNECTING TWO PARALLEL TRACKS.

TRAILING-POINT   NORMAL DIRECTION OF TRAFFIC   FACING-POINT

(SHOWN IN "NORMAL" POSITION)

(SHOWN IN "REVERSED" POSITION)

CROSSINGS A CROSSING CARRIES ONE TRACK ACROSS ANOTHER.

RIGID

MOVABLE-POINT
(ANGLE OF INTERSECTION LESS THAN 8°)

DOUBLE SLIP SWITCH

SHOWN IN POSITION CONNECTING (B) AND (D)

THE DOUBLE SLIP, USED ONLY WHERE SPACE IS LIMITED, COMBINES THE FUNCTIONS OF A CROSSING AND TURNOUTS TO ALLOW ANY ONE OF FOUR ROUTINGS

LADDER

A LADDER TRACK IS A SERIES OF TURNOUTS PROVIDING ACCESS TO ANY OF SEVERAL PARALLEL YARD TRACKS

Figure 3-7 Trackwork

from Class 1 (10 mph freight, 15 mph passenger) to Class 6 (110 mph, freight or passenger). State and Federal inspectors are empowered to suspend operation over sub-standard track. Civil monetary penalties are assessed for failure to correct reported deficiencies. At their present state of evolution, these FRA standards, which must attempt to provide the framework relating objective measurements to the minimum track conditions necessary for the safe passage of trains, do not necessarily cover all aspects of track structure affecting safety and may also be more restrictive than necessary in some other respects.

From a railroad operating standpoint the safety standards generally do represent a minimum, since most railroads find that track built and maintained to higher standards results in lower long-term maintenance of way and operating expenses.

Accelerated Track Testing

One of the main obstacles to the development and widespread adoption of a "better", i.e. more durable and economical, track design is the time it takes in normal service to wear out various components of the track system and thus get reliable "whole life cycle" cost comparisons. Since 1976, the FAST (Facility for Accelerated Service Testing) test track at the Transportation Test Center, Peublo, Colorado (Fig. 3-8) has been in operation to attack this problem. Under a cooperative FRA-industry program, a train of up to 11,000 tons circles the 4.5-mile test loop 16 hours a day, thus, accumulating gross tons of traffic over a spectrum of types of track and alignment at a rate at least ten times that on the most heavily-traveled main line in regular service. While the FAST experiments cannot simulate all the different operating speeds and consists found in "real life" railroading, results have already begun to speed up the evaluation and understanding of the effects of many individual aspects of track materials, geometry and maintenance. Some major experiments conducted include:

- Effects of track lubrication on wheel and rail wear.
- Comparative curve wear of standard and premium (heat-treated and alloy steel) rail.
- Effects of track structure and alignment on the development of rail corrugation (periodic shallow depressions in the wearing surface of the rail head from heavy traffic, which must be treated by removing metal with a rail-grinding train).
- Life and stability of various materials, sizes, cross-sections and treatments of ballast.
- Variation of wheel wear with axle loading (from which track wear may be deduced).

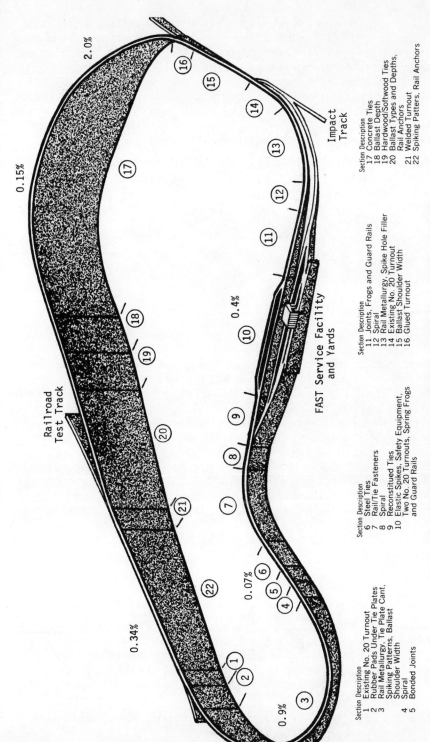

Figure 3-8 FAST (Facility for Accelerated Service Testing) Track Layout

4

THE LOCOMOTIVE

It was the development of a practical steam locomotive that revolutionized land transportation, and it is still the locomotive, diesel-electric or straight electric, that makes the railroad go. Though the locomotive is a complicated machine, there are just two factors, *horsepower* and *tractive force* (or *tractive effort*) which determine its ability to move trains. The particular combinations of horsepower and tractive effort needed for any particular job determine the type of locomotive that is needed. The range of assignments the motive power department of a railroad must handle will determine the make-up of its fleet of engines.

Tractive Force

Developing the tractive force to move a train involves several variables. Fig. 4-1 indicates the *tractive force* needed at the driving wheel rims to start and move tonnage up various grades. The locomotive generates this pull by gripping the rails with its driving wheels. To keep the wheels from slipping, the weight they carry (usually the entire weight of the locomotive, since all wheels are drivers on most of today's diesels) must be several times the tractive force to be developed. (Tractive force = weight on drivers x coefficient of adhesion.) The *coefficient of adhesion* of wheel on rail does not vary much with the size of the wheel or with the weight it is carrying, but it varies all over the lot with rail condition and it has recently been established that it also varies with the amount of *creep* (relative motion) between wheel and rail, being significantly higher when the tread is slipping slightly on the rail than when there is no slippage. Once *rapid* slippage occurs, the coefficient of friction drops far below the static value and power must be reduced to regain traction.

The static coefficient of adhesion may be less than 0.1 (10 percent) on slimy, wet rail or as high as 0.4 on dry, clean, sanded rail. With the adhesion-control systems used during most of the diesel era most railroads have found it possible to dispatch trains *reliably* on the basis of no more than about 0.18 (18%) adhesion, including the benefit of the sanders (a by-product of the steam era which blow dry sand on the railhead in front of each wheel) with which all locomotives are equipped. Recent advances (discussed later) make 25% adhesion an attainable figure, in which case the weight on drivers must be four times the tractive force needed to start the train and keep it moving. As is pointed out in the performance summary of Fig. 4-10, making full use of the *horsepower* of road locomotives requires high adhesion ratios only at the lower speeds.

46

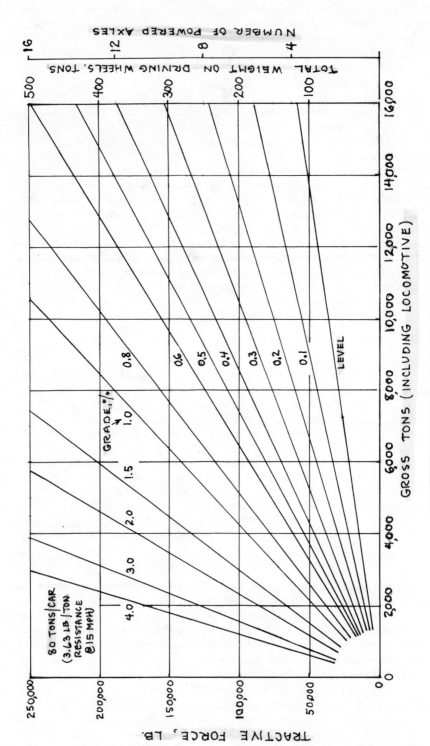

Figure 4-1 Tractive Force Vs. Tonnage and Grade

The right side of Fig. 4-1 shows the total locomotive weight needed for various amounts of tonnage and grade. Since most modern diesels for main line service carry about 60,000 to 70,000 lb. on each axle, there is another scale on the extreme right side of Fig. 4-1 that shows about how many powered locomotive axles it will take. The graph stops at 250,000 lb. because that is the point at which the possibility of coupler knuckle failure (minimum strength 350,000 lb.) begins to appear. If more force is needed, some of it should be supplied by a second locomotive, "pusher" locomotive or "helper." Other factors affecting the load a locomotive can pull are ruling grade and slack. On level track a locomotive can start a lot of tonnage. On practically any section of railroad, though, the track is not all level, and the *ruling grade* determines what can be hauled. This is the particular point on the run at which the combination of grade and curve resistance makes the train pull hardest and, therefore, "rules" how heavy a load can be given to the locomotive. It may not be the steepest grade on the route, since a short grade may not affect all the trains at the same time. And it may not occur at the same point for all trains. Also on a long train of lighter cars, the rear end may be coming downhill and helping push the front end over the top. Fig. 2-10 additionally shows that energy in a train going 60 mph is enough to lift its weight 115 ft., so a short incline may be run as a "momentum grade," if conditions are such that trains can get a good run for the hill.

The pull required to *start* moving a single freight car may be as much as 15 or 20 pounds per ton. The *rolling* friction of 4 to 6 pounds is used in calculation because the slack in the couplers and draft gear between cars allows the locomotive to start the train one car at a time, with the cars already moving helping start the ones to the rear. With the very large tractive force available with most diesel combinations, "taking slack" to start isn't usually necessary.

Horsepower

As discussed previously in connection with the amount of energy required to move trains by various routes (Fig. 2-10), horsepower is a measure of the *rate* of doing work. At zero speed, horsepower is by definition also zero, but to move the train at any desired speed above that takes horsepower. Fig. 4-2 shows how much it takes to move one gross ton (locomotive, cars and lading) at any speed, on level track and various grades. The curves on the graph are for straight track and cars averaging 50 tons weight, so the exact figure representing the best estimate for a particular situation will vary with factors such as wind, roadbed quality, uncompensated curves, heavier or lighter cars, etc. Some generalities from these curves will give a feel for motive power requirements:

- Power requirements for overcoming *rolling* friction are moderate; a 3,000-hp locomotive can move more than 5,000 tons at 30 mph on level track.

48

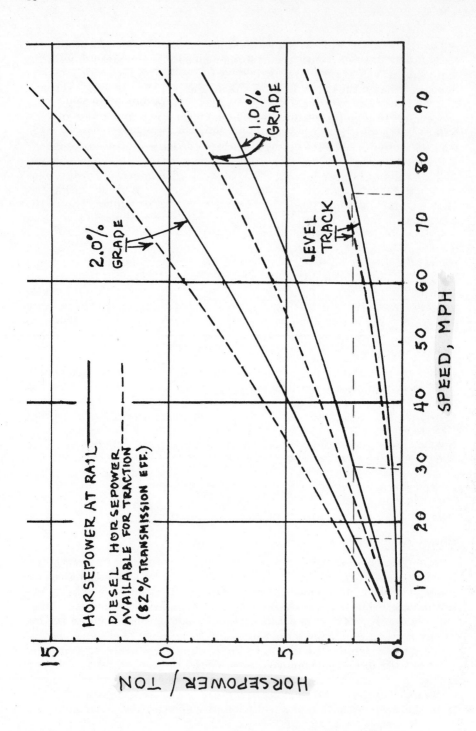

Figure 4-2 Power Required Vs. Speed and Grade

- Grade is highly significant for a heavy train; a train powered at 1.5 hp per ton, which could make 60 mph on level track, will slow to about 22 mph on a grade of one percent and to 10 mph on two percent. A train powered at 4 hp per ton (for example, having an 8-hp engine in your automobile) has a "balancing speed" (at which power available just balances train resistance) of more than 90 mph; it can make 55 mph up the one percent grade or 33 mph up two percent.

Balancing speed

- Compared to the effects of grade, the increase in train resistance with speed is moderate. Below 30 mph or so, horsepower increases only slightly more than directly with speed — twice the power to do the same amount of work in half the time if speed is doubled. Even at 70 mph with a train of empty cars where most of the power goes to overcoming air drag, resistance is less than that from a one percent grade (Fig. 2-8). Because it is a long, narrow thing which had to knock only a small hole in the atmosphere for its total weight, a freight train's energy consumption rises much less rapidly with speed than that of a highway vehicle.

Diesel Horsepower and Electric Horsepower

Fig. 4-2 shows two sets of curves; the upper curves are for the nominal "diesel horsepower available for traction" which is usually given as the locomotive's rating. Fig. 4-3 shows what happens to this power within the locomotive as it is converted to electricity and then back to tractive force by the traction motors. The lower curves on Fig. 4-2 represent the horsepower which is actually developed at the rims of the driving wheels. This is typically about 82 percent of the diesel horsepower available for traction.

Drawbar Horsepower

After some of the horsepower at the rail is used to move the locomotive itself, we have the useful horsepower at the rear coupler which moves the train. There is no "typical" percentage which goes into moving the locomotive because it varies due to relative weight of engine and trains. If a 400-ton locomotive is hauling 8,000 tons, over 95 percent of the rail power is being used to haul the cars, but if it has only 400 tons in tow it is using half its power to move itself, good reason for using, as closely as possible, the lightest locomotive that will do the job.

Acceleration

The rate at which a train can gain speed is determined by the amount of tractive force remaining after overcoming train resistance. To provide the same tractive force at *twice* the speed takes *twice* the horsepower, so gaining speed takes more and more locomotive power as speed increases. Fig. 4-4 shows a few of the innumberable combinations of acceleration rates and grade in terms of the horsepower per ton required at different

50

speeds. At low speed, acceleration may be fairly rapid -- up to 1.5 mph per second for a commuter train and up to 0.3 mph per second for a fast freight. As the speed increases, horsepower doesn't mean too much; our hotshot freight with 4.0 hp per ton can accelerate at only about 0.1 mph per second at 70 mph.

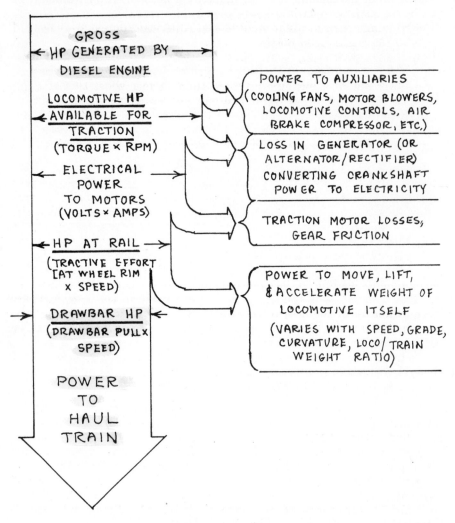

Figure 4-3 Different Horsepower Ratings

The Diesel-Electric Locomotive

The key invention that made the steam locomotive powerful enough to haul itself briskly and still have enough left over to haul a useful load was discovered by Richard Trevithick in 1803; he took the steam which was exhausted from the locomotive cylinders after it had pushed the pistons and directed it up the smokestack through a nozzle. The intermittent puffing action not only made the machine into a "choo choo" but sucked air so vigorously through the firebox that the boiler could generate steam at a rate many times greater than had been possible in a stationary engine of the same size and weight. The scheme was also self-regulating; the harder the locomotive worked, the more steam went out the stack, the faster the fuel burned, and the more steam was available.

Many other inventions, from equalizers (to keep the proper amount of weight on each wheel while going over rough track) to a headlight (to allow running trains at night on unfenced American routes), were needed to make the basic "iron horse" suitable for its work. However, for 125 years the reciprocating steam locomotive with its exhaust-stimulated white-hot fire represented the most effective way to get the necessary horsepower out of a machine no more than 11 feet wide, 16 feet high, short enough to swing around railroad curves at speed, and simple enough to be operated by two men. Numerous attempts to adapt more sophisticated and theoretically efficient steam generating systems to locomotive requirements were made; none had any lasting success.

Those involved in locomotive engineering and design eventually turned to another energy generating source, diesel power. The diesel engine was invented in 1901, at a time when the principles of electric railroad traction were fairly well understood. From the start it was apparent that the diesel could be several times more efficient in converting the energy in fuel to mechanical power. But it was not until the 1930's that the weight and bulk of the diesel began to be reduced to the point where it could compete with steam in other than low-speed switching service. The key developments leading to the eventual shift to diesel power for all railroad services (completed in the mid-1950's) were made in the 1920's. These were primarily in the area of reliable controls to match the load of the electrical generating and propulsion systems to the fuel input and power output of the diesel engine.

Diesel Locomotive Configurations

The American diesel-electric locomotive is now in its third generation of development, being a significant part of the motive power fleet for somewhat over 35 years and demonstrating a typical lifetime in heavy-main-line service of 15 to 20 years. For the most part, there have been only two to four companies manufacturing main line locomotives during the diesel era. Even though they have tried to standardize their designs to meet all railroad requirements with a few models, the total number of locomotive types is still considerable. Many are now extinct; others live on only in the form of components built into "remanufactured" locomotives.

Fig. 4-5 illustrates 12 representative types of diesel-electric locomotives. At least a few of each type shown are still in service. The number of locomotives in service on U.S. Class I railroads has remained within a few hundred of 28,000 since the completion of dieselization in 1958. The vast majority are now of types 5, 9 and 10; the ability to handle most main line assignments with just two basic types (4-axle and 6-axle) "road switchers") comes from connecting them together as multiple-unit (MU) locomotives under the control of a single engineer. Total fleet capability has increased steadily as the average horsepower of new units has risen from about 1500 hp to today's 3000+.

52

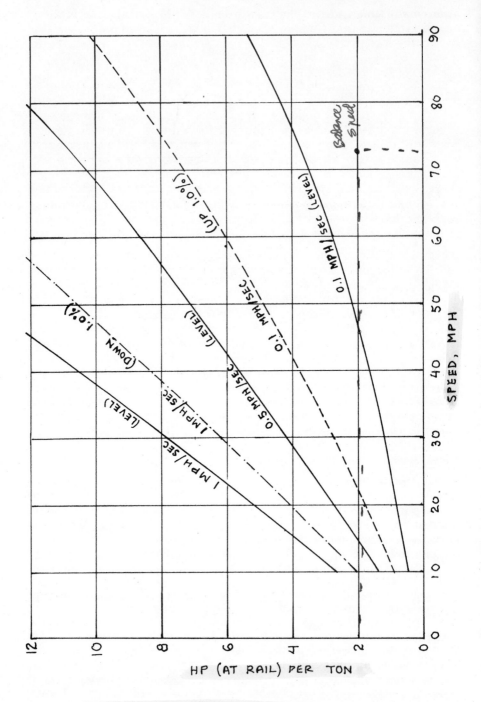

Figure 4-4 Acceleration-Horsepower Requirements

Anatomy of One Unit

Fig. 4-6 shows the arrangement of principal components in a typical high-horsepower (3,000 hp) "road-switcher" unit as built today. The term road-switcher"does not necessarily indicate a locomotive's function but refers to its body configuration, with a narrow hood (the "long end") enclosing the engine and other machinery and a short hood at the opposite end of the cab, a vestige of the enclosure providing space for a steam generator in the first such multi-purpose units (Type 7 on Fig. 4-5). With reasonable visibility from the cab in either direction, running gear and gearing suitable for road speeds and adaptability to supplying heat for passenger train use, these units could literally do anything and ushered in the second generation of diesel power in the early 1950's.

With the short hood chopped to a low-nose configuration, the road switcher (Fig. 4-7) with a full-width windshield (but still some degree of grade-crossing collision protection for the crew when running short-end forward) has become a more single-ended machine. Diesel locomotives *operate* equally well in either direction, so to avoid having to be concerned about the matter some railroads now locate the engineer's control stand on the *left* side (looking out över the low nose). When operating long-end forward, this places the engineer on the right where he can see signals, and the unit again becomes a bi-directional machine.

Units intended only for yard switching duties (Fig. 4-8) have less horsepower, simpler trucks not suitable for road speeds, a lower long hood for 360° visibility, no short hood, and, usually, no provisions for multiple-unit (MU) operations. Nevertheless, many of their components, from traction motors to cylinder assemblies, are interchangeable with those of road power -- an important saving in everything from parts inventory to the training of machinists. The general principles of locomotive design and operation in present-day Type 5 units are similar to those in the Type 9 and 10 units.

The Diesel Engine

The prime mover itself is a single V-type diesel with 8 to 20 cylinders rated at about 125 hp per cylinder if "normally aspirated" or 200 hp per cylinder if turbo charged. General Electric and Bombardier Inc. (Montreal) locomotives use 4-cycle engines (one power stroke for each two revolutions of the crankshaft), while General Motors units use two-cycle.

In accordance with North American practice, the diesel is a relatively low-speed machine, idling at about 400 rpm and developing full power at about 1,000 rpm, because it is designed for long life and low maintenance cost rather than for light weight. Even so, the diesel engine and its attached main generator represent less than 15 percent of the total locomotive weight. Many locomotives are "ballasted" (usually by making the underframe of thicker steel plate than necessary) to provide more tractive force.

The other part of the power plant is the generator or (on recently-built high-horsepower units) alternator which converts crankshaft motion into electrical energy (600 volt DC) for traction. In the same scheme as now used in automobile electrical systems, AC produced by the alternator is

DIAGRAM				TYPE OF LOCOMOTIVE UNIT	AAR STD. AXLE-TRUCK DESIGNATION SEE NOTE	TYPICAL HORSEPOWER (PER UNIT) (DATES BUILT)
DIESEL ENGINE & GENERATOR	POWERED AXLE	IDLER AXLE	TRAIN HEAT			
1				ROAD FREIGHT CAB ("A" UNIT)	B-B	1350 (1941) ↓ 1750 (1950)
2				ROAD FREIGHT BOOSTER ("B" UNIT, HOSTLER CONTROLS ONLY)	B-B	1350 (1941) ↓ 1750 (1950)
3				PASSENGER CAB UNIT ("B" UNITS ALSO BUILT)	A1A-A1A	1800 (1937) ↓ 2400 (1950)
4				LIGHT-DUTY/ INDUSTRIAL SWITCHERS "COMMERCIAL" DIESEL ENGINES; OFTEN RADIO CONTROLLED	B-B	300 (1926) ↓ 400 (DATE)
5				MEDIUM/HEAVY DUTY SWITCHERS (100 & 125 TON UNITS)	B-B	600/1000 (1936) ↓ 1000/1500 (DATE)
6				LOCO + SLUG COMBINATION ("POWERED TRAILER", SEMI-PERMANENTLY COUPLED)	VARIOUS- B-B & B-B ILLUSTRATED	1500 (USUALLY TO RE-BUILDS) 3600
7				GENERAL-PURPOSE ROAD-SWITCHER (HOOD-TYPE CARBODY; STEAM BOILER OPTIONAL)	B-B	1000 (1940) TO 2300 (DATE)
8				LOW-AXLE-LOAD ROAD SWITCHER	A1A-A1A	1000 (1946) ↓ 1800 (1950)
9				"SPECIAL-DUTY" SIX-AXLE ROAD-SWITCHER (LATER MODELS LOW-NOSE)	C-C	2400 (1955) ↓ 3600 DATE
10				HIGH-HORSEPOWER ROAD-SWITCHER (LOW NOSE)	B-B	2500 (1961) ↓ 3600 (DATE)
11				DUAL-ENGINE "UNIT REDUCTION" LOCOMOTIVE (WIDE-CAB HOOD CARBODY)	D-D (ALSO BUILT AS B-B + B-B)	5000 (1964) ↓ 6600 (1969)
12				COWL-CARBODY PASSENGER DIESEL "HEAD END POWER" ELECTRIC TRAIN HEAT/A-C	B-B (ALSO C-C)	3000 (1968) ↓ 3600 (DATE)

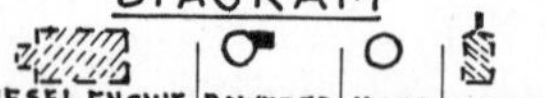

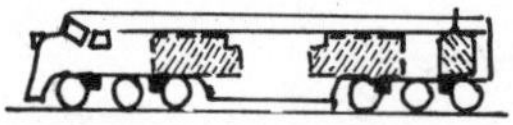

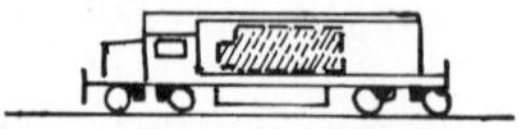

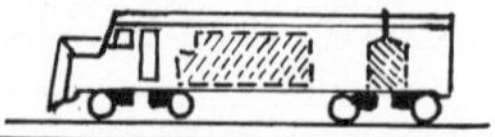

NOTE: "B₀-B₀," "C₀-C₀" IN EUROPEAN DESIGNATION, WHERE "B" AND "C" ARE USED TO DESIGNATE CONNECTED DRIVE BETWEEN AXLES OF TWO- OR THREE AXLE TRUCKS. 1, 2, 3 = IDLER (NON-POWERED) AXLES. IN BOTH SYSTEMS.

Figure 4-5 Representative Diesel-Electric Locomotive Types

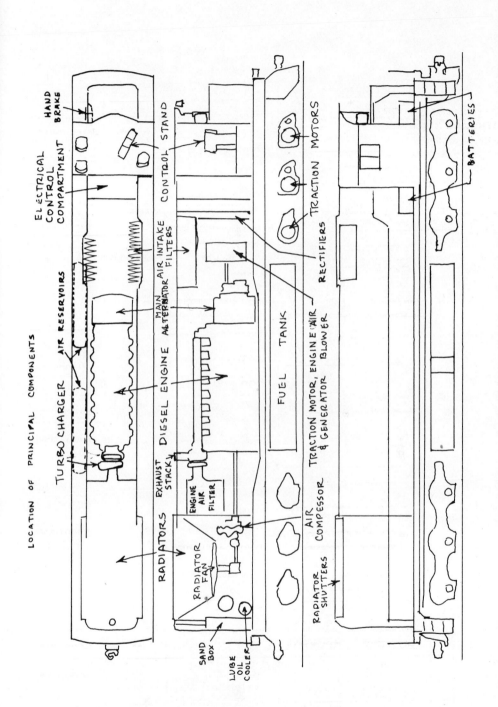

Figure 4-6 High-Horsepower, Six-Axle Road Switcher

Figure 4-7 The Modern Road Switcher — EMD SD40-2

immediately converted to DC by solid-state rectifiers. The alternator, with slip rings on its rotor instead of a multi-segment commutator and brushes, is somewhat simpler and, most important, smaller in diameter, so that up to 3,600 hp can be developed in the space available.

Numerous auxiliary systems in a locomotive provide: compressed air for the brakes; power for blowers for traction motors; cooling for lube oil, and dynamic brakes; and 78 v. DC for battery charging, fuel pump motors and locomotive controls. Typical capacities for a 3,000 hp unit are: engine cooling water, 300 gallons; engine lube oil, 250 gal.; fuel, 3,000 gal.; and sand, 2 tons.

The Turbocharger

High-horsepower units use a turbocharger driven by the diesel exhaust gases to ram extra air into the cylinders each power stroke. Since the amount of fuel that can be burned is determined by how much air is available, this increases the power of the engine by up to about 50 percent without increasing its size or operating speed. The turbocharger is a compact but high-speed device requiring considerable maintenance, so many two-cycle locomotives used in switching or local services where horsepower is less important are built without turbocharging.

Running Gear

Standard design uses two swiveling trucks per unit, each with two or three axles and traction motors. The traction motor is rated at 600 volts DC. Its magnetic field windings are connected in series with its armature to provide high starting torque. To adapt a common motor to all classes of service with the standard 40-inch diameter driving wheels, different gear ratios are used. Typical ratios range from a 15-tooth pinion on the motor shaft engaging a 62-tooth gear on the axle which provides a maxium speed of 71 mph to a 57:20 ratio for 102 mph. The traction motor speed is thus kept at a maximum of about 2,400 rpm.

The motors are arranged in the "nose-suspended" configuration illustrated in Fig. 4-9, exactly the same principle used in streetcars since 1890. This is the simplest way to allow the wheels to move up and down over track irregularities while transmitting the motor torque to the spring-supported truck frame. About half of the nose-suspended motor's weight is supported by the axle and is, therefore, "unsprung," subject to impact loads and, in turn, subjecting the track to similar forces.

The wheels, axles, gears, gear case and traction motor in the nose-suspended system constitute a single unit or "combo" which can be changed out for rebuilding with a minimum of out-of-service time. But the engineer is kept aware of the impact problem with this arrangement because of the requirement that power be shut off while the locomotive is passing over crossings with another railroad track. Otherwise, the bouncing of the motor brushes can cause big voltage transients and motor arc-overs.

Traction motors are cooled by a torrent of air supplied via flexible ducts from body-mounted blowers. Improvements in motor insulation and design have allowed continuous power ratings to approach 1,000 hp

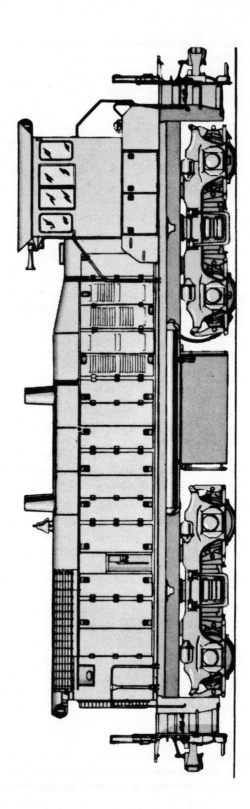

Figure 4-8 Switching Locomotive — EMD MP15

per motor in a unit that will fit between the wheels and clear the roadbed. At starting and low speed the current required to generate full tractive force creates more heat than the blowers can take away. At any current level above the continuous rating the motors will be burned out if the overload lasts too long. If the combination of tonnage and grade is appropriate for the locomotive power and gear ratio, the train will reach the summit of the hill or attain a speed where blower cooling can keep up with the heat being generated before the motor windings reach a dangerous temperature. If it doesn't, the engineer must stop and allow the motors to cool.

Locomotive Controls

Controls to utilize the locomotive's full capabilities in responding to the engineman and to allow several units to be coupled into multiple unit consists and controlled from one cab are among the most complex parts of the machine. The control stand itself now has a minimum of levers, but each works through elaborate circuitry (now mostly solid-state) to keep the diesel fuel supply and the electrical load on the generator in step so that properly graduated power levels are applied to moving the train.

Primary controls are the *reverse/selector handle* which determines the direction of travel and selects power or braking action (if the locomotive is equipped for dynamic braking) and the *throttle* handle with which it is interlocked so that improper combinations are impossible. The throttle has eight positions or run zones above "idle," each representing a higher horsepower output.

The primary throttle control adjusts the fuel injection control system of the diesel to maintain a specific rpm for each notch. This determines how much power it can develop, since it takes in a specific amount of air for each revolution and can thus effectively burn fuel and convert it into energy at a corresponding rate.

At the same time, the magnetic field of the generator is regulated so that the electrical power it is producing (and, therefore, the resistance it offers to the turning of the crankshaft) just matches the horsepower the diesel can develop, and the system is stable at the governed speed.

As the train speed increases, the traction motors generate more and more voltage ("back EMF") opposing the voltage they are receiving from the generator; at a certain speed, net available generator voltage will become insufficient to develop full traction motor power. At this *"transition"* point the motors, which have typically been connected in series to keep the low-speed motor current draw within limits, must be reconnected in parallel to put full generator voltage across them and let train speed continue to increase. In early-model diesels, transition (like shifting gears in an automobile) had to be made by the engineer; if required, it is now automatic.

The engineman's principal guide to locomotive performance is the ammeter, which shows the current actually going through the motors and, therefore, the rate at which they are heating up. It is marked to indicate the maximum continuous current draw allowable and the time limits which must not be exceeded at several values above this.

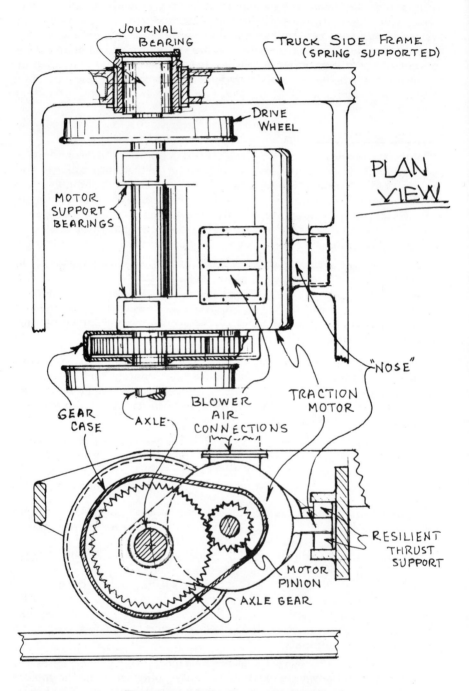

JOURNAL BEARING

TRUCK SIDE FRAME (SPRING SUPPORTED)

DRIVE WHEEL

PLAN VIEW

MOTOR SUPPORT BEARINGS

"NOSE"

GEAR CASE

AXLE

BLOWER AIR CONNECTIONS

TRACTION MOTOR

RESILIENT THRUST SUPPORT

MOTOR PINION

AXLE GEAR

Figure 4-9 Nose-Suspended Motor

Locomotive Performance

Fig. 4-10 shows what can be expected from a 3,000 hp diesel-electric unit and compares the two versions available -- the 4-axle locomotive with its short-wheelbase trucks and the 6-axle unit, weighing about 50 percent more, with its six traction motors but carrying the same diesel engine/alternator combination. Either can be equipped with different gear ratios for the desired maximum and minimum speed limits.

Why Six Axles Instead of Four?

The six-axle locomotive has two extra traction motors and gear sets to maintain, and its long-wheelbase trucks can be a problem on track with sharp curves. Over most of the speed range, tractive force is limited by engine horsepower, and the curve is the same for both types of units. The four-axle unit will actually haul a little more tonnage because it has some 55 tons less of its own weight to pull along.

The difference shows up below about 23 mph, where the adhesion required by the lighter unit to develop the tractive force corresponding to its horsepower begins to reach the limit for *reliable* traction -- 16 to 18 percent. To keep the engine from being "slippery," its control circuitry is arranged to cut back its power at lower speeds. The six-axle unit thereby moves out in front in hauling capacity. With 50 percent more traction motor thermal capacity, the C - C unit can "lug" that much more tonnage up a grade where low-speed horsepower is needed. As one would expect, six-axle units are prevalent on divisions where heavy trains must be hauled up long or steep grades, but scarce on lines whose loads are lighter and grades are such that all trains can get over them without dipping below 25 mph for more than brief periods.

Adhesion Control

To increase the spectrum of services in which the less costly 4-axles unit can do the job, recent design refinements emphasize achieving adhesion ratios higher than the traditional 18 percent which can be counted on to get the train over the ruling grade in any weather without tying up the main line.

In locomotives with electric drive, the axle with the poorest rail condition (usually the lead axle) governs the performance of the entire consist. One improvement results from connecting all motors in parallel, since this will tend to automatically reduce the power to an individual motor if it starts to run faster than its mates; advances in alternator and motor current and voltage ratings allowing the unit to develop full power over its operating range in permanent-parallel connection have been introduced. Previous methods of detecting incipient wheel slip by comparing the speed differential between axles have been supplemented with more sophisticated electronic computation of the acceleration of individual axles or of differences between wheel-rim and locomotive ground speed (as measured by a radar unit) in current automatic *adhesion-control* systems. These control instantaneous power levels to make full use of the wheel slip/adhesion relationship and replace manual control of the sanders in the case of more serious loss of traction. Under certain cir-

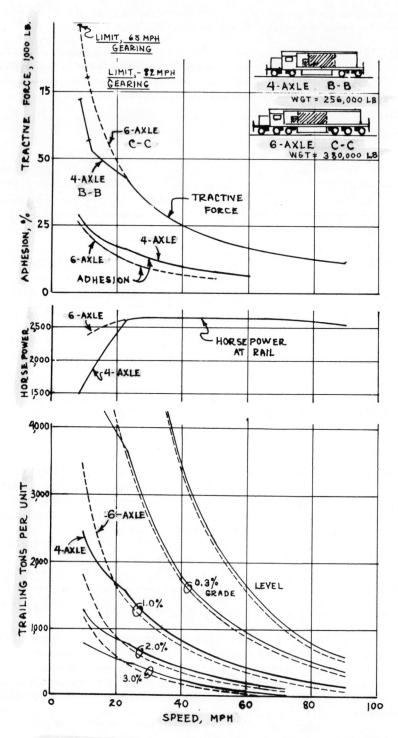

Figure 4-10 Performance Comparisons — 3,000-HP Units

cumstances these improvements may increase the tonnage rating of an engine of a given weight by as much as one third.

Since there is little indication in the cab when wheel slip is occurring somewhere in the locomotive consists, a "wheel slip" light in the control stand is provided in all road units to warn of persistent loss of adhesion requiring the engineer to reduce the throttle setting until conditions improve.

Multiple-Unit Arrangements

On level track a 3,000 hp unit will move the 4,760 gross tons of the "average" freight train at about 34 mph. Most lines, however, have at least some grades in the 0.3 percent range or greater where more than "drag" speeds must be maintained for practical schedules. Tonnage is likely to be assigned, in accordance with computer train performance analysis, on a *horsepower per ton* basis for the particular class of service, which results in more than one unit per train in most cases.

Units to be placed in multiple unit consists are provided with four or five air hose connections controlling braking and the sanders on all units and a standard 27-pin electrical connector controlling all other functions. It is possible to interconnect units of different makes, horsepower, number of motors, gear ratios and brake-control equipment and still have the resulting lash-up function as one locomotive. If the units are not matched, there is usually some loss of performance of the more capable units. Maximum speed will be limited to that of the unit with the lowest gearing, for example. But the flexibility of being able to use everything in the roundhouse while providing total power matched to the requirements of each train is a very important factor in achieving good locomotive utilization.

Remote-Control Units

Where heavy trains must be moved up steep grades, additional tractive force must come from somewhere back in the train, if the total required is beyond coupler strength limits. On fairly short grades, *helper locomotives* run by another engineman are used -- usually on the rear end to minimize time lost switching them in and out of the consist. Where there are several major grades scattered throughout a run, it is more economical to use *remote-control units* located at a point in the train where their tractive force will result in the smoothest handling (usually about two-thirds of the way back). These "slave" units are controlled by the engineman in the lead unit by radio control signals somewhat similar to those transmitted by jumper cable to MU'ed trailing units.

The receiver-decoder for these signals is located in one of the slave units (which in turn controls the units MU'ed with it), or in a separate car which can be used with any locomotives. A digital code is used to ensure that the slave listens only to its master's voice, and the slave units automatically go to "idle" if radio communication is not verified every few seconds.

Push-Pull

For commuter train service with its numerous short trips, a great deal

64

of terminal switching is saved by providing a control cab in the rear passenger car, connected to the locomotive by train-line control wires, from which the engineman can run the train on the return runs.

Dynamic Braking

Since a motor can act as a generator if its shaft is turned by an external source of power, the traction motors on most locomotives for over-the-road service are used to provide braking, particularly on descending grades. The current generated is fed to resistance grids where the energy developed from retarding the train is dissipated as heat. The controls are arranged so that the engineman can use the same throttle positions and ammeter readings to control braking and to guard against overheating the motors and sliding the wheels. The saving in wear and tear on brake shoes and rigging throughout the train is sizeable.

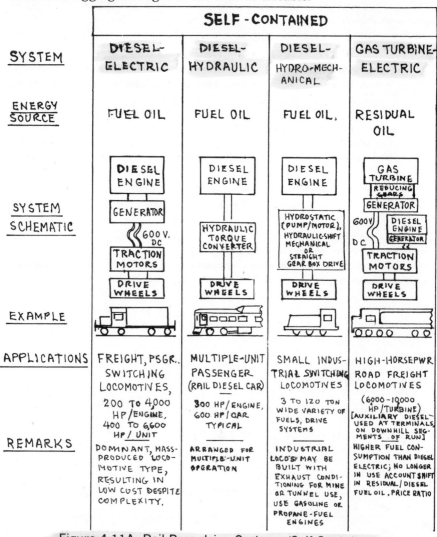

SYSTEM	**SELF-CONTAINED**			
	DIESEL-ELECTRIC	DIESEL-HYDRAULIC	DIESEL-HYDRO-MECH-ANICAL	GAS TURBINE-ELECTRIC
ENERGY SOURCE	FUEL OIL	FUEL OIL	FUEL OIL,	RESIDUAL OIL
SYSTEM SCHEMATIC	DIESEL ENGINE / GENERATOR / 600 V. DC / TRACTION MOTORS / DRIVE WHEELS	DIESEL ENGINE / HYDRAULIC TORQUE CONVERTER / DRIVE WHEELS	DIESEL ENGINE / HYDROSTATIC (PUMP/MOTOR), HYDRAULIC-SHIFT MECHANICAL OR STRAIGHT GEAR BOX DRIVE / DRIVE WHEELS	GAS TURBINE / REDUCING GEARS / GENERATOR / 600V DC / DIESEL ENGINE GENERATOR / TRACTION MOTORS / DRIVE WHEELS
EXAMPLE				
APPLICATIONS	FREIGHT, PSGR., SWITCHING LOCOMOTIVES, 200 TO 4,000 HP/ENGINE, 400 TO 6,600 HP/UNIT	MULTIPLE-UNIT PASSENGER (RAIL DIESEL CAR) 300 HP/ENGINE, 600 HP/CAR TYPICAL	SMALL INDUSTRIAL SWITCHING LOCOMOTIVES 3 TO 120 TON WIDE VARIETY OF FUELS, DRIVE SYSTEMS	HIGH-HORSEPWR ROAD FREIGHT LOCOMOTIVES (6000-10000 HP/TURBINE)
REMARKS	DOMINANT, MASS-PRODUCED LOCO-MOTIVE TYPE, RESULTING IN LOW COST DESPITE COMPLEXITY.	ARRANGED FOR MULTIPLE-UNIT OPERATION	INDUSTRIAL LOCOS MAY BE BUILT WITH EXHAUST CONDI-TIONING FOR MINE OR TUNNEL USE, USE GASOLINE OR PROPANE-FUEL ENGINES	AUXILIARY DIESEL USED AT TERMINALS ON DOWNHILL SEGMENTS OF RUN] HIGHER FUEL CONSUMPTION THAN DIESEL ELECTRIC; NO LONGER IN USE ACCOUNT SHIFT IN RESIDUAL/DIESEL FUEL OIL, PRICE RATIO

Figure 4-11A Rail Propulsion Systems (Self-Contained)

Slugs and Mates

Sometimes, the traditional locomotive set-up isn't capable of performing certain tasks. When it comes to pushing cars over the crest in a hump yard at a steady 2 to 4 mph, a single unit has plenty of horsepower but not enough tractive force or traction motor cooling capacity. To remedy this situation, excess power is fed from the diesel unit's generator to a "slug" unit. The slug is a ballasted four- or six-axle unit having traction motors but no engine or generator. This usually home-made combination provides multi-unit, low-speed tractive force with single-unit fuel consumption and engine maintenance. For some over-the-road services where particularly heavy loads must be handled at moderate speeds, "road slug" or "mate" units married to standard road locomotives also furnish that needed tractive force.

Head-End Power

Passenger trains require "hotel" power for heating, lighting and air conditioning, traditionally obtained from axle-driven generators on the cars and steam piped from a steam-generating boiler on the locomotive. The HEP (Head-End Power) system now in practically universal use in the United States uses 480 volt, three-phase power trainlined from the locomotive unit to provide all such power. In most cases, an alternator coupled directly to the propulsion diesel engine generates the power, with the engine controls programmed to "idle" it at high enough speed to develop full HEP output when no traction power is being produced. Typical HEP output is 500 kw or about 675 hp, which is subtracted from the diesel horsepower available for traction.

Fuel Efficiency. A fundamental shift in locomotive design goals has occurred as a result of the many-fold increase in diesel fuel prices which started in 1974; in 1979, fuel consumed by locomotives for the first time exceeded the cost of maintaining them and was the second largest expense item (after labor) in railroad operation. Some of the fuel-saving items in design and operating practices resulting include:

- Engines and controls are adapted to lower idling speeds (e.g. 250 rpm) where low ambient temperatures represent a hazard; locomotives are shut down rather than idled between runs (again, if temperatures permit; present diesel engines are not adapted to the use of anti-freeze and major modifications in lubrication, starting equipment and batteries would be required to achieve below-freezing restart): individual units in a consist may be shut down during portions of the run where their horsepower is not needed to maintain schedule; schedules are re-calculated to reflect the new balance between fuel and other costs.

- Locomotive auxiliaries such as cooling fans and turbochargers are sized and regulated more precisely to match demand and redesigned for greater aerodynamic efficiency.

- Trade-offs in the basic diesel engine design between fuel efficiency and mechanical refinement, first-cost and complexity are reexamined.

Other Locomotive Types

Although 99 percent of all locomotive horsepower in the United States is diesel-electric, a number of basically different types of motive power are also in use. Multiple-unit, self-propelled commuter and rapid transit train operations, which are discussed later (Fig. 17-1), amount to several million horsepower. The other important form of locomotive is the straight electric, usuable, of course, only where overhead catenary or third-rail power supply is available. Fig. 4-11 summarizes the various types of motive power in use, including some hybrids developed to allow running across power-supply boundaries.

The Electric Locomotive

The straight electric locomotive draws its power from an overhead conductor via a sliding shoe held against the wire by a pantograph. The important difference between the electric and diesel-electric is in the electric's ability to draw almost unlimited power from the wire while accelerating its train. The traction motors have a continuous rating, the same as that on their diesel counterparts. But the electrics have a short-time rating (five-minute, for example) which may be almost double the rating. At low speed, the tractive force is adhesion-limited, just as on the diesel, but as the speed increases, the extra horsepower can be used to keep the tractive force at a high value. As Fig. 4-4 shows, the result is much better. A six-axle electric with a continuous-duty rating of 6,000 diesel-equivalent horsepower (about 5,000 hp at the rail) loaded to 4 hp per ton could still be accelerating at 0.2 mph per second at 70 mph on level track and reach that speed well before the five-minute rating period had been used up. Over an entire run involving many stops or speed restrictions, the time difference is considerable; an electric can be loaded considerably more heavily than an equivalent diesel and still make the same schedule.

The electric locomotive cannot be considered apart from *electrification,* the process of providing the power distribution system. Recent developments in locomotive design (Fig. 4-11) which allow the use of lightweight catenary carrying 25,000 or 50,000 volt 60 HZ ("commercial frequency") power provided by public utilities rather than railroad-built power plants are being reflected in extension/conversion of portions of the Northeast Corridor electrification at this frequency. This is, at present, the only main-line electrification outside of commuter districts in the United States, although numerous studies have been and are being conducted on the desirability of electrifying other high-traffic-density lines in all parts of the continent.

Locomotive Maintenance

The principal emphasis in recent locomotive design changes has been on improving reliability and reducing required maintenance rather than simply increasing power. For example, internal locomotive compartments, particularly the high-and-low-voltage electrical control cabinets, in current models, are fed filtered air maintaining them at a pressure a little above atmospheric so that dirt is blown out of these sensitive areas instead of leaking in.

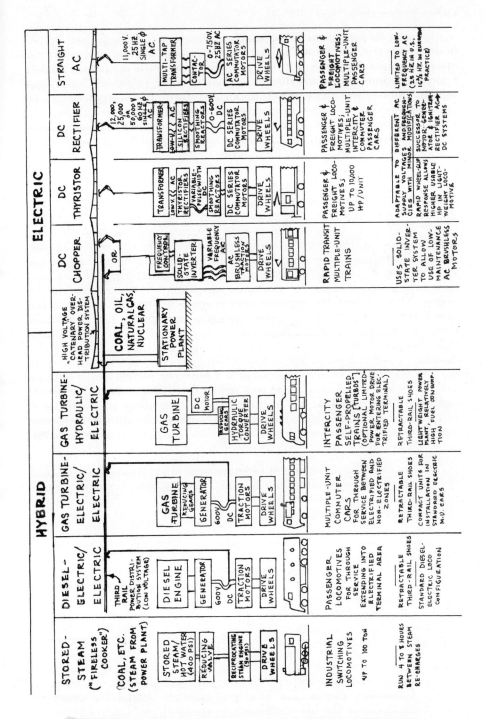

Figure 4-11B Rail Propulsion Systems (Hybrid and Electric)

There is also a continuing battle to simplifty the design of basic components and help compensate for the increased complexity that creeps in with each improvement in performance. The pressure-retaining 26L air brake control stand allows trains to descend grades without having to stop to set up brake retainers on the freight cars. But the added features do make air brake equipment more complicated, especially since it must be made compatible with older units not so equipped; in partial compensation for this, composition brake shoes with their higher coefficient of friction have made it possible to reduce the number of brake shoes per wheel on the locomotive from two to one, getting rid of considerable brake rigging in the process.

Inspection and Running Repairs

One of the most obvious hazards of early railroading was the boiler explosion. The design, construction, inspection and maintenance of steam locomotive boilers have been regulated by the federal government since 1911. By extension from the boiler inspection, power brake and safety appliance acts and the Railroad Safety Act of 1970, diesels and other types of locomotives and MU cars are subject to mandatory daily, 92-day, annual and biennial inspections and tests of all components and adjustments that are considered to affect safety; compliance is subject to verification by FRA inspectors and enforcement by civil monetary penalties. The 92-day inspection requires such items as calibration of air gauges and putting the locomotive over a pit where the underside can be thoroughly examined.

Safety inspections are accompanied, as a matter of good maintenance practice, by increasingly refined diagnostic tests such as spectrographic analysis of the lube oil to detect early indications of unusual engine wear or internal leaks. A major recent advance in efficiently checking out the ability of a unit to pull its weight as it leaves the shop is a built-in capability to test the diesel and electrical systems under load by running them with the full generated power being dissipated in the locomotive's own dynamic brake resistors.

Major Repairs

Most of the repairs and adjustments found necessary at periodic inspections can be taken care of with little time out of service; modern diesel design is such that even major casualties to prime mover, auxiliary or electrical components can be handled by quick exchange with spares in running-repair shops. Components removed are then remanufactured on a production-line basis in railroad, contractor or manufacturer shop facilities. Nevertheless, after four years (possibly 250,000 miles) or so, depending, of course, on the severity of the service to which it has been assigned, a unit willl be ready for a major overhaul. This could entail rebuilding trucks, replacing a "power assembly" or other major work.

After about eight or ten years, complete rebuilding may be in order, with new engine crankshaft bearings, trucks whose frames have been built up by welding to as-new tolerances, and a new paint job.

End of the Line?

The nominal life of a diesel electric in its original form is typically about 20 to 25 years, but at the end of this time there are several options. Some components, such as traction motors and truck frames, may still be useful as parts for remanufacturing to updated specs. For this reason, the units may be "traded-in" on new locomotives, not necessarily to the original manufacturer, since there is considerable interchangeability of components between makes and considerable mortality among manufacturers. The new locomotives may not contain any parts of the trade-in's, but there is a substantial credit on the purchase price.

The units may be "remodeled" (by the railroad's own shops, by a contract rebuilder, or even by another railroad's shop which does such work on a contract basis) into essentially new locomotives of the type the railroad now needs, changed from streamlined road freight engines into chopped-nose road-switchers, perhaps, with new engines of a later, higher horsepower series. Since locomotive underframes are fabricated by welding them up from heavy steel plate, even this most basic component may be redesigned in the process.

As a third alternative, the units may be cannibalized for parts to keep sister engines in service and finally cut up for scrap.

5

THE RAILROAD CAR

Railroad cars, primarily, are designed to conveniently carry and protect their contents and to stay on the track as individual vehicles, but they also must serve as links in a very strong chain. Within the first few years of railroading in the United States, the basic durable car configuration evolved: a long car body built around a strong center sill and supported on two swiveling four-wheel trucks.

The Basic Eight-Wheel Car

The basic eight-wheel car may not be the perfect design for railroad cars, but it has proven to be a solid performer. All of the hundreds of major and minor deviations from the basic design — four-wheel cars, guided trucks, six-wheel trucks, articulated (hinged) cars — seem to be less satisfactory and efficient on an overall system cost basis. This has been borne out in all types of services, from high tonnage ore hauling to high-speed passenger trains and in car lengths from 24 to 95 feet.

It was also quickly found best by early railroaders to have the wheels attached rigidly to an axle which in turn revolved in stationary metal bearings, in contrast to the previous horse-drawn carriage practice (in which the wheels revolved on a stationary axle). These bearings could readily be provided with a continual source of lubrication by enclosing them in a "journal box" packed with oil-saturated wool fibers (waste). It was found that, once in motion, the bearing actually carries its load on a film of oil, floating with a friction load equal to only about two pounds of pull to move a ton of weight. The total friction, including that of the wheel rolling on the rail, is about twice that.

Early cars, primarily of wood construction, weighed about as much as their loads. As freight cars grew bigger and changed from wood to steel, the loaded-to-empty-weight ratio improved and is currently almost four to one, even though every item of the car has been strengthened to withstand service at higher speeds and the increased longitudinal forces from longer, heavier trains.

Standardization and Interchange

Car design is a compromise between two conflicting goals — diversity to achieve the most efficient loading, transport and unloading of a particular lading vs. standardization on a minimum variety of general-purpose cars likely to cost less and achieve better utilization. Specific car types and designs for the principal classes of freight are illustrated in a later section on railroad operations.

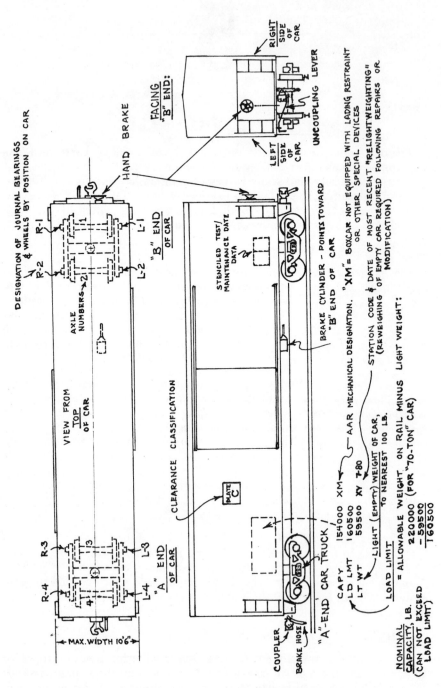

Figure 5-1 The Freight Car

Most freight cars, specialized or general purpose, are interchanged between railroads and may be traveling in a train coupled to any of the other nearly 2,000,000 cars making up the North American car fleet. In a continuation of the process started with the formation of the association of Master Car Builders in 1873 and now administered by the Mechanical Division of the Association of American Railroads (AAR), the basic dimensions, design criteria, construction and maintenance standards for the operating parts of a car making it suitable for interchange are rigidly specified.

Interchangeability and Evolution

The parts of a car subject to wear or damage in service must be as few in number and as interchangeable as possible, since they may need repair or replacement at repair ("rip") tracks or car shops anywhere. Even cars in "captive" service on a single railroad enroute are for the most part built to interchange requirements, since the cost of developing and building non-standard designs usually outweighs other possible advantages.

Who Pays for Repairs?

Interchangeability of parts allows the nearly 2,000,000 cars in existence to go just about anywhere, and be repaired just about anywhere. Interline repair billings of hundreds of millions of dollars are run up every year by cars operating in interchange service. These are charges for work done by a railroad on another company's car which was due for preventive maintenance or developed problems on line. To avoid confusion and litigation, standards must be set to determine who pays for which repairs. These standards are contained in the Bible of the railroad industry, the "Field Manual of the A.A.R. Interchange Rules", a pocket-size book of inspection standards, comparability of parts, repair and paperwork procedures and responsiblity rules. Pricing of all parts and repairs is determined by the A.A.R. "Office Manual."

Who Pays How Much for What?

In general, repairs are divided into those of a normal wear and tear nature, such as worn out wheels, and those associated with damage from treatment received (from railroad, freight shipper or receiver, act of God, or vandalism) on the handling line after it received and accepted the car at the interchange point. Wear and tear is "owner's responsibility." The handling line pays for damage. Over the years, solutions to most of the thousands of common ("Who pays for the grease?") and questionable ("Who flattened the wheels?") problems have been determined; an arbitration board continues to decide new issues as they arise.

Car Capacity

The basis for much of the rather remarkable degree of standardization in car repair parts that has been achieved is *nominal car capacity*. Wheels, axles, journal bearings, truck side frames and many other components whose size and strength is affected by the load they must carry come in 30, 40, 50, 70, 100 and 125-ton sizes. The two smallest capacities are rarely found except for cabooses, since practically all cars remaining in service are larger; 125-ton cars are restricted to use by special interline agreement on roads and routes with track rated to support their 79,000-lb. axle load. Thus, just three car capacities encompass most of the fleet, and most cars now being built are either 70- or 100-tonners.

Not all "70-ton" cars can carry exactly 140,000 lb., however. Total load on the rail is the governing force.

Nominal Car Capacity		Total Load on Rail (4-axle car)	Journals (diam. & length)
30-ton	60,000 lb.	103,000 lb.	4¼ × 8 in.
40-ton	80,000	142,000	5 × 9
50-ton	110,000	177,000	5½ × 10
70-ton	154,000	220,000	6 × 11
100-ton	200,000	263,000	6½ × 12
125-ton	250,000	315,000	7 × 12

Load Limit

The "load limit" for a particular car then becomes the difference between its empty (light) weight and the above total load on the rail. Some 100-ton cars, such as hopper cars intended for a dense commodity like rock which requires only a small cubic capacity, may weigh only 55,000 lb. empty and be able to carry 208,000 lb. A 100-ton tank car built to carry relatively light liquified petroleum gas and which must be built to take 350 psi pressure, on the other hand, may weigh over 100,000 lb. and thus have a load limit equal to only about 80 tons. Both cars will use the same size wheels, roller bearings, axles and other weight-related parts.

Car Clearances

Overall car size is also standardized by AAR interchange regulations. A car fitting within the diagram "Plate B" (10 ft. 8 in. wide by 15 ft. 1 in. high, maximum, with further restrictions on width for extra-long cars so they will clear structures near sharp curves) can go anywhere. A "plate C" car, up to 15 ft. 6 in. high, is subject to clearance restrictions on a few locations on some specified railroads. Beyond that, cars such as "high-cube" automobile parts boxcars which are built to Plate F and may be 17 ft. 1 in. high may require a clearance check for any new routing.

For tracking quality reasons, overall car body length is limited to 89 ft. (about 95 ft. over the couplers). When the center of gravity of a loaded car exceeds 98 in. above the rail, "high-wide" handling is required.

Safety Appliances

The Federal Safety Appliance Act of 1893, which required automatic couplers and power brakes on railroad cars, also included standardization of the steps, ladders, grab irons and running boards necessary for a brakeman to climb from car to car atop the train. A brakeman's original function was to control train speed with the hand brakes and, in the air-brake era, to pass hand or lantern signals to the engine crew. Radio communication has made it unnecessary for trainmen to traipse up and down the train; employees are now expressly forbidden to go atop cars in motion, and the ladders and running boards are being eliminated except where needed in connection with loading or unloading operations. The hand brake (now primarily a "parking" brake to keep stationary cars where they belong) has been relocated to a lower, safer position. For many years it has been of a geared design which can be set without using a "brakeman's club" to twist the wheel. Grab irons and steps for riding the cars during switching movements continue to be required, in standardized locations so that an employee can count on a foot or handhold where expected, regardless of car age or ownership.

The Railroad Safety Act of 1970 extended FRA authority to all aspects of car design and maintenance, not just brakes, couplers and safety appliances. The principal effect of this has been to give many requirements originally established for interchange purposes the force of law. After a period in the 1970's when what proved to be a very expensive program of periodic safety inspections and certifications of all freight cars was mandated, safety regulations were changed in 1980 to eliminate subsequent periodic inspection requirements. Inspection for defects judged critical for safe operation is required at the location where cars are placed in trains for road movement and penalties ($500 to $2500 per offense) may be assessed for any car subsequently found in service with such a defect. Cars developing defects must be tagged and moved for repair under restrictions determined by a qualified person.

Outlawed Designs and Components

Over the years a great many design improvements have become mandatory and outmoded designs, whether single components or major aspects of design such as wooden underframes, outlawed. Passenger car structural design requirements are descended, for example, from Railway Mail Service specifications developed in the process of requiring that all railway post office cars be the equivalent of "all steel" construction.

Critical Car Components

Within all these constraints, the job of the car designer in coming up with a vehicle that will make money is made possible only by the fact that there is considerable flexibility in using standard parts for the items where compatibility and interchangeability are required and then conceiving a car body and its specialty items that will best meet the demands of traffic. From about 1962 on, there has been an increase of about 1.5 tons a year in the *average* freight car capacity, as new cars averaging over 80 tons capacity have replaced retired 40-, 50- and even 70-ton cars. Wheel-rail stress levels are such that it appears that the 100-ton car represents about the heaviest economically practical on even the best of conventional trackage. If handling more tons as a single unit is desirable from cost and competitive standpoints it is likely to be accomplished by grouping individual vehicles of about the present size; articulation connections for supporting adjoining carbodies on standard four-wheel trucks while connecting them without slack are well-developed items, in use for special service in "cars" of up to 10 permanently-connected units.

The freight cars being built new today are bigger, lighter, stronger, require less maintenance and are a great deal more expensive (about four times the cost versus 20 years ago) than the ones they replace. Taking a closer look at the critical components that determine how the freight car does its job as a vehicle and a container will show how the freight car has become larger, better and costlier.

Car Truck Design

Fig. 5-2 shows the standard freight car design now in use, giving the established names for its parts. The individual pieces undergo constant improvement and change, but the basic arrangement which allows quick disassembly and assembly in changing out worn parts is of long standing. The whole 9,000 lb. truck is held together only by gravity and the interlocking surfaces on the principal parts. In the roller-bearing truck, wheel and axle assemblies are changed out simply by lifting the truck. Jacking up the bolster allows the spring group to be lifted off its seat in the side frame and taken out sidewise; the bolster can then be lowered, disengaging its gibs from the side frame. The entire truck is disassembled as simply as that.

Car Suspensions

Almost from the beginning it was apparent that some kind of system to isolate the car and its contents from the impacts of the unyielding metal wheels on the hard rails was needed. Also, since the wheel flanges are only an inch high, the vehicle must have enough flexibility to insure that all its wheels are on the rails at all times. Although the theory underlying a "good ride" was not at all well understood at that time, the rough track typical of American railroading was a powerful incentive to develop effective suspension systems. Both passenger and freight car suspensions of a basic type which has proven hard to beat (steel coil or leaf springs) were in existence by the 1870's.

Unsprung Weight and Spring Deflection

It is now known that the ability of the suspension to reduce shocks and vibrations at the wheel depends primarily upon two factors. The smaller the portion of the car's weight that is "unsprung," that is, supported directly on the rail without intermediate cushioning by something flexible, and the greater the deflection of the suspension under the weight of the car (the softer the springing), the better the ride can be. Obtaining a lasting and satisfactory ride in a simple, affordable system is certainly a great challenge.

Freight Suspensions

The freight truck has a single-stage suspension, one set of springs isolating the bolster (upon which the car body rests) from the side frames which are supported directly from the wheels. The inventory of car springs is greatly reduced by the fact that anything from a 30-ton to a 125-ton truck is supported on the same springs, nesting inner and outer coils in different numbers and combinations to produce the required total load capacity.

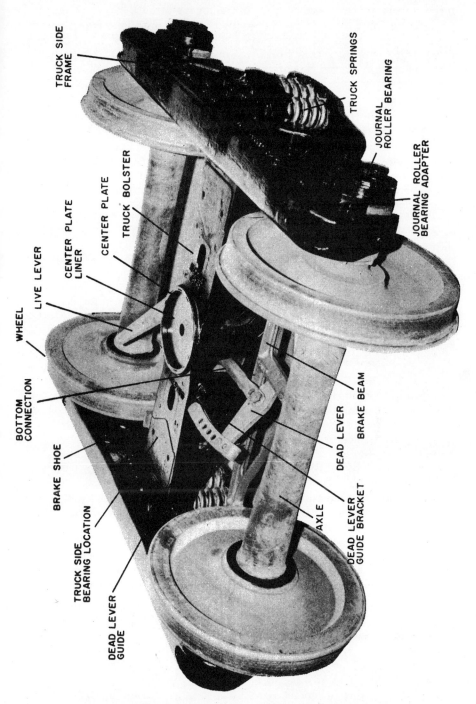

Figure 5-2 Freight Car Truck — Component Nomenclature

The softness of the suspension depends on the spring travel, the difference between the "free height" of the spring and its length when compressed by the weight of the car loaded to the limit. This travel ranges from 1 5/8 in. in the D-1 spring (now rarely used) to 4 1/4 in. in the new D-7's. Most cars have D-3, 4 or 5 springs with 2 1/2- to 3 11/16-in. travel. The suspension cannot be softer than this in freight service because the difference in coupler height with a car empty and loaded would be too great and lead to breaks in the train. Longer-travel springs not only provide a better ride but have greater reserve margin against "going solid" under severe track conditions and subjecting the car and its load to very high loads.

Locomotive and Passenger-Car Suspensions

Passenger train and rapid transit cars and most locomotives have two-stage suspensions, with one set of resilient elements between wheels and truck frame and another between the truck frame and the bolster. This reduces the unsprung weight, improving the ride and reducing track loads at high speeds. They usually include _swing hangers_ (Fig. 5-3) or equivalent systems which isolate the body from lateral impacts and tend to keep it upright. Spring travel can total up to about seven inches, since there isn't much difference between empty and loaded weight. On passenger cars, "air bag" suspension which can use train-line air to maintain car floor height with different loads is now widely used. Premium freight car truck designs which include some of these more expensive features at reasonable cost (including maintenance) are a continuing inventor's goal.

Rock and Roll

Any single-stage suspension has a _resonant frequency_. Repeated jolts at or near this frequency, such as from "low joints" on bolted rail, will build up motion until something drastic happens, unless there is _damping to_ sop up energy. This was automatically provided in passenger cars by the use of leaf springs, which absorbed energy in friction between their leaves. Freight car suspensions now include one or another of various proprietary "snubber" arrangements which reliably generate an appropriate amount of friction between the bolster and side frame, preventing excessive vertical bounce of the car body at the resonant speed.

Certain cars have a high center of gravity and truck spacing about the same as the 39-ft. lengths of rail in jointed track. These cars can build up a resonant _rocking_ motion to a point where wheels on one side lift off the rail. They can easily derail if on curved track at the time they go through the 15 to 25 mph speed range at which the resonance occurs. This rocking mode is harder to control because it happens at a lower speed, and much more damping is required. The problem is being attacked by the combination of welded rail, additional snubbing arrangements and (in the interim) operating restrictions in the attempt to keep trains out of the forbidden speed range on curved track.

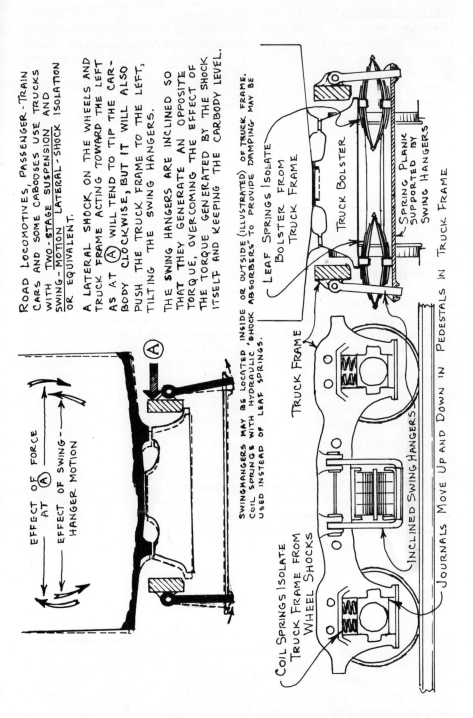

Figure 5-3 Locomotive and Passenger Car Suspensions

80

Journal Bearings

A most critical element in car design is the journal bearing. From an efficiency standpoint, the babbit-faced brass bearing resting atop the axle and lubricated by oil-saturated wool waste enclosed in a hinged-lid journal box, the plain bearing assembly, is still unbeatable. One man using only a jack can replace a bearing in three minutes. Also, the lateral motion between bearing and axle tends to reduce wheel wear in comparison to that of roller-bearing trucks. However, the journal bearing has barely enough heat dissipating capacity under adverse conditions for 70-ton cars and requires frequent attention if "hot boxes" are to be avoided.

Hot Boxes

The overheated journal bearing or hot box is one of the most hazardous aspects of railroad operation. If undetected, bearing malfunction rapidly results in friction heating of the end of the axle to a point where the steel is so weakened that the weight of the car breaks it off. This drops the truck frame to the roadbed, resulting in a potentially major derailment.

Following World War II increased loads and speeds lead to an intolerable number of delays in setting out cars with hot boxes. This rate was reduced by better than 90 percent within the space of a few years in the early 1960's by a mandatory replacement of the loose waste packing with spring-loaded, wick-fed lubricator pads. These keep loose strands from getting into the bearing (waste grabs) and are less sensitive to packing methods. At the same time, improvements and cost reductions in roller bearings (which had long before become standard for passenger cars) made their use in freight cars more practical. All cars built since 1963 have been required to have roller bearings; by 1980, about 80% of all freight car mileage in the U.S. was on cars so equipped.

The principal cost benefit from roller bearing application is reduction in maintenance; plain bearings must be inspected by opening the journal box lid to verify the condition of bearing assembly, lubricator and oil supply, whereas carefully monitored service measurements of grease consumption in latest-design roller bearings have allowed them to be certified to run the full ten years before disassembly and refurbishing on an "NFL" (No Field Lubrication) basis. However, a roller bearing assembly which does fail can progress to disaster more quickly and with less warning than a plain bearing, so the detection of incipient trouble is even more important, as will be discussed in the section on signaling devices.

Axles

The rotating axle which solved the problem of keeping the wheels in gauge also produces a bending stress which changes from compression to tension at any point in the axle every time the wheel revolves. This condition can result in *metal fatigue,* in which a crack develops progressively at a stress level below that which would cause any effect on a single steady application of load. Study of axle failures as far back as the 1850's was the first situation in which this condition was recognized. The most recent change to design a more durable axle was the development of the _raised wheel-seat_ axle. This design lowers the concentrated stress in the axle at the inner face of the wheel, which comes from the heavy force-fit used to keep the wheel in place.

Today, axles are forged from medium carbon steel, machined all over to reduce surface fatigue possibilities, weigh as much as 1,200 lb. and have a very low failure rate.

Wheels

Freight car wheels for cars of up to 70-ton capacity have been standardized at 33 in. diameter for many years. Larger wheels (36 in. for 100-ton and 38 in. for 125-ton cars) are used in high-capacity service to help spread out the concentrated load at the point of contact between wheel and rail head. A special 28 in. wheel is used on some piggyback flat cars to lower the deck three inches and help accommodate high truck trailers on routes where clearances are tight.

Cast and Wrought Wheels

When iron is cast into a metal mold, the sudden cooling produces a white "chilled iron" structure extending a half-inch or so from the surface and then blending into the soft "grey iron" of the rest of the casting. The chilled iron is extremely hard -- so hard that it can't be machined. Until the 1930's most freight car wheels were made of iron, cast into a "chill ring" surrrounding a sand mold so that the tread and flange were hard but the center was soft and reasonably tough. The axle hole could then be bored concentric with the rim and pressed onto the axle. These economical, long-wearing wheels were not adequate for the heavier loads of the postwar years; all freight car wheels are now made of steel, either cast or forged.

Thermal Loads

In addition to its functions of carrying the load and serving as the guiding element, the wheel tread must also survive the heat shock of serving as the brake drum and dissipating much of the heat energy resulting from descending grades and emergency stops. The locomotive dynamic brake is a big help, but wheel tread temperature of 800° F. from a single high-speed emergency stop on a passenger car wheel is typical. The most severe stresses inside the wheel rim occur when the train has descended a long grade, raising it to a dull red heat; when these hot wheels are hit by the icy blasts of a blizzard, it takes a tough material to stand up to such torture.

Wheel material selection is a compromise between wear and thermal-shock properties. Class A, B, and C heat-treated wheels are of increasingly higher carbon content, hardness and wear-resistance but decreasing resistance to developing thermal cracks in service where extreme braking loads are frequent. Thus, a passenger train making frequent stops might require the use of the softer Class A wheels, while a heavily-loaded unit-train car would get high wheel mileage from Class C wheels if its route did not involve long grades.

Wheel Wear

The exact contour of the tread and flange of the wheel as it has been refined over the years is also a compromise. It's designed to ride well over its life and to last as long as possible before it begins to wear to a hazardous shape, either by developing a high flange with a vertical face which can climb the rail or a hollow tread with a "second flange" on the outside which can take the wrong route at a track switch. Wheel contour is one of the most closely gauged items in freight car inspection. Rail cant also affects wheel wear and is a subject of continuing research to find the best value for cars and track.

In heavy service, the point at which 50 percent of a given lot of wheels have been changed should range from 150,000 to 250,000 miles. Two-wear and multiple-wear wheels are made with a thicker tread so that they can be turned to a new contour once or twice before becoming scrap. With some 1,600,000 wheels to be replaced or turned per year, the process of handling them (they weigh from 700 to 1,000 lb. each) has been highly automated.

Car Body Structure

The car body structure for the most part is built around a *center sill* connecting the two trucks and the pockets for the draft gear and coupler assemblies which transmit pull and push ("buff") loads associated with motion of the train as a whole.

Freight cars rely on gravity to hold the car body in place on its trucks; a standardized *center plate* from 12 to 16 in. in diameter (depending on car capacity) on the car body extends one inch into a corresponding *center plate bowl* on the truck bolster whose rim keeps the truck moving with the car body. *Side bearings* spaced 4 ft., 2 in. apart are the other points of contact between truck and car body; to allow the car to keep all its wheels on the rail on warped track, the side bearings have some clearance or are resilient.

Truck Hunting

The center plate/side bearing system has conflicting requirements. It should let the trucks swivel freely on entering curves to minimize friction and wheel wear, but it should provide resistance to control *truck hunting* on tangent track. Truck hunting is a rapid oscillation occurring in empty cars at speeds of about 50 mph and above in which the wheel flanges zoom alternately from contact with one railhead to the other, with bad effects on both and generating damaging forces and wear in trucks and car-body. As a result of this problem, there have been developed a number of proprietary designs for resilient side bearings, center-plate extensions and bolster/side frame elements which are intended to delay the onset of hunting as speed increases; some also fight rock and roll. None of these designs has been universally accepted as fully meeting requirements for all classes of service at a satisfactory price.

Radial Trucks

In standard truck designs the two axles remain parallel as the train goes around curves; if they could move within the truck so that each remains radial with respect to the curve, wheel treads with the proper angle of "conicity" could pass around the curve without flange contact or wheel slippage on the railhead, reducing friction and resulting fuel consumption, wheel and rail wear, and track lateral forces. Competing designs for accomplishing this with a minimum of added truck complexity, cost and maintenance, based on theoretical studies of wheel-rail action extending over many years, have been tested extensively in the 1980 era as part of an industry-government Truck Design Optimization Project (including FAST track experiments) and may prove economical in high-mileage service over routes where much of the mileage is on curves.

The Rolling Bridge

The car body also must serve as a bridge holding up a load supported only at the truck centers. The load is always heavy, may be concentrated in a short part of the car length, or may be dumped into the car with little regard for its feelings in the matter. To do this job with as little weight as possible, the car body is designed as a unit with the center still. This is why a box car may actually be lighter than a flat car of the same length and capacity -- its sides, roof and underframe form a box structure which is quite efficient structurally in comparison to the deck of a flatcar designed to be as shallow as possible.

Critical parts of the car must be strong enough to take incidental loads that make it a more efficient carrier of freight, such as wheel loads of as much as 50,000 lb. from forklift trucks on box car floors and clamp loads from rotary dumpers that empty gondola cars by simply overturning them.

Car Body Materials

The body must also withstand the lading itself, which may be corrosive, abrasive, contaminating and/or flammable. As a result, most car bodies are built with many parts of copper-bearing low-alloy high-tensile steels; the extra cost of the premium material is counterbalanced not only by longer life and reduced cost of hauling dead weight but also by the smaller quantity required to do the structural job. Aluminum alloy car bodies are used in specific services where their corrosion resistance to a particular lading together with the extra load permitted by the weight saving will justify the extra cost.

Car Maintenance

On the average, costs of car maintenance amounted to some $800 per car per year (1978) or more than $1.4 billion for the U.S. fleet. Maintenance ranges from terminal and interchange inspections through running repairs which keep the car in serviceable condition to heavy repairs in which such major components as hopper-car side sheets may be replaced. Based on current replacement rates, the average life of a freight car is about 22 years, during which it will have had at least one major overhaul. Types of cars made less popular by changes in the rate structure and commodities handled, such as the 40-ft. boxcar, are frequently rebuilt almost beyond recognition, in railroad, contract or car builders' shops. Cars undergoing such conversions as stretching from 40 to 50 ft., adding sliding-sill underframes and increasing capacity from 50 to 70 tons with new trucks emerge as essentially new units. However, AAR regulations now prohibit the general acceptance in interchange of cars over 40 years old regardless of whether their current state meets all other requirements.

Interchange and Inspections

Current FRA rules allow a train to operate a maximum of 500 miles between car inspections and brake performance tests provided that there is no change in the consist of the entire train. Establishment of responsibility for repairs and other aspects of operation requires inspection and acceptance of cars and their loads at the point where they are interchanged between railroads in an interline movement; for unit trains (Chapter 14), agreements are in force allowing interchange on the basis of inspections only at the point of train origin and as required by the 500-mile rule.

Periodic work legally required includes *in-date tests* of air brake performance and "COT&S" (Clean, Oil, Test and Stencil) disassembly and rework as necessary of the brake valve assemblies; for the current ABDW design the interval (on the basis of demonstrated reliability in service) of 144 months is long enough to take the car to its likely first major overhaul.

6

THE TRAIN

The business of the railroad is the selling and delivery of transportation. From an economic standpoint, it's the ability to assemble and move a large number of coupled cars as a unit that distinguishes rail systems: so the real name of the game is running *trains*. The rails and the flanged wheels guide the individual cars and let them roll with minimum friction, but action of the train as a whole is considerably more complicated than just the sum of the actions of its parts.

What's A Train?

The track is not known to be clear until *all* of a train has passed, so it's extremely important for safety sake to identify each train and be sure that it's intact. For operating purposes, the Book of Rules defines a train very specifically as "an engine or more than one engine coupled, with or without cars, *displaying markers*." Basic markers are a headlight or other white light on the front of the "consist" and a red flag, lantern or reflector plate on the rear end.

Couplers

In order to have a train, cars and locomotives must be coupled together. The original coupler, an eyebar or a piece of chain connecting the train cars, evolved in two directions. In Great Britain and Europe it became a system with spring buffers at the corners of the cars (to make the thud less sickening as the engine stopped) and a short chain (freight) or tightened turnbuckle (passenger) tying the cars together. Since the buffers provide refuge room for the trainman as he stands between the rails to drop the link over the hook as the cars come together, this system is still in general use.

In the United State, the coupling evolved into the "link and pin" arrangement. A single loop of iron held by a pin through a vertical hole in the "draw-head" on one car was guided into a slot on the approaching car by the switchman and secured by dropping a loose pin in place through the link. While in theory it was possible to hold up the link with a stick, and some draw-head designs supposedly left room for the fingers as their striking surfaces came together, in practice the link and pin coupler was treacherous. Thousands of fingers, hands and lives were lost due to its use. The Federal Safety Appliance Act of 1893 required the adoption of couplers which would permit cars to be connected without requiring a person to go between them. Of the thousands of patented devices designed to do this, the swinging-knuckle design of Major Eli H. Janney was selected for standardization.

E's and F's

The current standard coupler for general freight service is the Type E shown in Fig. 6-1. Like all Janney couplers, it works on the "clasped-hand" principle. To couple automatically, one or both of the knuckles must be open when the cars are pushed together; the knuckle swings to the closed position and a lock drops in place and holds it closed. Various internal features prevent the knuckle lock from jiggling or bouncing open under shock and vibration. To uncouple, the cars are pushed together enough to take the load off the coupler ("the slack is taken in") and the "cut" or uncoupling lever is turned by hand, lifting the lock pin. One knuckle opens as the cars move apart, and uncoupling has taken place.

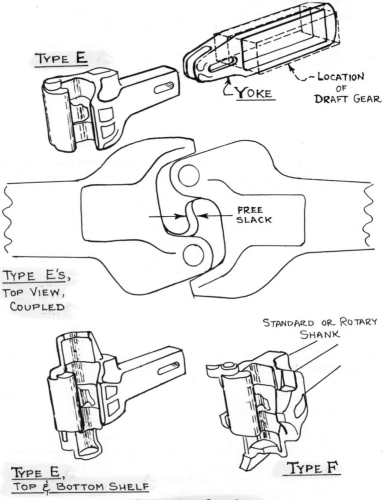

Figure 6-1 Couplers

The E coupler does not interlock in the vertical direction. Coupler height is maintained between 31½ and 34½ in. above the rail with the car either loaded or empty. The coupler knuckles are 11 in. high, so there is always a nominal engagement of at least 8 inches. Under extreme conditions it is possible for couplers to "slip by" in a moving train.

Interlocking Couplers

Passenger-train cars, hazardous-material tank cars and many other freight cars are now equipped with couplers which also interlock in the vertical direction. Fig. 6-1 shows some of these. The passenger Type H "Tite-lock" is similar to the Type F freight coupler but uses some machined parts to restrict free slack between mating surfaces to a minimum. F and H couplers do not allow the knuckles to slide vertically on each other and so must be hinged in the vertical plane to allow some up-and-down swiveling as cars move over vertical curves in the track and coupler carrier irons must allow vertical motion as well.

The E-shelf couplers, like F's and H's, will tend in a derailment to reduce the severity of the accident by preventing the cars from disengaging, reducing jacknifing and the possibility of puncturing cars of hazardous materials. Shelf clearance is enough, though, to eliminate the vertical-swiveling complication. Also, if the shank of an E coupler mated to a shelf coupler should be pulled out, it will be prevented from dropping to the track and perhaps causing a derailment.

Rotary-shank couplers which allow a car to be rotated 180° to dump its contents without uncoupling are an important feature of cars for unit-train service where this form of unloading is used. They must be of interlocking design.

Couplers for long cars, such as 89-ft. piggyback flats, must have extra long (60 in.) shanks and wide coupler pockets to allow enough coupler swing for sharp curves. On these cars in particular, it may be necessary to line up the couplers manually so they will couple.

Draft Gear

Even before the automatic coupler was invented it became clear that some controlled "give" between the drawhead and the car body could greatly reduce shock and strain on the cars. The importance of *draft gear* and the difficulty of meeting all its requirements is well illustrated by the fact that over 21,000 U.S. patents have been issued in this field. At first a stout spring was used, but it was soon found far better to use an arrangement which would dissipate the energy of a starting, stopping or coupling impact in *friction* between its internal parts rather than springing back. Another essential feature of the draft gear was to provide relative motion or "slack" between the cars to help the locomotive start a heavy load, as mentioned in Chapter 4. With high-tractive-force, multi-unit diesel power this has become less important.

Impact Protection

The role of draft gear in protecting cars and lading remains and indeed has become more significant as train weight has increased. There is about ¾ in. "free slack" between a pair of E's and half that between two F's; there is a total of somewhat over six inches of stretch per car in the head end of a heavy train being started. Management of this slack to avoid breaking the train in two is one of the biggest challenges to the engineer's skill.

Draft Gear Capacity

The space into which draft gear must fit has been standardized; most cars have draft gear pockets 24 5/8 in. long, with total coupler travel of 5½ in. draft (pull) and buff (compression). In 1956 an alternate standard pocket 36 in. long was established, with maximum travel of 9½ in. The impact energy which can be absorbed at any given level of maximum force is directly proportional to the distance over which the impact can be spread out; improved rubber-friction or friction-hydraulic draft gears fitting in these pockets can keep car impact forces within the 500,000 lb. limit in loaded 70-ton cars striking at about 4 mph. Car center sills now have a compressive strength without serious distress of about 1,250,000 lb. The cars may take the punishment, but merchandise within may not, even if held in place with rugged load-restraining devices to prevent damage from internal impacts in the lading.

Cushion Cars

As a result, about one sixth of all freight cars are equipped, with longer-travel cushioning systems, either sliding center sill (Fig. 6-2) or end of car. Fig. 6-3 shows typical maximum-force curves for different lengths of travel as impact speed increases. Nobody *wants* to bang cars together this vigorously, but impacts in the range above the "safe coupling" limit of 4 mph do occur often enough to make the extra complication and cost of the cushion car a reasonable investment for carrying sensitive freight.

End-of-car cushioning devices have up to 15-inch travel, sliding-sill cars up to 30 in., with most providing 20-inch motion. The effectiveness in spreading out impact of the two types, within their limits of travel, is essentially the same. Action in the train may be considerably different. In the sliding-sill car the two couplers and their regular, short-travel draft gears are held the same distance apart at all times by the sill; train slack per car is not increased. The end-of-car devices, acting like very long-travel draft gears, may let each car shorten by more than two feet.

Draft System Strength

As trains have become heavier and locomotives more powerful, all parts of the system, knuckles, coupler shanks, yokes (holding coupler to draft gear), draft gear parts, center sill lugs (against which the draft gear acts), and the center sills themselves have been strengthened. This has been done by increasing the size of parts where interchangeability is not affected and by using stronger alloys and heat treatment. However, the knuckle is deliberately kept weaker than the coupler shank, the shank weaker than the yoke, and so on. Thus, in case of failure out on the road, it will usually be the knuckle, which can be readily replaced by the crew, that breaks, and the likelihood of something serious such as a buckled center sill is remote. Accordingly, coupler knuckles for general service are made of Grade B steel and have a strength of 350,000 lb. For "captive" service where all cars in the train will be designed to the latest and strongest standards, Grade E knuckles with an ultimate strength of 650,000 lb. are available, giving the railroad much more leeway in adding tractive force on the head end.

Power to Stop

In moving traffic over a railroad, *power to stop* can be more important than tractive force, big cars or strong couplers. If the motive power can handle only a few cars at a time, more trains can be run until the job is done, provided that a steady procession of them can move at reasonable speed without running into each other. That takes reliable braking power.

Before any train leaves its terminal, its crew must follow a specified test procedure to verify: that pressure at the rear end is within 15 psi of that being fed into its train line by the locomotive; that system leakage with brakes applied does not exceed 5 psi per minute; and that brakes on each car have applied and released properly.

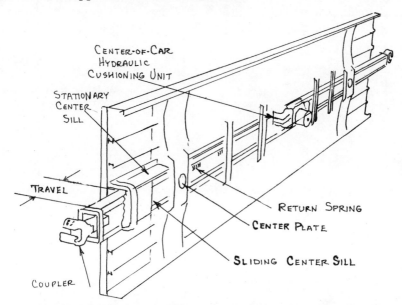

In the sliding center sill system, the car body, with its trucks, "floats" on the separate sill connecting the couplers, which are isolated from shocks by a center-of-car hydraulic cushioning device with travel of 15, 20 or 30 in. in either direction. A return spring re-centers the sill between impacts. A regular draft gear is still needed at each coupler to prevent a blow from traveling through the cushioned car and hitting the next car, with the added mass of an uncushioned center sill. The sliding sill system adds about 3 tons to the weight of a 50-ft. car.

Figure 6-2 Sliding Center Sill Cushioning

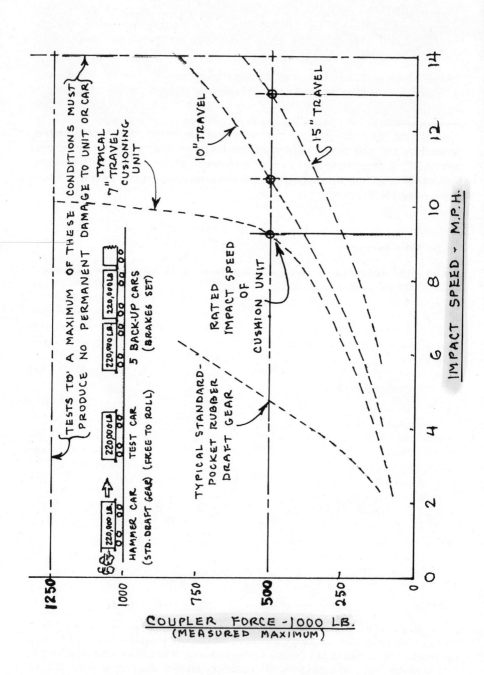

Figure 6-3 Hydraulic Cushioning Performance and Requirements

The Air Brake

Since 1900, the common factor on all trains in American railroading has been the air brake -- the most complex set of equipment on the freight car fleet, and the only one that has some components which could possibly be called "delicate."

Like wheel and coupler contours, air brake components have had to be standardized throughout the system. Despite the restriction of having to insure that each innovation would work satisfactorily in a train with its predecessors, brake performance has continued to improve in major respects as the various systems have been invented, developed, tested, phased in and phased out. Each of the features of the present ABD and new ABDW freight brake system has come about as a result of some limitation in earlier equipment which became enough of a problem to require improvements.

Brake Pipe Pressure

The chief function of the air brake system is to provide adequate, uninterrupted pressure from car to car. With the train assembled in the departure yard, the single air hose at the end of each car is manually connected to its neighbor, with all the angle cocks (shut-off valves) except at each end of the train in open position. Automatic coupler assemblies which also make the air connection have been perfected and are widely used in rapid-transit service, but they are not compatible with the existing system, and the formidable job of making a changeover has so far not been judged worthwhile.

The brake system is charged, either by the air compressors on the locomotives or from a yard air supply (usually quicker), if available. Maximum braking power varies, within limits, simply by adjusting the feed valve on the locomotive. On a solid train of empties headed for a relatively level run, pressure would probably be set at a value near the lower legal limit of 70 psi, providing adequate braking with minimum chance of sliding any wheels flat. More demanding conditions would call for trainline pressure up to the 90 psi maximum for normal freight train operation. Passenger train pressure is 110 psi.

Release

When the pressure throughout the train has built up, the brake valve on each car is in the "release" position (Fig. 6-4), with the brake pipe connected to the reservoirs and the brake cylinder exhaust connected to the atmosphere (via a special "wasp excluder" fitting that insures that mud daubers can't frustrate brake action). There will always be some leakage, resulting in lower pressure at the rear end of the train. But the actual pressure in the reservoirs on each car is the system's reference, and its response to *change* in brake pipe pressure is unaffected.

92

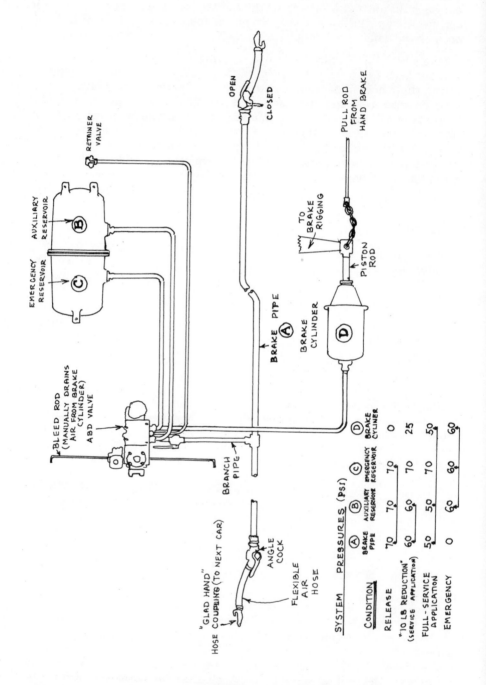

Figure 6-4 The Automatic Air Brake

The Fail-Safe Principle

When braking is required, the engineer (on a locomotive with the current 26L equipment) moves his automatic brake valve handle to a position within the "service" range corresponding to the amount of retardation he wants. This *reduces* pressure in the brake pipe leading back through the train, at a controlled rate. This reduction causes the ABD valve on each car to use air from the auxiliary reservoir to *build up* pressure in the brake cylinder, applying the brakes.

This fail-safe, reverse action is the basis for the whole technology of the automatic air brake as it has developed from George Westinghouse's invention of 1872. With a supply of air on each car, a train break-in-two, a burst air hose, an air compressor failure or any other situation causing loss of pressure will bring the train to a stop. The scores of improvements which have been and still are being incorporated into the system work to speed up, smooth out, fine-tune and otherwise improve braking action throughout the train.

Service Application

For each pound of reduction in brake pipe pressure, the valve will build up 2 1/2 psi in the brake cylinder, until a "full service" reduction of 20 psi from the 70 psi brake pipe pressure produces a full service application of 50 psi cylinder pressure (Fig. 6-4). At this point, the pressures in reservoir and cylinder are equal, and any further reduction in the pipe pressure will have no further effect.

Slack Action Control

In the days of hand brakes, in an emergency the engineer could only: set the steam brake on the locomotive drivers (or put the engine in reverse); whistle "down brakes" to signal the brakemen to start winding 'em up on the cars; and pray. The locomotive would start to slow down, and then the cars would run into it, one by one. The crude draft gear of the time would probably be enough to keep the impacts from throwing cars off the track, since the engine didn't have much braking power anyway, but it was not a graceful process.

With the first version of the automatic air brake, the brake on each car would begin to apply only after there had been time for the air in its section of the brake pipe to flow up toward the opening to atmosphere in the locomotive brake valve. This took time, time enough for the slack to run in before the brakes of the rear of a long train even began to take hold. With good braking power on the head end of the train, the result was quite violent, often, enough to buckle the train.

Quick Service

The remedy was to add a "serial action" feature to the brake valve on each car. As the valve sensed the reduced pressure, it not only applied pressure to its own brake cylinder but also vented brake pipe air. This would in turn speed up the pressure reduction in the brake pipe of the next car. The modern valves use this basic idea in a variety of ways to move air among the various reservoir, brake pipe and brake cylinder volumes and the atmosphere, not only to speed up and improve the certainty of brake applications but to speed up release as well.

94

Emergency Braking

For an emergency application, the brake valve opens the brake pipe wide (the big hole position). The resulting rapid rate of brake pipe pressure reduction causes the car valves to dump the contents of both auxiliary and emergency reservoirs into the brake cylinder (Fig. 6-4). This builds up a brake cylinder pressure equal to 6/7 of brake pipe pressure (as compared to 5/7 for full service). The rate of application back through the train is as fast as 900 ft. per second, rather impressive considering that the speed of sound in air is only 1,100 ft. per sec., and that is the theoretical absolute maximum rate of "passing the word" pneumatically.

Brake Rigging and Braking Ratio

Br. Ratio := Braking ratio is the relation of the weight of the car or locomotive to the braking force; that is, the percentage obtained by dividing the braking force by the weight of the car or locomotive. Brake cylinder pressure is translated into stopping power at the wheel treads by the brake rigging and brake shoes. Most freight cars use a single cylinder on the car body, connected by levers and rods to one brake shoe per wheel. There is a single rod connection to the brake gear on each truck, and this is the only disconnection to be made in separating truck from car. The same rigging is actuated by a connecting chain from the geared hand brake, now used only in switching individual cars and to keep "parked" equipment from moving. An alternative to this standard "foundation" brake rigging, used particularly on cars whose carbody design would complicate the rigging — (such as large-diameter tank cars where the tank serves as the car's "center-sill" structural element), is the use of two smaller brake cylinders on each truck which apply force directly to the brake beams.

The brake ratio is calculated by the following formula:

$$\frac{P \times L \times A \times N \times 100}{\text{Weight in Lb.}} \text{ (for percentage)}$$

Where P = Brake Cylinder Pressure (50 lbs.)
A = Area in square inches of brake cylinder piston
L = Ratio of brake levers
N = Number of brake cylinders

As an example, let's take a box car that weighs about 80,000 lb. and has a gross rail load of 220,000 lb. This car has a brake lever ratio of 12.2 to 1, a piston area of 78.54 in. and one brake cylinder. Using the formula from above, we can determine the light weight ratio:

$$\frac{50 \times 12.2 \times 78.54 \times 1 \times 100}{80,000} = 59.89\%$$

For the gross rail load, we get the following formula:

$$\frac{50 \times 12.2 \times 78.54 \times 1 \times 100}{220,000} = 21.77\%$$

The calculated ratio is strictly theoretical, as it does not take into account such items as the force of the return spring in the brake cylinder and friction in the brake rigging from angularity, dirt, etc. The actual brake shoe force measurement is called the Golden Shoe ratio, and is usually about 65% of the calculated measurement. Golden Shoe ratios are determined by test mechanism which is substituted for the shoes on a car. The device has a digital display that gives a direct reading in pounds of brake force when air pressure is put into the brake cylinder.

AAR standards call for the following calculated ratios:

cast iron shoes -- 13% (gross rail load)
                 53% (light weight)
composition -- 6.5% (gross rail load)
shoes   30% (light weight)

Slack Adjustment

The distance which the brake cylinder piston must travel to move the shoes against the wheels depends on the wear of all the parts of the rigging and particularly on the remaining thickness of the brake shoes. The longer the travel, the greater the volume of the brake cylinder and the lower the equalizing pressure in a full-service or emergency brake application. All cars are now required to have automatic brake slack adjusters which keep piston travel within limits.

Brake Force Ratios

The braking force applied to the brake shoes (expressed as its ratio to the car weight) results in a retarding effect with cast-iron shoes which is quite low at high speed (say 65 mph and above) but becomes as much as 2 1/2 times higher as the train speed is reduced. The friction attainable between wheel and rail to slow the train also varies in the same direction with speed, but to a much smaller degree. In practice, the braking ratio could be about 150 percent for an emergency passenger-train application and no more than 70 to 80 percent for any empty freight car in full-service. Otherwise, there would be too much likelihood of sliding wheels flat. This causes two problems.

Empty and Load Brakes

In freight service, the difference in weight between a loaded and empty car is now as much as 4 to 1. The same braking power for a loaded car will thus result in only one quarter the stopping rate of the empty. And at the higher speeds, the stopping distance will become very long; the most economical operating speed for a loaded train, considering the cost of energy against the cost of equipment-time, may not be practical because stopping distance becomes too long for the signaling system.

Extra-cost "empty and load" braking systems which automatically adjust the braking power to the weight of the car have been available for many years, but haven't been widely used except where heavily-loaded trains must be lowered down particularly steep grades. Further simplification and cost reduction in the latest designs of empty and load systems may result in some reconsideration of the matter.

High-Speed Braking

Early streamlined trains had to use elaborate speed-governor-controlled brake systems to allow very high braking ratios during the high-speed portion of a stop, progressively reducing it as the brake shoe friction increased. Individual wheel-slip controls, similar to those on locomotive driving axles, acted to momentarily reduce braking on an axle that started to slide, avoiding the need for a reduced average braking force to take care of local adhesion problems.

Composition Brake Shoes

Many problem areas have been mitigated considerably by the development of composition brake shoes, first used extensively in the early 1960's. These have both a higher coefficient of friction (simplifying brake rigging and reducing the force it must generate)and one whose variation with speed better matches rail-wheel adhesion.

Release, Runaways and Retainers

The freight brake system can *apply* braking power in steps but does not have the *graduated release* capability which is practical in relatively short trains and is provided in passenger brake systems so that the engineer can make accurate station stops and come to rest without a "stonewall" effect.

In freight trains, once release is initiated by increasing brake-pipe pressure, the brake valve completely exhausts the brake cylinder while recharging the reservoirs. The only way to reduce braking is to release the brakes completely and then re-apply them at a lower level. With the earlier systems, this could take a matter of minutes in a long train. If brake application was made at less than 30 mph in a long train, it was necessary to stop completely and allow all the brakes on the rear end to release before starting again. The ABD system largely eliminates this problem by its accelerated release (450 ft./second) and relatively rapid re-application capabilities.

Retainers and Pressure-Maintaining

When air brakes were still in the early stages of development, there was always the chance that the train could run away while the brakes were being released prior to being re-charged to make up for the gradual leakage that eventually reduces brake cylinder pressure. This was initially overcome by the *retainer,* a valve on each car (manually turned up at the top of a descending grade) which retained some pressure in the brake cylinders after release. At the foot of the grade, the train would have to stop again while retainers were turned down.

In most cases, use of retainers has been eliminated by the *pressure maintaining* feature of the 26L locomotive brake valve (also retrofitted to earlier models). This maintains brake pipe pressure at a level that gives the desired degree of braking, making up for leakage by feeding air into the brake pipe at the appropriate rate. With the dynamic brake on the locomotive, to adjust for differences in train action, e.g. curves, it is usually possible to hold the train at the desired speed throughout a descent. Occasionally, retainers are still useful in holding heavy tonnage trains on grades while recharging after a stop, where the independent alone would not hold the train.

Braking Horsepower and Hot Wheels

Since it's effective on all the wheels of the train, air braking horsepower can greatly exceed locomotive horsepower, as well it should. A 13,000 ton train going down a two percent grade must dissipate 83,000 hp in heat to remain at a steady speed of 30 mph. Dynamic-brake horsepower may be about equal to the traction horsepower rating of the locomotive, perhaps 12,000 to 18,000 hp in this case. Every bit helps save brakeshoes, which is why you'll see "helper" locomotives attached to trains going *downhill*, to contribute to dynamic braking capacity, though all railroads do not agree on this practice. In trains of less than 100 tons per operative brake, downhill dynamic brake helpers can cause undesired slack status changes. On a grade this steep, though, most of the work will have to be done by the brakeshoes. If the grade is long, it may be necessary to stop and cool the wheels.

Since the brake heating environment is a wheel's toughest task, why not use a disc brake in which the thermal load has been taken off the wheel tread? Disc brakes are used widely in passenger service, but the relative simplicity, wheel-cleaning characteristics, minimum weight and minimum cost of tread brakes has so far made them the most cost-effective system for general freight service. Even though brake shoe replacement is by far the most frequent item of maintenance on the freight car, it's also one of the easiest and quickest.

The Independent Brake

Brakes on the locomotive units themselves are controlled by the separate *independent* brake valve. This is a "straight air" system in which braking force can be applied and released to any desired degree without delay. It is used in switching cars when their brakes are not connected and is very important in train handling, allowing the engineer to gently "bunch" the slack, for example, before applying the train brake. Since retarding forces of independent and dynamic braking would be compounded and applied to the same wheels, they should not be used at the same time, as the wheels would slide.

Electro-Pneumatic Braking

The time lag in the best air braking is a matter of several seconds. Where trains must run on close headway or make many stops, this is a serious limitation which can only be overcome by transmitting braking signals at the speed of light instead of the speed of sound. Westinghouse himself felt at one point in the 1880's that only an electrically-controlled air brake would be usable in long trains. But he went ahead and improved the quick-service features of his air brake to such a degree that it has continued to do the job satisfactorily for general freight service. The enormous problem of maintaining reliable electrical connectors between 1,800,000 freight cars has been averted.

Electrically-controlled air brakes are used in all multiple-unit electric trains (where control circuits must be maintained throughout the train anyway) in railroad and rapid-transit service.

Two-Pipe Systems

For special situations involving operation of loaded trains down steep grades the addition of a second brake pipe can eliminate stops to set up and turn down retainers and may be worth the extra cost on unit trains used intensively in a specific service. One option is to use pressure in the second brake pipe to set the retainers from the locomotive cab. In another system, the second brake pipe is connected to the brake cylinders on each car by way of a simple differential pressure valve which allows pressure from the regular brake system or the second pipe, whichever is higher, to enter the cylinder. The second pipe thus functions as a *straight air* system in which the engineer controls retardation directly. Since reducing pressure in this system will *reduce* braking, graduated release is provided and precise control during the descent is possible; at the same time, the standard automatic air brake system is fully charged and is available at all times should the straight air system fail.

Passenger-train cars have traditionally used a second train line for the *air signal* system allowing trainmen to communicate with the engine cab. The signal valves in each car reduce pipe pressure, blowing a whistle in the locomotive.

Track-Train Dynamics

A 150-car train of mixed loads and empties stretches more than a mile and a half. When starting up, the locomotive will move about 75 ft. before the caboose even quivers. Drawbar pull in moving the weight of 9,500 tons on level track is about 25 tons, more than the weight of some of the cars in the train. However, most track is not level but is a series of ups and downs. When the rear of the train is on a 1.0 percent downgrade and the forward half is headed uphill at the same rate, there will be a net compression at mid-train of about 30 tons, pushing the slack in and compressing the draft gears. This compressed section of train must shift along the consist as it moves over grades. Add in the effects of curves, braking time lags, cars of different weight and with short- or long-travel cushioning, and the dynamics of this enormous snake becomes most complex. This is, of course, an extreme situation. When proper train handling methods are observed, when long car-short car coupling locations are regulated, and extreme "loads rear, empties forward" situations are avoided, then track-train dynamics problems can be minimized.

Ideally, a trainmaster would like to make up trains according to where the cars are going, rather than by where they must go in the consist to stay on the track. He or she would also like every engineer to have the experience and skill to be able to run any train smoothly, safely and quickly over the division.

Train-Dynamics Analysis

Fortunately, it is now practical to study by computer analysis the effects of train make-up and handling by calculating the forces developed and absorbed by the components of each car as it moves along a representation of the grades and curves of any specific rail route. In-train forces developed can be determined with good accuracy, and the limits of train-handling technique in minimizing run-in and run-out forces can be worked out for favorable and unfavorable arrangements of light and heavy, short and long cars within the train.

Using test data on individual car behavior in Transportation Test Center experiments with instrumented cars subjected to pull and buff forces up to 250,000 lb. between multi-unit locomotives while on curves and grades, the train forces can be interpreted in terms of the margin of safety against derailment.

The L-V Ratio

The key factor is the ratio of lateral forces on each wheel to the vertical load holding it down to the rail. This value reflects the combination of: the weight of the car; the bounce, rock and other dynamic effects on the truck suspension; weight shifts between axles from braking and train forces; brake shoe reactions; and (usually most important) the effects of

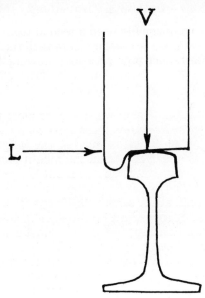

Effect	Lateral to Vertical Wheel Force Ratio
Incipient Wheel Climb (New Rail)	1.29
Incipient Wheel Climb (Worn Rail)	0.75
Rail Overturn	0.64
Wheel Lift (Zero Speed on Superelevation)	0.82

Figure 6-5 The L-V Ratio

lateral coupler forces as affected by the angle of the coupler shanks through which pull and buff forces must reach the car. Fig. 6-5 shows some examples of critical L-V ratios for a car with a high (98 in.) center of gravity. The rail-overturn figure is conservative since it assumes the rail has no stiffness against twisting (which would let the weight of other wheels help keep it upright), but other values are considered realistic.

Under various test and analysis projects which make up the Track-Train Dynamics Program, jointly sponsored by the FRA, AAR, RPI (Railway Progress Institute, an association of rail equipment manufactures) and the Canadian TDC (Transport Development Commission), the tools are becoming available for predicting the performance of any consist over any route and determining if restrictions, such as avoiding long-short coupled car combinations, are necessary. The programs and principles developed also provide guidance in throttle and brake handling in efficiently moving trains over difficult routes. Some railroads are also using this information in programming simulators used to train engineers, and in devices which continually display, in the cab, the position of the entire consist with respect to the profile of the route it's traversing.

Of course, the general principles of train make-up and handling have been developed over the years by experience, bitter and otherwise, and are reflected in the features of current brake, coupler, car and locomotive design. The ability to get better answers with hypothetical rather than real-life accidents promises more efficient railroading all the way around.

7

SIGNALS AND COMMUNICATION

The railroad is classified as a "single degree of freedom" mode of transport, that is, rail vehicles can only go back and forth along the "guideway." With only this one degree of freedom in which to maneuver, attaining high unit capacity and safety on an all-weather basis depends on a control system that keeps its vehicles in proper relation to each other. If paths cross or vehicles overtake each other from the same or opposite directions, a collision is inevitable.

The steam railroad was the first system where speeds could be high enough for stopping distance to exceed sighting distance; therefore, a clear track had to be assured by some means other than an alert driver. The railroad pioneered in the development of several principles and techniques which today form the basis for all successful traffic control systems.

Scheduling and Dispatching

American railroads quickly evolved to operation by timetable. Many of the lines were single-track affairs, so meeting points had to be established at stations where there were sidings, and the short trains of the time meant that traffic was rather dense in terms of number of trips per day. Delaying one train essentially paralyzed the line, since a train had no alternative but to wait until the train it was required to meet eventually showed up. In turn, it would delay all the following trains which couldn't move until it came through.

Timetable and Train-Order Operation (T & TO)

In 1851 Superintendent Charles Minot of the Erie used his recently-installed telegraph line to issue the first *train order* -- a message changing the meeting point between two trains, to the benefit of both, but doing it safely by first determining that the train being held at the meeting point had in fact "got the word." Minot had to run the train himself, since the engineer would have no part of disobeying the timetable. This organized system of train dispatching by "timetable and train order" (T & TO) was rapidly adopted due to the significant benefits. Procedures were standardized by committees of the Standard Rules Convention, forerunner of today's Association of American Railroads (AAR).

Train Orders

Rules have been developed over the years to specify the form of train orders and to eliminate any uncertainty as to their meaning, and to insure their accurate transmission, delivery and observance. Train movements are still authorized in the name of the superintendent of each railroad division, by the current employees timetable and orders issued by the *train dispatcher*. The process is safe but time consuming, and takes about 35 pages in the Book of Rules. As Fig. 7-1 shows, our East-West System uses this method of operation on its single-track line from W to C, which handles heavy trains but not very many per day.

Superiority by Direction

Many of the rules governing T & TO operation relate to "superiority of trains" -- principally, which train will take siding at a meeting point. Misinterpretation of these rules can be a source of either hazard or delay.

Time Spacing

For trains following each other, T & TO operation must rely upon *time spacing* and *flag protection* to keep each train off the back of its predecessor. A train may not leave a station less than five minutes after the preceding train has departed. There's no assurance that this spacing will be retained as the trains move along the line, so the flagman (rear brakeman) of a train slowing down or stopping will light and throw off a five-minute red flare ("fusee") which may not be passed by the next train. If the train has to stop, he must trot back with red flag or lantern a sufficient distance to protect the train, remaining there until the train is ready to move and he is called back (in pre-radio days) by whistle signal -- four long blasts to return from west or south, five from east or north, plus one toot per track number if in multiple track territory, to be sure only the right flag comes in.

A fusee and two track torpedoes provide protection as he scrambles back and the train resumes speed. There is no reason the system can't work, but it depends on a series of human activities and is no fun in bad weather.

Safety and Capacity -- Block Signaling

It is perfectly possible to operate a railroad safely without signals, and about half of the route miles in the U.S. make do without them; most of this mileage, of course, represents branch-line trackage, usually occupied by only one train at a time. The purpose of signal systems is not so much to increase safety as it is to step up the *efficiency* and *capacity* of a line in handling traffic. Nevertheless, it's convenient to discuss signal system principles in terms of the three types of collisions they must prevent— rear-end, side-on, and head-on.

Manual Block Signaling

Block signal systems prevent a train from ramming the train ahead by dividing the main line into segments ("blocks") and allowing only one train in a block at a time, with *block signals* indicating whether or not the block ahead is occupied. In *manual block,* the signals are set by a human operator. Before clearing the signal, he must verify that any train which has previously entered the block is now clear of it; a written record is kept of the status of each block, and a prescribed procedure is used in communicating with the next operator.

The degree to which manual block frees up operations depends on whether "distant" signals (Fig. 7-2) are provided and on the spacing of "open" stations, those in which an operator is on duty. If (as is usually the case these days) it is many miles to the next block station, trains must be equally spaced. Nevertheless, manual block does afford a high degree of safety, and federal rules allow a maximum speed of 79 mph in manual-block territory, as compared to 59 and 49 mph for passenger and freight trains, respectively, in "dark" (no signals) territory.

Our E-W System operates the line from V and U to D on this basis. This route, which usually is not busy, experiences seasonal traffic "rushes," during which additional block stations can be assigned operators to keep things moving.

Automatic Block Signaling (A.B.S.)

The block signaling which does the most for increasing line capacity is *automatic* block signals (A.B.S.), in which the signals are controlled by the trains themselves. Presence or absence of a train is determined by the *track circuit.* Invented by Dr. William Robinson in 1872, the track circuit's key feature is that it is *fail safe.* As can be seen in Fig. 7-3, if the battery or any wire connections fail, or if a rail is broken, the relay can't pick up, and clear signal will not be displayed.

Vital Circuits

The track circuit is also an example of what is designated in railway signaling practice as a *vital* circuit, one which can give an unsafe indication if some of its components malfunction in certain ways. The track circuit is fail safe, but it could still give a "false clear" indication should its relay stick in the closed or "picked up" position. Vital-circuit relays, therefore, are built to very stringent standards: they are large devices; rely only on gravity (no springs) to drop the armature; and use special non-welding contacts which will not stick together if hit by a large surge of current (as from nearby lightning).

Track Circuit Adjustment

Getting a track circuit to be absolutely reliable is not a simple matter. The electrical leakage between the rails is considerable and varies greatly with the seasons of the year and the weather. The joints in bolted-rail track are by-passed with bond wires to insure low resistance at all times, but total resistance still varies. It is lower, for example, when cold weather shrinks the rails, and they pull tightly on the track bolts or when hot weather expands the rail to force the ends together tightly.

Battery voltage is limited to 1 to 2 volts, requiring a fairly sensitive relay. Despite this, the direct-current track circuit can be adjusted to do an excellent job, and false-clears are extremely rare.

104

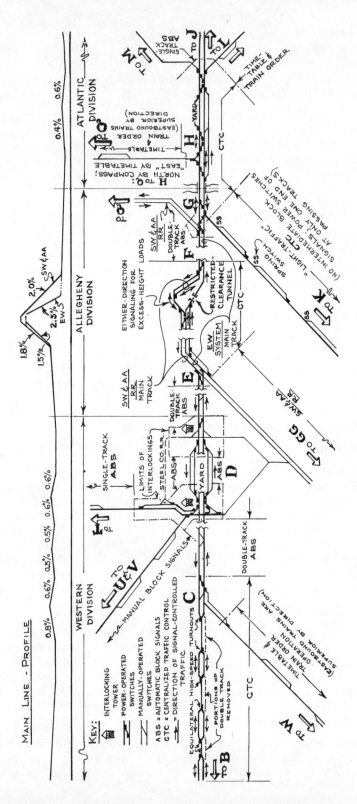

Figure 7-1 E-W System — Track and Signalling Arrangement

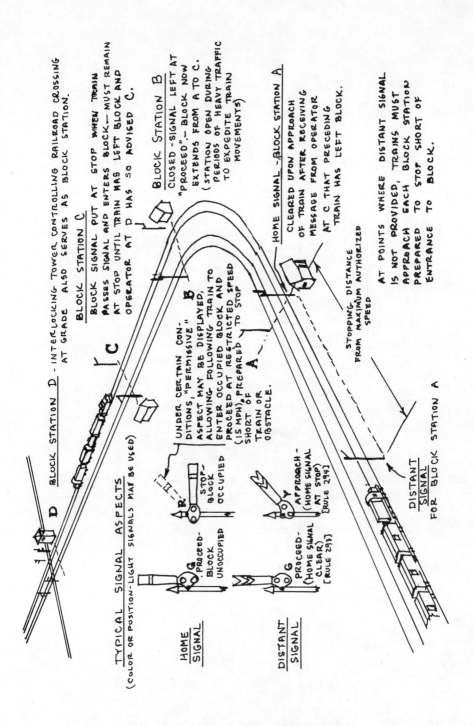

Figure 7-2 Manual Block Signalling

106

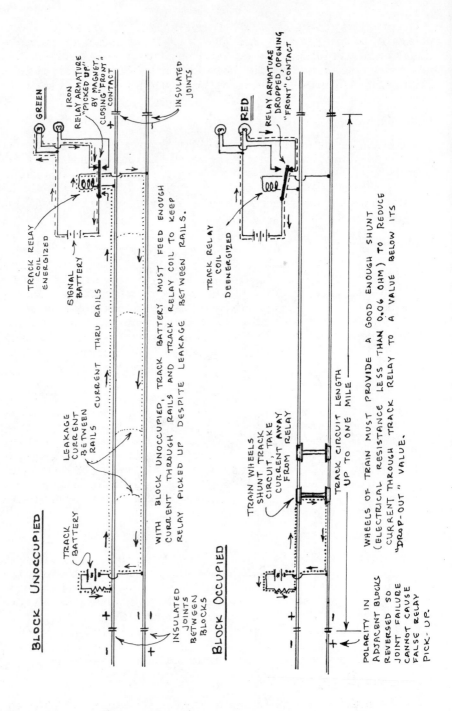

Figure 7-3 The Track Circuit (Note: Symbols for Electrical Components Are Pictorial, and Are Not Those Used in Railway Signalling Practice)

The principal improvement in the basic circuit has been to use slowly-pulsed DC so that the relay drops out and must be picked up again continually when the block is unoccupied. This allows use of a more sensitive relay which will detect a train, but additionally work in track circuits twice as long (about two miles) before leakage between the rails begins to threaten reliable relay operation.

Insulated Joints

The insulated joints defining block limits (usually used in dual sets in case one should get leaky) must be of rugged constuction and are now frequently bonded with the toughest plastic adhesives available in addition to being secured with permanently-crimped bolts. An alternative is the use of tuned audio-frequency track circuits which can do the job without insulated joints, which will be discussed later.

Signal and Train Spacing

Fig. 7-4 shows the situations determining the minimum block length for the standard "two-block, three-indication" A.B.S. system. Since a train may stop with its rear car just inside the rear boundary of a block, a following train will first receive warning just one block-length away. By law, no allowance may be made for how far the signal indication may be seen by the engineer. So the block must be as long as the longest stopping distance (with a service, not an emergency, brake application) for any train on the route, traveling at its maximum authorized speed.

Track Capacity

From this standpoint, it is important to allow trains to move along without receiving any "approach" indications which will force them to slow down. This requires a train spacing of *two* block lengths -- twice the stopping distance -- since the signal can't clear until the train ahead is completely out of the *second* block. If heavily loaded trains running at high speeds, with their long stopping distances, are in the picture, block lengths must be long, and it may not be possible to get enough trains over the line to produce appropriate revenue.

Multi-Aspect Signaling

The "three-block, four-indication" signaling shown in Fig. 7-4 reduces the "excess" train spacing by 50 percent. With warning two blocks to the rear, signal spacing need be only half the braking distance. In particularly congested areas, such as downgrades where stopping distances are long and trains are likely to bunch up, four-block, five-indication signaling may be provided. Advance approach, approach medium, approach and stop indications give a minimum of three-block warning, allowing further block-shortening and keep things moving.

Signal Aspects and Indications

Fig 7-4 uses aspects of "upper quadrant" semaphores to illustrate block signaling. These signals, with the blade rising 90° to give the clear indication, began to replace the lower-quadrant semaphores in the early 1900's and are still used in diagrams to show available aspects on each signal head. Since World War I, when electric lamps and lens systems bright enough to be seen against the sun were developed, most new wayside signals have used the same aspects day and night, avoiding the maintenance of the moving semaphore arm which still must be supplemented with lamps and lenses at night.

Some of the systems developed by different railroads are shown in Fig. 7-5. Within the general rules discussed below, a railroad is free to establish the simplest and most easily maintained system of aspects and indications that will keep traffic moving safely and meet any special requirements due to geography, traffic pattern or equipment.

Aspects such as flashing yellow for "approach medium," for example, may be used to provide an extra indication without an extra signal head. This is safe because a stuck flasher will result either in a steady-yellow "approach" or the more restrictive light-out aspect.

Special Aspects

System-wide aspects are illustrated in the Book of Rules. The signal-system rules in effect on each segment of line and each track (as illustrated on Fig. 7-1), along with rules for any special signal indications at particular locations, are established by the Employees Timetable on a divisional basis. The important thing, of course, is that there be no uncertainty whatsoever as to the meaning of a signal.

General Design Rules

Some rules regarding signaling practices are established and enforced by the FRA as law. An example is prohibiting the use of white as a "clear" aspect -- a missing colored lens would give a false indication. Other recommended practices come from the work of the Signal Section of the AAR. To abide by the "fail safe" rule, most two-light aspects are arranged so that the *absence* of *either* light will result in a more restrictive indication; if this is not the case, a filament-checking circuit must be used so that a burned out bulb will either cause the signal to "go red" or be completely extinguished. By rule, a dark signal must be regarded as being at the most restrictive aspect possible.

Absolute and Permissive Signals

Automatic block signals, whose purpose is to prevent rear-end collisions, have as their most restrictive indication "stop and proceed." Once the train has come to a stop, it is permitted to proceed at restricted speed (usually 15 mph maximum) but prepared to stop short of any obstruction, a train, broken rail, open switch, which has caused the red signal to be displayed. The permissive nature of a signal must be indentified by the presence of a number plate on the mast or a second marker light in a staggered position (Fig. 7-5). A marker light or second signal head in vertical position with respect to the main signal is an "absolute" signal, such as at a junction or at the end of a passing track, which indicates that a conflicting movement has been authorized and requires that an approaching train stop and *stay* stopped. Such a "stop and stay" signal can be passed only by the authority of a specific train order.

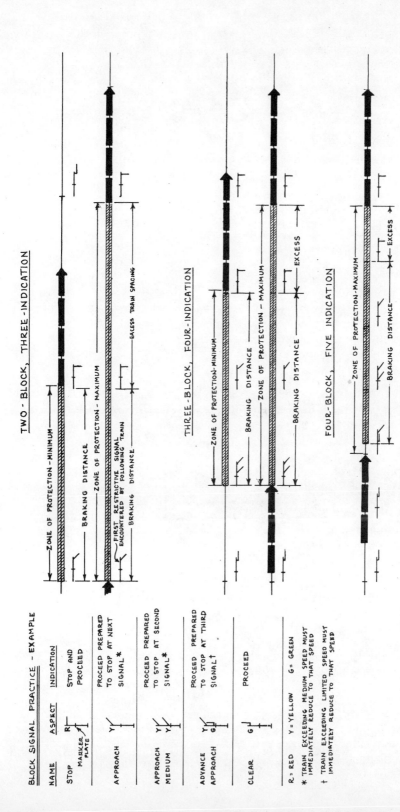

Figure 7-4 Block Signalling and Track Capacity

110

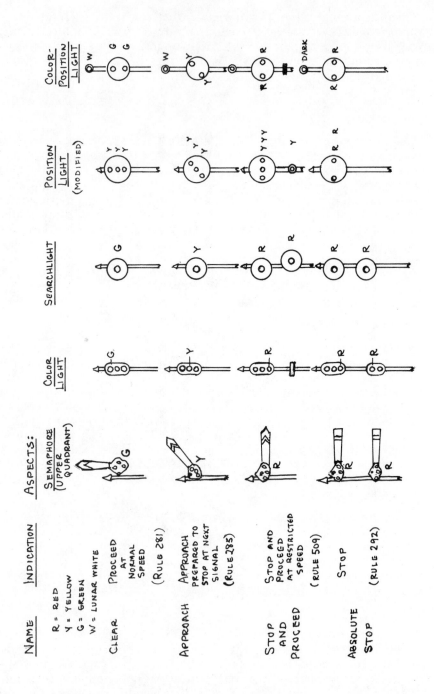

Figure 7-5 Signals of Different Types — Examples of Indications and Aspects, Interlocking and Automatic Block Signal Rules

Grade Signals

On an ascending grade, a tonnage train (one carrying its full rated load) will have a difficult time starting again if it's stopped by a block signal. Since its stopping distance on the grade is short, it can safely be allowed to proceed past a "stop and proceed" signal at restricted speed without a stop. Signals where this is the case are marked, usually with a "P" (for permissive) or "G" (for grade).

Cab Signaling

The earliest industrial use of electronics outside of communication systems was in the early 1920's in the form of *cab signaling* on "steam" railroads. By using a slow-pulsed AC, it was possible for the signal system to send a continuous message through the rails to a receiver/amplifier on the locomotive. Bringing the signal indication inside the cab where it cannot be obscured by fog and providing an audible alarm to further alert the engine crew to a restrictive indication increases the safety factor. The most attractive feature is that it allows a train to resume speed promptly when a block is cleared, even though the signal may not become visible for some distance. Subsequent improvements in electronic technology have allowed use of DC or audio-frequency transmission through the rails.

Automatic Train Stop/Automatic Train Control

Systems for automatically stopping the train (ATS) were a popular subject for inventors even before reliable train brakes had gone into general use. Systems using a mechanical trip, moved out of the way only when the signal is clear, to hit a brake actuator on the train are successfully used in rapid transit systems where: all the equipment is alike; the right of way is protected; and ice is not a problem. The first relatively satisfactory ATS for steam railroading was the intermittent inductive system of the late 1920's. In this scheme a magnetic device on the locomotive passes near and is actuated by an iron lineside "inductor," *unless* the effect of the inductor is nullified by an electromagnet inside. The magnet is energized only if the block signal is clear.

Since ATS provides only an on-off control, it must take effect at the first restrictive signal, where there is still stopping distance. Before passing the restrictive signal, the engineer has a few seconds to retain control of the brakes by operating a "forestalling" lever; if he fails to do so, or if he holds it down more than 15 seconds, a "penalty application" of the air brakes will occur.

ATC

More precise automatic supervision of train operation is available with continuous-coded *automatic train control* in which pulses at various repetitive rates in the rails are decoded by a receiver on the train and used to ensure that train speed is brought into accord with approach-medium, approach or stop indications. ATC systems, usually in combination with cab signaling, are in use on several thousand miles of the most heavily traveled routes.

By ICC (now FRA) order of 1951, train speeds in excess of 79 mph are permitted only where ATS, ATC or cab signals are in use.

Interlocking

Once turnouts and crossings were developed so that tracks could branch from or across each other, it became apparent that some way of assuring a clear route was needed if trains were to take advantage of their speed capabilities. The answer was *interlocking*, developed as early as 1857.

Railroad Crossings at Grade

At any crossing the law requires a "statutory stop" to verify that the way is clear before a train can proceed, unless the crossing is protected by an "interlocking plant." Operation was originally completely mechanical, with the levers in the control tower connected by long runs of "rodding" (actually, pipe) to cranks working the signal arms and track switches. In the "interlocking machine" (many of which are still in use), "tappets" and "dogs" on locking bars between the levers make it physically impossible to work the levers in clearing a route in anything but the proper sequence; signals must be at stop and derails open on the conflicting routes before the signal can be moved to "clear" from its normal stop position.

Throwing a track switch under a train had to be avoided, so a complex arrangement of detector bars was included which, when held down by the presence of wheels, impeded the movement of the levers. As soon as reliable circuits became available, they replaced the detector bars for this "occupancy locking" purpose.

Electric Interlocking

Interlocking functions can now be performed electrically (*not* electronically) by vital-circuit relays while switches and signals are power operated, but the things to be accomplished remain the same. Actually, a number of distinct types of locking is required to prevent all possible accidents. Before a route is cleared, for example, the system must also assure that no other trains are approaching at such a speed that they could not be stopped before intruding on the route being set up; this is handled by *time* or *approach* locking.

Junctions

To take care of junctions where trains are diverted from one route to another, the signals must control train speed. A train traveling straight through must be able to travel at full speed. Diverging routes will require some limit, depending on the turnout numbers (Fig. 3-6) and the track curvature, and the signals must control train speed to match.

Route or Speed Signaling?

One approach would be to have signals indicate which route has been set up and cleared for the train. American practice is to use *speed signaling*, in which the signal indicates not where the train is going but rather what speed is allowed through the interlocking. If this is less than normal speed, distant signals must also give warning so that the train can be brought down to this speed in time. Fig. 7-6 shows typical signal aspects and indications as they would appear to an engineer on the E-W approaching H from the west.

Once a route is established and the signal cleared, *route* locking must insure that nothing can be changed to *reduce* the route's speed capability from the time the train approaching it is committed to enter until it has cleared the last switch. Additional refinements to the basic system to speed up handling trains in rapid sequence include *sectional route locking* which unlocks portions of the route as soon as the train has cleared so that other routes can be set up promptly. Interlocking signals also function as block signals to provide rear-end protection.

Automatic and Route Interlocking

At isolated crossings at grade, an *automatic interlocking* can respond to the approach of a train by clearing its route, if there are no opposing movements cleared or in progress. Automatic interlocking returns everything to stop after the train has passed. Busy, complex interlockings, such as at the throat of a busy commuter-train terminal, may be handled by automated *route interlocking*, allowing one operator to take care of traffic which would require several levermen and a supervisor, if each switch and signal had to be thrown individually. Pushing a button at the entrance and exit of a route causes the machine to locate the best (highest speed) path that's available, set up all switches in that route, and clear the signal.

Other situations which must include interlocking protection if trains are to proceed without statutory stops or flag protection include drawbridges and "gantlets," sections of double track on bridges or in tunnels where the two lines overlap or are so close together that only one train can pass at a time.

Train Operation By Signal Indication

Where all trackage in a territory is controlled by block signals and interlockings, it is common practice to institute operation by signal indication, superseding the superiority of trains and eliminating the necessity for train orders in moving trains on designated tracks in the same direction (Rule 251) or in both directions (Rule 261). In effect, all trains become "extras," and instructions for their movement are conveyed directly by the signal system as supervised by the dispatcher, directly or through the block and interlocking station operators.

Centralized Traffic Control

When a system is so arranged that the dispatcher controls the throwing of switches and the clearing of signals for train operation by signal indication from a machine in his office, the terms TCS (Traffic Control System) and CTC (Centralized Traffic Control) are used to describe the system.

On many sections of double track, where trains move along under block-signal protection without too many stops, pass each other or en-

114

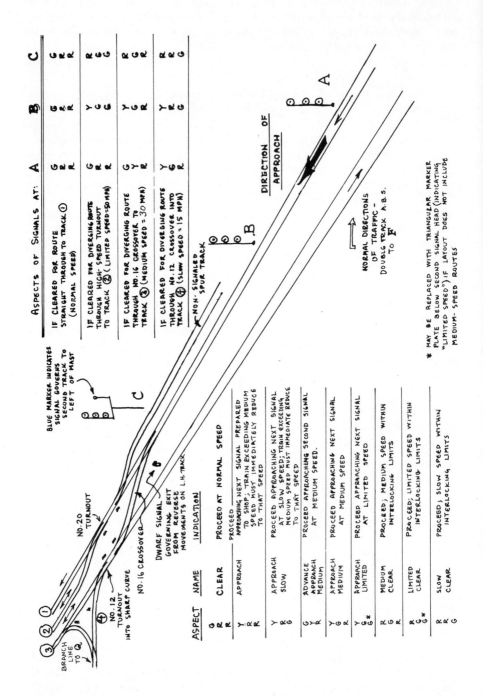

Figure 7-6 Example of Speed Signalling in Approach to a Junction (East-West System, Eastbound at West End of H)

counter other interruptions, timetable and train order operation is satisfactory in moving heavy traffic without serious delay; in practice, only occasional train orders are needed. Such a section of the E-W System as that from C to E (Fig. 7-1) continues to be operated under double-track and block-signal and interlocking rules. Most trains travel in the "normal direction of traffic" on the right-hand track; train orders are issued when track work or serious delay requires a left-hand movement. For heavily-traveled single-track lines or congested sections of multi-track routes, however, CTC is usually the answer.

Single-track with CTC is considered to have about 70 percent of the traffic-handling capability of ABS double-track, so the E-W line between B and C, like thousands of miles of other main line in the U.S., has been so converted. Pulling up some of the second track but leaving long "passing track" sections connected with high-speed turnouts reduces track investment, maintenance and taxes while improving the flexibility of handling traffic which must move at much different speeds in the same direction (piggyback trains vs. ore extras). About 50,000 miles of line on U.S. railroads are so controlled.

CTC Controls

Controls for an extensive section of line are located on a panel with a diagram of the trackage. The dispatcher plans his moves based on lights which show the locations of all trains. He can implement his orders by sending instructions to what are, in effect, interlocking plants at the ends of each passing siding. The dispatcher gives instructions by turning a knob and pushing a button; when the switch points have shifted or the signal has cleared dozens or hundreds of miles away, a message is received that the action is complete.

Vital and Non-Vital Circuits

CTC was originally made economically feasible, starting about 1930, by pulse-code technology making it practical to control all the signals and switches in an extended territory over only two line wires; today much CTC control goes by microwave. These are "non-vital" circuits, which can use up-to-date electronics to speed up, simplify and reduce the cost of transmitting information because safety is not involved. The vital-circuit relays out in the field control and interlock switches, signals and track circuits so that: the points cannot be thrown in the face of an approaching train; signal indications correspond to the route lined up; and so on.

Absolute Permissive Block

The CTC system on single track also usually includes APB (Absolute Permissive Block), a very ingenious arrangement of circuit functions among individual block signals between passing tracks. These circuits can determine the *direction* in which a train is moving and act to put all *opposing* signals from one passing track to the next at red as soon as a train heads out onto single track. At the same time they will allow signals *behind* the train to clear as it passes from block to block, allowing following trains to move along without a delay.

The CTC machine is arranged so that it cannot send out conflicting messages, such as trying to clear signals in both directions on the same track. But should any such instructions get through, the local APB circuitry would prevent conflicting messages from affecting safety.

Control Centers

The logical extension of CTC is to consolidate all installations to the point where virtually an entire railroad can be controlled from one room. Fig. 7-7 shows such a control center, one which uses both the older engraved-panel CTC consoles with individual knobs to control each signal and switch and newer extended-territory systems with TV-monitor displays which are programmed to show the particular section of line where the operator is exercising control.

Computer-Aided Dispatching

With the advent of digital minicomputers of lowered cost but steadily increasing computing speed and memory capacity, varying degrees of *computer-aided dispatching* have become commonplace. The CTC system may, for example, recognize the need for a meet between two opposing trains, calculate the best meeting point on the basis of the trains' anticipated performance (based on hp per ton and route characteristics), check progress as the trains approach each other, and (subject to override by the dispatcher at any point) send switch and signal instructions to the field to execute the meet.

The computer may also free up dispatcher time for overall planning by taking care of much record keeping and paperwork, such as generating the "train sheet" record of all movements required by law.

Computer Control

For rapid transit systems where trains making many stops are operated on extremely close headway, various degrees of "computer control" have been developed. Supervision of overall system performance, including regulation of the speeds and station-stop times of individual trains, may be provided, along with automatic spotting of the train at platforms, station announcements and so on, leaving the on-board operator in a monitoring and emergency manual control role. However, all successful systems of this type still separate the functions of automatic train operation (ATO) from those of ATC; that is, the computer-controlled ATO tells the train how to proceed, but it will only do so to the extent that the vital-circuit ATC has independently assured the computer that it is safe to do so.

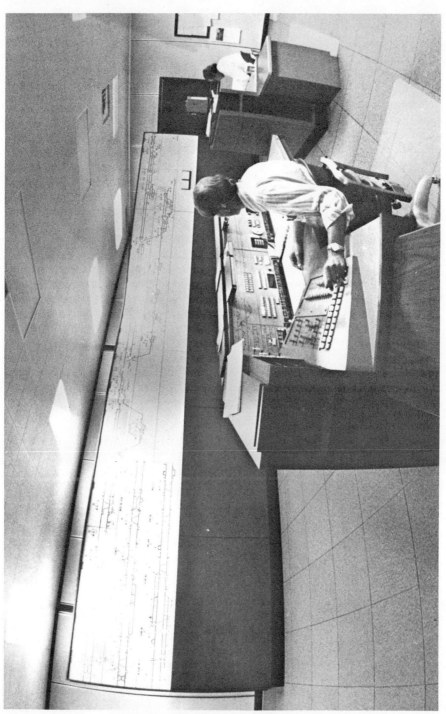

Figure 7-7 CTC Control Center

Communications

From the very beginning of railroading, communication has been recognized as a key element. Superintendent Minot was so sure that Morse's new telegraph would be crucial in running his railroad that he had already put up poles and strung wire alongside the Erie and was prepared to make his own illegal instruments if necessary, before he reached agreement with the inventor on providing service.

Advent of telephone communication helped make operations a great deal more flexible; train crews could communicate with the dispatcher from wayside phone sheds without knowing Morse code. Allocation of VHF FM frequencies for railroad use after World War II and the development of portable radio equipment which could remain reliable under rugged conditions caused a rapid system-wide increase in radio communication between engine and caboose and train and base stations.

Radio Rules

Apart from the intermittent refinement in train crew language caused by the need to observe FCC rules, use of radio in railroad operations has required great care in establishing proper areas for its safe use. Receiving word when "the rear end's moving" lets the engineer accelerate his long train promptly when the slack has been taken up in starting. The dispatcher can plan meets much better when he can determine the up-to-date position and progress of a train from its crew rather than by calculations based only on the time reported at its last "OS" (train passing recorded "on sheet") point.

Nevertheless, the constant need to insure against mistaken identity and to prevent actions on the basis of assumptions from overheard conversations has been a challenge to operating officials. When train orders are transmitted by radio, established procedures must be strictly adhered to. Interchange of information as to the aspect of signals between station employees and train crews is forbidden.

Railroad Communication Networks

Like any business geographically far-flung and with many customers, the railroad has a seemingly insatiable need for communication which has been augmented within the last two decades by the use of centralized digital computation for both operational and business aspects. Large railroads now find their long-haul communication load about evenly divided between voice and digital (mostly computer) traffic; the heaviest-traffic routes may require capacity equivalent to 1200 simultaneous voice circuits. Much traffic is over leased lines, but most railroads have found it economical to establish their own microwave transmission networks serving their main routes and terminals with local telephone and radio interconnections.

Because of the remote locations of some relay and signal installations, railroads have pioneered in the use of solar-panel power sources.

Other Signal Devices

Among other devices or systems whose electrical or electronic nature places them under the responsibility of the Signal and Communications Department on most railroads are: 1. grade crossing protection flashers and gates 2. hotbox and dragging equipment detectors.

1. Highway Grade Crossing Protection

Except for the absolute safety of an underpass or overpass, flashing signals with automatic crossing gates provide the best available assurance against rail-highway collisions and continue to be added or updated at a rate of 1,500 or more a year. These installations require sophisticated circuitry to initiate the warning action sequence a safe distance ahead of the train but halt the sequence when the train has cleared the crossing. If nearby switching movements are common, manual controls are also needed to let the train crew start or release the warning and preserve their credibility and acceptability with the public.

With the wide-spread use of welded track, the DC track-circuit installation requirement of four pairs of insulated joints has become an undesirable break in rail continuity. "Frequency Shift Overlay" circuits, operating in the low audio range around 1,000 Hz, are now likely to be used. Since current at these frequencies will travel only a short, predictable distance along the rails before fading out, and since different frequencies can be used to cause a receiving relay pick up only in response to current from one source, these systems can do the job with uninterrupted rails. They can also detect the *rate* at which a train is approaching by how fast the current is being shunted by its wheels. A *grade crossing predictor* which lowers the gates a relatively constant time ahead of the arrival of trains traveling at widely different speeds is thus possible. However, the cost of such systems and the fact that typical changes in track ballast resistance with weather conditions can upset their performance (with the fail-safe circuitry required usually resulting in continuous warning of a non-existent train) has resulted in limited use; some research on other constant-warning-time principles of operation continues.

2. Safety Detectors

Fig. 7-8 shows a wayside infra-red hotbox detector which scans the journal bearings of trains passing at any speed. Such detectors are typically maintained at intervals of 20 to 50 miles on main lines. Temperature of each bearing is measured; two basic approaches to evaluation of this data are in use:

- A tape printout of the signature of each train may be transmitted to a central point where it is visually examined; suspiciously warm journal locations are reported to the train crew by radio. This method takes advantage of the fine degree of discrimination developed by experienced human observers.

- Hot journals as determined at the detector site by such increasingly sophisticated techniques as measuring the temperature differential between bearings on the same axle and using different alarm thresholds for roller and plain bearings (roller bearings run at a higher normal temperature), are reported directly to the train crew — either by a wayside "scoreboard" displaying an axle-count to the end of the train from the suspect bearing or by a taped-message "talker" reporting over the train radio.

Hot wheels (statistically much more frequent that hot boxes) resulting from stuck or unreleased brakes and a hazard because of their potential for subsequent broken wheels can be similarly detected and reported.

Figure 7-8 Wayside Hot Box Detector

Dragging equipment detectors are located ahead of major bridges and interlocking plants where the potential cost of any resulting accident is high. Rock *slide detector fences* alongside (and even overhead in vulnerable cuts) are connected to the block signal system to provide advance warning. High-water, earthquake-motion, shifted-load and high-car detectors are used in particular situations where the potential for hazard is high.

Reliability of detection with these devices is generally high; *complete* protection is not economically feasible with wayside detectors because their cost (typically $25,000 to $100,000 per installation) precludes spacing them so closely that a disastrous failure cannot occur within the time between detectors.

8

RAILROAD OPERATION --
MOVING FROM HERE TO THERE

During every business day, approximately 100,000 freight cars are loaded in the United States, Canada and Mexico. Some are loaded with bulk commodities while in motion and without being uncoupled from their trains, and others have their loads placed aboard in piggyback trailers or sealed containers which started their journey by highway or water. The typical freight shipment, however, is an individual car, loaded where its contents was produced or processed and destined for a particular consignee hundreds or thousands of miles away. It may start on its journey as a lone car or coupled to others similarly loaded at the same time and place, and it will finish its trip at an unloading point where its specific load is awaited, to be consumed, processed, distributed or sold.

Even with recent mergers, it is expected that more than 60 percent of all U.S. rail shipments will travel over more than one line. Frequently a shipment will be riding in a car belonging to none of the lines over which it is routed. Statistics as to the *average* length, net lading and overall speed of freight trains (66 cars, 2080 tons, 17.2 mph including all road and terminal delays) in a typical year don't begin to describe the variety of operations involved in railroad freight movement. Unit trains may cover over 1,500 miles without change of consist and gross from 6,500 to 13,500 tons, while a car in a local freight may move only a couple of miles at a jump and at some point in the run represent the entire train consist. Dedicated piggyback trains may be limited to 25 to 50 cars but run through over several railroads with few if any intermediate stops, setting out and picking up large blocks of cars at major terminals.

Obviously, the labor and energy involved in a specific shipment will vary widely with the tonnage, distance, route and handling involved. *On the average*, the 64 net tons of each carload travels 600 miles, and requires the expenditure of 50 hours of railroad employee time in total — including maintenance of equipment and right of way, bringing back the empties, de-bugging computer programs, quoting tariffs and so on. Total diesel fuel consumption for all movements — switching and road — amounts to 30 gallons for that hypothetical average revenue carload.

To get some idea of how this major task is accomplished year in and year out, the process of handling carload traffic from receipt to delivery will be examined in sequence. Some of the other integral services will be explored.

The Paperwork Path

By tracing just one carload from origin to final destination, we can get a good idea of what kind of paperwork and to what degree a railroad's computer system is involved in moving a shipment from here to there.

Jones Cannery is located on the East-West Railroad at city B (see system map, Fig 2-4). Jones contacts the E-W's freight agent to request a car to ship 100,000 lbs. of canned goods to their customer, Smith Company in the port city of AA. The E-W's Car Service Division will then pick out the appropriate car for placement at Jones Cannery's railroad siding. With a west to east shipment, such as this, the Car Service Division will select an eastern line car, so that the car will be heading back towards its home railroad.

They select a box car (identified as PR 123456) belonging to the Peninsular Railway, as AA is in the same general direction as Peninsular trackage. While the E-W is using this particular box car, they are paying "rent" to the Peninsular in the form of mileage and per diem charges, much the same as one would pay when renting an automobile.

After the car is obtained and inspected by the mechanical department to see if it's mechanically fit for loading, the car is then spotted by the switching crew to Jones' siding (more about switching in Chapter 11). On the E-W, the car is processed through the yard by the continuous inventory car location system with IBM cards or CRT display, rather than physical checks.

Demurrage

Once the car has been delivered to Jones, it is subject to the Demurrage Rules. Demurrage is a tariff established and assessed by the railroads and enforced by the ICC to encourage shippers to load and unload quickly to get the cars back in revenue service. The customer generally has 24 hours to load and 48 hours to unload. The amount of time varies according to commodities, rate and tariff applications. After the allotted time has expired, the customer is subject to a demurrage charge. The demurrage bill is issued by the local freight agent to the customer and is paid at that point.

Bill of Lading

Following receipt and loading of the car, Jones presents to the railroad a straight bill of lading (Fig. 8-1). The bill of lading is a contract of carriage between Jones and the E-W. It is also Jones' receipt that states the customer has issued the railroad a carload of goods and a bill of lading. In most cases, the shipper pays the freight charges, so the bill of lading is marked "Prepaid." If the consignee is to pay the freight bill, the bill of lading is to be marked "Collect." Once the bill of lading is signed by the shipper and the railroad, it is a legal contract, admissible in a court of law, in the event of any contention about the shipment. The legalities concerning bills of lading and agreements between shippers and transporters are spelled out in the law of bailments, often summarized in the "fine print" on the back of most bills of lading (Fig. 8-1A).

UNIFORM STRAIGHT BILL OF LADING — **ORIGINAL — Not Negotiable**

SHIPPER NO.
DATE

MARK EACH COLLECT ON DELIVERY SHIPMENT WITH THE LETTERS "COD" BEFORE CONSIGNEE'S NAME

CONSIGNED TO		SHIPPED FROM	
STREET		STREET	
CITY, STATE	ZIP	CITY, STATE	ZIP
ROUTE		SINGLE SHIPMENT PICK-UP CHARGE APPLICABLE ☐	CUBE	VEHICLE NO.

NO. SHIPPING UNITS	* HM	KIND OF PACKAGES, DESCRIPTION OF ARTICLES, SPECIAL MARKS AND EXCEPTIONS	WEIGHT	(SUBJ. TO CORRECT)	RATE	CHARGES (FOR CARRIER USE ONLY)
	◆					

* MARK EACH COLUMN WITH "X" THAT CONTAINS ARTICLES DESIGNATED AS HAZARDOUS MATERIAL AS DEFINED IN TITLE 49 OF THE CODE OF FEDERAL REGULATIONS

C.O.D.	REMIT C.O.D. TO _____ ADDRESS	1	C.O.D. FEE TO BE PAID BY ☐ SHIPPER ☐ CONSIGNEE	C.O.D. AMOUNT
				C.O.D. FEE

Note - Where the rate is dependent on value, shippers are required to state specifically in writing the agreed or declared value of the property.
The agreed or declared value of the property is hereby specifically stated by the shipper to be not exceeding.

$_____ per _____

Subject to section 7 of the conditions, if this shipment is to be delivered to the consignee without recourse on the consignor, the consignee shall sign the following statement: The carrier shall not make delivery of this shipment without payment of freight and all other lawful charges.

_____
(Signature of Consignor)

TOTAL CHARGES ▶

FREIGHT CHARGES
FREIGHT PREPAID except when charges are is checked
Check box if charges are to be collect ☐

RECEIVED, subject to the classifications and tariffs in effect on the date of the issue of this Bill of Lading, the property described above, in apparent good order, except as noted (contents and condition of contents of packages unknown) marked, consigned, and destined as shown above, which said company (the word company being understood throughout this contract as meaning any person or corporation in possession of the property under the contract) agrees to carry to its usual place of delivery at said destination, if on its own railroad, water line, highway route or routes, or within the territory of its highway operations, otherwise to deliver to another carrier on the route to said destination. It is mutually agreed, as to each carrier of all or any of said property over all or any portion of said route to destination, and as to each party at any time interested in all or any of said property, that every service to be performed hereunder shall be subject to all the conditions not prohibited by law, whether printed or written, herein contained, including the conditions on the back hereof, WHICH ARE HEREBY AGREED TO BY THE SHIPPER AND ACCEPTED FOR HIMSELF AND HIS ASSIGNS. SHIPPER HEREBY CERTIFIES THAT HE IS FAMILIAR WITH ALL THE BILL OF LADING TERMS AND CONDITIONS IN THE GOVERNING CLASSIFICATION AND THE SAID TERMS AND CONDITIONS ARE HEREBY AGREED TO BY THE SHIPPER AND ACCEPTED FOR HIMSELF AND HIS ASSIGNS.

SEE COMPLETE CONTRACT TERMS AND CONDITIONS ON REVERSE SIDE

THE AGREED VALUATION OF HOUSEHOLD OR PERSONAL EFFECTS DOES NOT EXCEED 10¢ PER LB. PER ARTICLE, UNLESS OTHERWISE SPECIFIED. I UNDERSTAND THE MEANING OF RELEASED OR ACTUAL VALUE, WHERE RATE OR CHARGES ARE DEPENDENT ON SUCH DECLARED VALUES.

SHIPPER NAME	CARRIER NAME		NO. SHIPPING UNITS
AUTHORIZED SIGNATURE	AUTHORIZED SIGNATURE	DATE	

CHECK YOUR MARKS
COUNT YOUR FREIGHT

Figure 8-1 Straight Bill of Lading

CONTRACT TERMS AND CONDITIONS

Sec. 1. (a) The carrier or party in possession of any of the property herein described shall be liable as at common law for any loss thereof or damage thereto, except as hereinafter provided.

(b) No carrier or party in possession of all or any of the property herein described shall be liable for any loss thereof or damage thereto or delay caused by the act of God, the public enemy, the authority of law, or the act or default of the shipper or owner, or for natural shrinkage. The carrier's liability shall be that of warehouseman, only, for loss, damage, or delay caused by fire occurring after the expiration of the free time allowed by tariffs lawfully on file (such free time to be computed as therein provided) after notice of the arrival of the property at destination or at the port of export (if intended for export) has been duly sent or given, and after placement of the property for delivery at destination, or tender of delivery of the property to the party entitled to receive it, has been made. Except in case of negligence of the carrier or party in possession (and the burden to prove freedom from such negligence shall be on the carrier or party in possession), the carrier or party in possession shall not be liable for loss, damage, or delay occurring while the property is stopped and held in transit upon the request of the shipper, owner, or party entitled to make such request, or resulting from a defect or vice in the property, or for country damage to cotton, or from riots or strikes.

(c) In case of quarantine the property may be discharged at risk and expense of owners into quarantine depot or elsewhere, as required by quarantine regulations or authorities, or for the carrier's dispatch at nearest available point in carrier's judgment, and in any such case carrier's responsibility shall cease when property is so discharged, or property may be returned by carrier at owner's expense to shipping point, earning freight both ways. Quarantine expenses of whatever nature or kind upon or in respect to property shall be borne by the owners of the property or be a lien thereon. The carrier shall not be liable for loss or damage occasioned by fumigation or disinfection or other acts required or done by quarantine regulations or authorities even though the same may have been done by carrier's officers, agents, or employees, nor for detention, loss, or damage of any kind occasioned by quarantine or the enforcement hereof. No carrier shall be liable, except in case of negligence, for any mistake or inaccuracy in any information furnished by the carrier, its agents, or officers, as to quarantine laws or regulations. The shipper shall hold the carriers harmless from any expense they may incur, or damages they may be required to pay, by reason of the introduction of the property covered by this contract into any place against the quarantine laws or regulations in effect at such place.

Sec. 2. (a) No carrier is bound to transport said property by any particular train or vessel, or in time for any particular market or otherwise than with reasonable dispatch. Every carrier shall have the right in case of physical necessity to forward said property by any carrier or route between the point of shipment and the point of destination. In all cases not prohibited by law, where a lower value than actual value has been represented in writing by the shipper or has been agreed upon in writing as the released value of the property shall be borne by the owners of the property or be a lien thereon. The carrier shall not be liable for loss or damage determined by the classification or tariffs upon which the rate is based, such lower value plus freight charges if paid shall be the maximum amount to be recovered, whether or not such loss or damage occurs from negligence.

(b) As a condition precedent to recovery, claims must be filed in writing with the receiving or delivering carrier, or carrier issuing the bill of lading, or carrier on whose line the loss, damage, injury or delay occurred, within nine months after delivery of the property (or, in case of export traffic, within nine months after delivery at port of export); or, in case of failure to make delivery, then within nine months after a reasonable time for delivery has elapsed; and suits shall be instituted against any carrier only within two years and one day from the day when notice in writing is given by the carrier to the claimant that the carrier has disallowed the claim or any part or parts thereof specified in the notice. Where claims are not filed or suits are not instituted thereon in accordance with the foregoing provisions, no carrier hereunder shall be liable, and such claims will not be paid.

(c) Any carrier or party liable on account of loss of or damage to any of said property shall have the full benefit of any insurance that may have been effected upon or on account of said property, so far as this shall not avoid the policies or contracts of insurance: Provided, That the carrier reimburse the claimant for the premium paid therein.

Sec. 3. Except where such service is required as the result of carrier's negligence, all property shall be subject to necessary cooperage and baling at owner's cost. Each carrier over whose route cotton or cotton linters is to be transported hereunder shall have the privilege, at its own cost and risk, of compressing the same for greater convenience in handling or forwarding, and shall not be held responsible for deviation or unavoidable delays in procuring such compression. Grain in bulk consigned to a point where there is a railroad, public or licensed elevator, may (unless otherwise expressly noted herein, and then if it is not promptly unloaded) be there delivered and placed with other grain of the same kind and grade without respect to ownership (and prompt notice thereof shall be given to the consignor), and if so delivered shall be subject to a lien for elevator charges in addition to all other charges hereunder.

Sec. 4. (a) Property not removed by the party entitled to receive it within the free time allowed by tariffs, lawfully on file (such free time to be computed as therein provided), after notice of the arrival of the property at destination or at the port of export (if intended for export) has been duly sent or given, and after placement of the property for delivery at destination has been made, may be kept in vessel, car, depot, warehouse or place of delivery of the carrier, subject to the tariff charge for storage and to carrier's responsibility as warehouseman, only, or at the option of the carrier, may be removed to and stored in a public or licensed warehouse at the place of delivery or other available place, at the cost of the owner, and there held without liability on the part of the carrier, and subject to a lien for all freight and other lawful charges, including a reasonable charge for storage.

(b) Where nonperishable property which has been transported to destination hereunder is refused by consignee or the party entitled to receive it, or said consignee or party entitled to receive it fails to receive it within 15 days after notice of arrival shall have been duly sent or given, the carrier may at the option of the carrier sell the property at public auction to the highest bidder, at such place as may be designated by the carrier: Provided, That the carrier shall have first mailed, sent, or given to the consignee notice that the property has been refused or remains unclaimed, as the case may be, and that it will be subject to sale under the terms of the bill of lading if disposition be not arranged for, and shall have published notice containing a description of the property, the name of the party to whom consigned, or, if shipped order notify, the name of the party to be notified, and the time and place of sale, once a week for two successive weeks, in a newspaper of general circulation at the place of sale or nearest place where such newspaper is published: Provided, That 30 days shall have elapsed before publication of notice of sale after said notice that the property was refused or remains unclaimed was mailed, sent, or given.

(c) Where perishable property which has been transported hereunder to destination is refused by consignee or party entitled to receive it, or said consignee or party entitled to receive it shall fail to receive it promptly, the carrier may, in its discretion, to prevent deterioration or further deterioration, sell the same to the best advantage at private or public sale: Provided, That if time does not permit of notification to the consignor or owner of the refusal of the property or the failure to receive it and request for disposition of the property, such notification shall be given, in such manner as the exercise of due diligence requires, before the property is sold.

(d) Where the procedure provided for in the two paragraphs last preceding is not possible, it is agreed that nothing contained in said paragraphs shall be construed to abridge the right of the carrier at its option to sell the property under such circumstances and in such manner as may be authorized by law.

(e) The proceeds of any sale made under this section shall be applied by the carrier to the payment of freight, demurrage, storage, and any other lawful charges and the expense of notice, advertisement, sale, and other necessary expense and of caring for and maintaining the property, if proper care of the same requires special expense, and should there be a balance it shall be paid to the owner of the property sold hereunder.

(f) Property destined to or taken from a station, wharf, or landing at which there is no regularly appointed freight agent shall be entirely at risk of owner after unloaded from cars or vessels or until loaded into cars or vessels, and, except in case of carrier's negligence, when received from or delivered to such stations, wharves, or landings shall be at owner's risk until the cars are attached to and after they are detached from locomotive or train or until loaded into and after unloaded from vessels.

Sec. 5. No carrier hereunder will carry or be liable in any way for any documents, specie, or for any articles of extraordinary value not specifically rated in the published classifications or tariffs unless a special agreement to do so and a stipulated value of the articles are indorsed hereon.

Sec. 6. Every party, whether principal or agent, shipping explosives or dangerous goods, without previous full written disclosure to the carrier of their nature, shall be liable for and indemnify the carrier against all loss or damage caused by such goods, and such goods may be warehoused at owner's risk and expense or destroyed without compensation.

Sec. 7. The owner or consignee shall pay the freight and average, if any, and all other lawful charges accruing on said property, but, except in those instances when it may lawfully be authorized to do so, no carrier by railroad shall deliver or relinquish possession at destination of the property covered by this bill of lading until all tariff rates and charges thereon have been paid. The consignor shall be liable for the freight and all other lawful charges, except that if the consignor stipulates, by signature, in the space provided herein that purpose on the face of this bill of lading that the carrier shall not make delivery without requiring payment of such charges and the carrier, contrary to such stipulation, shall make delivery without requiring such payment, the consignor (except as hereinafter provided) shall not be liable for such charges. Provided, that where the carrier has been instructed by the shipper or consignor to deliver said property to a consignee other than the shipper or consignor, such consignee shall not be legally liable for transportation charges in respect of the transportation of said property (beyond those billed against him at the time of delivery for which he is otherwise liable) which may be found to be due after the property has been delivered to him, if the consignee (a) is an agent only and has no beneficial title in said property, and (b) prior to delivery of said property has notified the delivering carrier in writing of the fact of such agency and absence of beneficial title, and, in the case of a shipment reconsigned or diverted to a point other than that specified in the original bill of lading, has also notified the delivering carrier in writing of the name and address of the beneficial owner of said property, and, in such cases the shipper or consignor, or, in the case of a shipment so reconsigned or diverted, the beneficial owner, shall be liable for such additional charges. If the consignee has given to the carrier erroneous information as to who the beneficial owner is, such consignee shall himself be liable for such additional charges. On shipments reconsigned or diverted by an agent who has furnished the carrier in like reconsignment or diversion order with a notice of agency and the proper name and address of the beneficial owner, and where such shipments are refused or abandoned at ultimate destination, the said beneficial owner shall be liable for all legally applicable charges in connection therewith. If the reconsignor or diverter has given to the carrier erroneous information as to who the beneficial owner is, such reconsignor or diverter shall himself be liable for all such charges.

If a shipper or consignor of a shipment of property (other than a prepaid shipment) is also the consignee named in the bill of lading and, prior to the time of delivery, notifies, in writing, a delivering carrier by railroad (a) to deliver such property at destination to another party, (b) that such party is the beneficial owner of such property, and (c) that delivery is to be made to such party only upon payment of all transportation charges in respect of the transportation of such property, and delivery is made by the carrier to such party without such payment, such delivering carrier shall not be liable (as shipper, consignor, consignee, or otherwise) for such transportation charges that the party to whom delivery is so made shall in any event be liable for transportation charges billed against the property at the time of such delivery, and also for any additional charges which may be found to be due after delivery of the property, except that if such party prior to such delivery has notified in writing the delivering carrier that he is not the beneficial owner of the property, and has given in writing to such delivering carrier the name and address of such beneficial owner, such party shall not be liable for any additional charges which may be found to be due after delivery of the property, but if the party to whom delivery is made has given to the carrier erroneous information as to the beneficial owner, such party shall nevertheless be liable for such additional charges. If the ship or is or consignee has given to the delivering carrier erroneous information as to who the beneficial owner is, such shipper or consignor shall himself be liable for such transportation charges, notwithstanding the foregoing provisions of this paragraph and irrespective of any provisions to the contrary in the bill of lading or in the contract of transportation under which the shipment was made. The term "delivering carrier" means the line-haul carrier making ultimate delivery.

Nothing herein shall limit the right of the carrier to require at time of shipment the prepayment or guarantee of the charges. If upon inspection it is ascertained that the articles shipped are not those described in this bill of lading, the freight charges must be paid upon the articles actually shipped.

Where delivery is made by a common carrier by water the foregoing provisions of this section shall apply except as may be inconsistent with Part III of the Interstate Commerce Act.

Sec. 8. If this bill of lading be issued on the order of the shipper, or his agent, in exchange or in substitution for another bill of lading, the shipper's signature to the prior bill of lading as to the statement of value or otherwise, or election of common law or bill of lading liability, or in connection with such prior bill of lading shall be considered a part of this bill of lading as fully as if the same were written or made in or in connection with this bill of lading.

Sec. 9. (a) If all or any part of said property is carried by water over any port of said route, and loss, damage or injury to said property occurs while the same is in the custody of a carrier by water the liability of such carrier shall be determined by the bill of lading of the carrier by water (this bill of lading being such bill of lading if the property is transported by such water carrier thereunder) and by and under the laws and regulations applicable to transportation by water. Such water carriage shall be performed subject to all the terms and provisions of, and all the exemptions from liability contained in the Act of the Congress of the United States, approved on February 13, 1893, and entitled "An act relating to the navigation of vessels, etc.," and of other statutes of the United States according carriers by water the protection of limited liability, as well as the following subdivisions of this section, and to the conditions contained in this bill of lading not inconsistent with this section, when this bill of lading becomes the bill of lading of the carrier by water.

(b) No such carrier by water shall be liable for any loss or damage resulting from any fire happening to or on board the vessel, or from explosion, bursting of boilers or breakage of shafts, unless caused by the design or neglect of such carrier.

(c) If the owner shall have exercised due diligence in making the vessel in all respects seaworthy and properly manned, equipped, and supplied, no such carrier shall be liable for any loss or damage resulting from the perils of the lakes, seas, or other waters, or from latent defects in hull, machinery, or appurtenances whether existing prior to, at the time of, or after sailing, or from collision, stranding, or other accidents of navigation, or from prolongation of the voyage. And, when for any reason it is necessary, any vessel carrying any or all of the property herein described shall be at liberty to call at any port or ports, in or out of the customary route, to tow and be towed, to transfer, trans-ship, or lighter, to load and discharge goods at any time, to assist vessels in distress, to deviate for the purpose of saving life or property, and for docking and repairs. Except in case of negligence such carrier shall not be responsible for any loss or damage to property if it be necessary or is usual to carry the same upon deck.

(d) General Average shall be payable according to the York-Antwerp Rules of 1924, Sections 1 to 15 inclusive, and Sections 17 to 22, inclusive, and as to matters not covered thereby according to the laws and usages of the Port of New York. If the owners shall have exercised due diligence to make the vessels in all respects seaworthy and properly manned, equipped and supplied, it is hereby agreed that in case of danger, damage or disaster resulting from faults or errors in navigation, or in the management of the vessel, or from any latent or other defects in the vessel, her machinery or appurtenances, or from unseaworthiness, whether existing at the time of shipment or at the beginning of the voyage (provided the latent or other defects or the unseaworthiness was not discoverable by the exercise of due diligence), the shippers, consignees and/or owners of the cargo shall nevertheless pay salvage and any special charges incurred in respect of the cargo, and shall contribute with the shipowner in general average to the payment of any sacrifices, losses or expenses of a general average nature that may be made or incurred for the common benefit or to relieve the adventure from any common peril.

(e) If the property is being carried under a tariff which provides that any carrier or carriers party thereto shall be liable for loss from perils of the sea, then as to such carrier or carriers the provisions of this section shall be modified in accordance with the tariff provisions, which shall be regarded as incorporated into the conditions of this bill of lading.

(f) The term "water carriage" in this section shall not be construed as including lighterage in or across rivers, harbors, or lakes, when performed by or on behalf of rail carriers.

Sec. 10. Any alteration, addition, or erasure in this bill of lading which shall be made without the special notation hereon of the agent of the carrier issuing this bill of lading, shall be without effect, and this bill of lading shall be enforceable according to its original tenor.

Figure 8-1A Reverse Side of Bill of Lading

There are several different types of bills of lading, but they all fall into one of two categories, "open or straight" and "order." The open bill of lading is used for most collect and prepaid shipments. The order bill of lading comes into use when the shipper wants to be paid for his goods before the shipment is released to the consignee. The finances are taken care of by the shipper's and consignee's respective banks. Freight charges may be prepaid or collect. Other types of bills of lading include individualized forms used by the federal government and some private industries and export bills of lading.

Compiling a Waybill

When the E-W receives the bill of lading from Jones, the local E-W rate clerk will rate the shipment, that is, he or she will check the various tariff documents to find out the actual rate for the products Jones is shipping. From all the information received and determined to this point, the E-W makes up a waybill (Fig. 8-2) to help keep track of the car and shipment and to inform the rest of the railroad that the shipment is moving on the E-W system. A waybill contains the following information:

> Car initial and number
> Waybill number, which is assigned to the freight agent by
> the railroad
> Waybill date
> Origin station
>
> Name of shipper
> Consignee, or customer at destination
> Destination city
> The route the car will travel
> The Standard Transportation Commodity Code, a seven-
> digit number assigned by the ICC to a particular com-
> modity
> Physical description of articles
> Weight of shipment
> Applicable rate
> Total freight charges (weight x rate = freight charges)
> Prepaid or collect
> Whether the shipment is perishable; if so, perishable in-
> structions will be included

All of this information is fed from the yard office into the E-W's computer in headquarters, which keeps track of all cars on the system, the freight being carried and its destination.

The waybill is a contract between the railroads moving the shipment. The junction stamps applied to this document as it travels between carriers determine the divisions which will apply and provide the basis for misroute claims between carriers. The last handling road haul carrier takes the waybill into account and is responsible for collecting the freight charge and allocating it among the handling lines. The handling lines match up waybill numbers in interline settlements to assure they have not been left out of the payments for any car they handled on a road haul. Thus, the waybill is a great deal more than a simple movement instruction.

The original waybill will travel with the car from its origin to destination and is carried by the train conductor. One copy will be sent to railroad headquarters; several copies are kept on file at the local freight office. Other copies of the waybill may go to other departments or offices in the railroad, depending on individual practice.

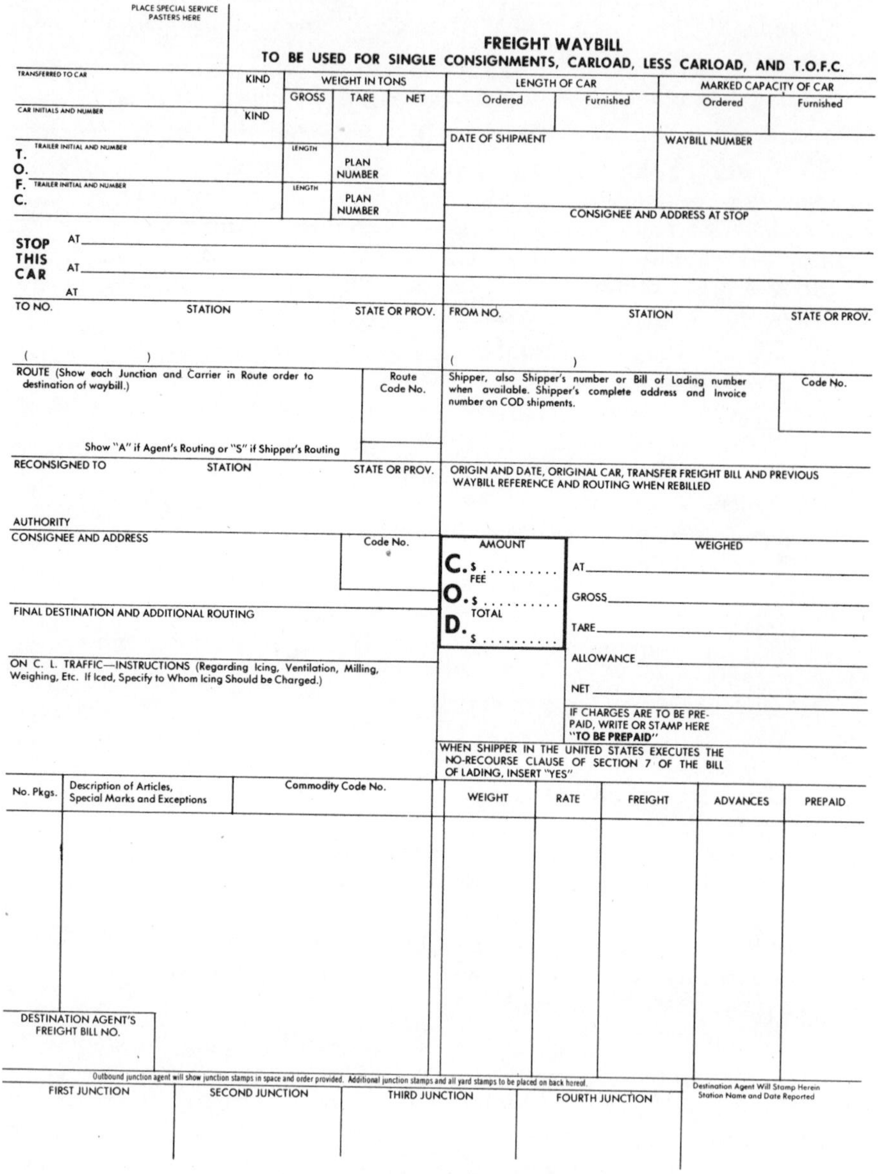

PLACE SPECIAL SERVICE PASTERS HERE

FREIGHT WAYBILL

TO BE USED FOR SINGLE CONSIGNMENTS, CARLOAD, LESS CARLOAD, AND T.O.F.C.

TRANSFERRED TO CAR — KIND — WEIGHT IN TONS — LENGTH OF CAR — MARKED CAPACITY OF CAR

GROSS | TARE | NET — Ordered | Furnished — Ordered | Furnished

CAR INITIALS AND NUMBER — KIND

T. TRAILER INITIAL AND NUMBER — LENGTH — PLAN NUMBER — DATE OF SHIPMENT — WAYBILL NUMBER
O.
F. TRAILER INITIAL AND NUMBER — LENGTH — PLAN NUMBER
C.

CONSIGNEE AND ADDRESS AT STOP

STOP THIS CAR — AT__ AT__ AT

TO NO. — STATION — STATE OR PROV. — FROM NO. — STATION — STATE OR PROV.

( ) — ( )

ROUTE (Show each Junction and Carrier in Route order to destination of waybill.) — Route Code No. — Shipper, also Shipper's number or Bill of Lading number when available. Shipper's complete address and Invoice number on COD shipments. — Code No.

Show "A" if Agent's Routing or "S" if Shipper's Routing

RECONSIGNED TO — STATION — STATE OR PROV. — ORIGIN AND DATE, ORIGINAL CAR, TRANSFER FREIGHT BILL AND PREVIOUS WAYBILL REFERENCE AND ROUTING WHEN REBILLED

AUTHORITY

CONSIGNEE AND ADDRESS — Code No. — AMOUNT — WEIGHED

C. $......... FEE — AT__
O. $......... TOTAL — GROSS__

FINAL DESTINATION AND ADDITIONAL ROUTING — D. $ .... — TARE__

ON C. L. TRAFFIC—INSTRUCTIONS (Regarding Icing, Ventilation, Milling, Weighing, Etc. If Iced, Specify to Whom Icing Should be Charged.) — ALLOWANCE__

NET__

IF CHARGES ARE TO BE PREPAID, WRITE OR STAMP HERE "TO BE PREPAID"

WHEN SHIPPER IN THE UNITED STATES EXECUTES THE NO-RECOURSE CLAUSE OF SECTION 7 OF THE BILL OF LADING, INSERT "YES"

No. Pkgs.	Description of Articles, Special Marks and Exceptions	Commodity Code No.	WEIGHT	RATE	FREIGHT	ADVANCES	PREPAID

DESTINATION AGENT'S FREIGHT BILL NO.

Outbound junction agent will show junction stamps in space and order provided. Additional junction stamps and all yard stamps to be placed on back hereof.

FIRST JUNCTION	SECOND JUNCTION	THIRD JUNCTION	FOURTH JUNCTION	Destination Agent Will Stamp Herein Station Name and Date Reported

Figure 8-2 Freight Waybill

Other Computer Operations

Several steps involving the use of the continuous inventory car location system and the railroad's computer operating data base follow the preparation of the waybill. These procedures vary from railroad to railroad in their details, but in most cases, several events will be reported to the computer plus changes made in the continuous car inventory, whether in the form of IBM cards or in the mini-computer/CRT systems. These events include the set, release and pull of the car, any bad orders (cars that have defects that may prevent their safe movement over the railroad), weighing or inspection movements and holding for billings. The car inventory system produces the switch lists used in picking up and in classifying the outbound load.

While the waybill is being prepared in the yard office, a switch crew goes to Jones' siding to pick up the car and take it to the classification yard, where the car will be switched into the proper outbound train. All the waybills for the particular train are gathered together, and a wheel report is compiled for the conductor. The wheel report is a list of cars in a train showing destination, weight, load or empty status, etc. for each car, and which the conductor updates as the train picks up or sets out cars enroute. The wheel report is used by the conductor for the haul over his territory, in this case from city B to city C. At city C, the wheel report is turned over to the conductor on the haul from C to D, and so on. Wheel reports are turned into headquarters and are sometimes used to figure mileage on the cars.

Many roads no longer use the conductor's wheel report to figure mileage, but rely on computer-generated wheel reports and computation programs. The mileage calculations are for interline settlements of the mileage charges on cars which the railroads are "renting" from each other.

The next report entered in the computer, just prior to train departure, is the consist report. This report now lists only time, date, location and car numbers, since on any sophisticated system, waybill data was previously entered, and train symbol itinerary is already established in the computer. The division point will now be aware of what train is coming in, what's on it, and whether they will have to add or cut out cars. When the new crew comes on at the division point, the old crew hands over the waybills for the cars continuing and the wheel report.

Interchange

In order to get Jones' shipment to Smith in city AA, the car must be turned over to the SW & AA Railroad at city G. Before the train gets to G, the E-W yardmaster in G has already received a consist report from the computer. From this report, he makes up a switch list for his switching crews, so that they will know whether each car stays with the train, stays in the area for local delivery or, as in this case, interchanges to the SW & AA Railroad to continue on to city AA.

The switching crew brings car PR 123456 and any other cars being interchanged to the SW & AA yard to be made up into a train heading for city AA. The E-W yard office personnel must enter into the computer an interchange delivery report which confirms that the car(s) has been turned over to the SW & AA. The report includes the initial and number of the car, its contents, destination and time and date it was delivered to the SW & AA. As soon as the car is turned over, the E-W's per diem and mileage charges end, and the SW & AA's charges begin.

The waybill that was filled out in city B and that has traveled with the car to city G is turned over to SW & AA yard personnel, who make waybill entries into their computer to advise their people of the destination, contents, etc. of this car. They also will make a wheel report for their crew.

Arriving at Destination

The SW & AA train then continues on to city AA. When the freight agent in city AA receives the waybill, he or she will notify Smith Co. that the car containing their shipment of canned goods has arrived. Smith will either order the car to be sent to their siding as soon as feasible or will order it in by number, i.e., a specific sequence of cars. The SW & AA switch crew will then bring the car to Smith Company, if it has established credit with the railroad or the freight bill has been prepaid. If not, Smith must pay for freight charges before the car can be delivered.

Car PR 123456 then goes on to Smith's demurrage. Smith has an allotted amount of time to unload the shipment and notify the SW & AA to pick up the car. If Smith goes over the allotted time, then the SW & AA charges and collects the demurrage fee.

The local freight agent prepares a freight bill for the consignee which is made up from the information on the waybill. Smith remits its check for these charges to the SW & AA Railroad, unless the charges have been prepaid.

Order Bill of Lading

If the shipment carries an order bill of lading, the last road haul line cannot turn over the shipment to the consignee or to the switching company making final delivery until it has proof that the goods have been paid for. Proof of payment includes: order bill handed over by the bank that has made payment; a consignee bond that is on file with the railroad's credit and collection department; or a certified check of 125% of the value of the shipment. Mistakes can sometimes happen. Improper communication between railroad employees may allow the shipment to be delivered before proof of payment is received. Should something go awry, and the consignee cannot pay for the goods, the last road haul company is responsible for the cost of the merchandise.

Regardless of who pays the freight charges, the company has 120 hours (not including weekends and holidays) to pay the charges. U.S. government agencies have 30 days to pay. If the railroad does not show evidence of attempting to collect, it could be found in violation of the Elkins Act. The railroad may also be liable to fines if it unduly denies credit to shippers. Credit regulations are spelled out in Section 1320 of the ICC Act.

Rate clerks are entrusted to accurately rate shipments and supply the proper data for freight bills. In the event of undercharges or overcharges due to errors on the bill, the railroad is not absolved of the responsibility of refunding the overcharges, nor is the shipper excused from paying to the railroad the difference between the undercharge and actual charge. The originating carrier must make the refund or collect the difference when the shipment is prepaid. For collect shipments, it's the delivering line's responsibility. The payee has 30 days to make payment to the railroad after he has been notified of undercharges.

The Complexities of Switching

The road-haul freight that brings a car into town usually doesn't deliver it to the consignee's siding, but must rely on switching to get the car to its final destination. Basically, there are three types of switches--intra-plant, intra-terminal and inter-terminal. Intra-plant switching involves the movement from one track to another or between two points on the same track within the same plant or industry. Intra-terminal switching is the movement from a track, industry of firm to another track, industry or firm on the same road within the same district. Inter-terminal switching covers movements from a track of one road to a track of another road within the same district.

When an inter-terminal switch is called for, things can get complicated. Inter-terminal switching involves complex agreements between the railroads in every city. Each railroad establishes a switching district (See Chapter 11) in which it will arrange to have a car delivered, regardless of whose tracks the siding is located on. Railroads establish reciprocal agreements ("we'll switch your cars, if you'll switch ours") to ensure that cars are delivered.

Switching Charges

The road handling the switch will be paid a switching charge which is determined by each railroad within each switching district. These charges are computed via careful analysis of crew time, fuel cost, etc. The rates are then published and usually approved by the ICC. They can be determined by any basis the railroad selects--commodity, weight, distance, type of car or any combination.

Settlement of charges among railroads is taken care of by monthly switching settlement statements based on lists provided by the freight agent. The accounting department arranges for settlement of charges via a process similar to interline settlements which follows.

Interline Settlements

In order for the E-W Railroad to receive its share of revenue from this shipment, it must get its money from the SW & AA Railroad, which collected the freight charges from Smith Company. It would seem that the SW & AA would simply issue a check to the E-W for its fair share. But with the large number of cars being interchanged from one railroad to another, this seemingly simple method of payment would become very complicated due to the mountains of checks the railroads would be issuing to each other. Railroads do not send checks every time they owe another railroad from a shipment, such as in our example.

Every month railroads compile interline settlement statements that list all the carloads for which each railroad owes another railroad revenue. For example, the East-West Railroad's interline settlement statement with the SW & AA Railroad may show that the E-W owes the SW & AA $2.9 million dollars for revenue collected in February. The SW & AA statement may show that the SW & AA owes the E-W $3 million dollars. At this point, the SW & AA would issue a draft or check for the difference.

Railroad Regulation

Since it would be virtually impossible to obtain a right-of-way through settled country without the back-up capability of invoking the government's power of *eminent domain* to set a reasonable price, railroads must in practice be chartered by public authority. These charters, in turn, require that railroads operate as *common carriers*. Since the railroad by its very nature can carry just about anything that's worth transporting, this isn't just an academic matter. Most of the Federal regulation of railroads in the United States is based on the Interstate Commerce Act of 1887 and subsequent extensions; these in general were established at a time when railroads were in a monopoly situation in land transport and have had the primary thrust of keeping the overall level of rates low and equalizing access to regulated transportation among shippers and consignees in different locations and situations.

Since rates have been regulated by the Interstate Commerce Commission, railroads have been exempt from the anti-trust provisions of the Clayton Act and allowed to propose rates and establish standardized tariff provisions (and formats) collectively through the workings of *rate bureaus*.

Although the steady growth of the state and, later, Federally-financed highway systems and the Federally-constructed and maintained internal and coastal waterways systems have made the monopoly aspects of rail transportation a thing of the past for most commodities, regulation of railroad (and common-carrier trucking except for any commodities however remotely related to agriculture, which were exempt) continued in full flower until the passage of significant *deregulation* legislation in 1980.

Full effects of the Staggers (deregulation) Act of 1980 (which followed the "4 R" Railroad Revitalization and Regulatory Reform Act of 1976, a less far-reaching piece of legislation whose effects were largely postponed by ICC interpretations), can only be assessed with the passage of time as they are interpreted by litigation and the thought patterns and habits of railroaders, shippers and regulators ingrained over the years adapt to the shifts in philosophy implied. A few of the provisions of the act:

- Railroad pricing is subject to anti-trust law; rate-bureau functions are severely limited, with only railroads participating in an interline (joint) rate allowed to vote in establishing its level.

- Within broad limits, especially on traffic for which other modes of transport provide an alternative to the shipper, individual rail rates may be raised and lowered rapidly in response to the competitive situation from unregulated carriers, seasonal factors and other service and cost effects.

- "Blanket" rate changes under the "Ex Parte" procedures are phased out, except for limited changes directly related to specific cost increases.

- *Contract rates* between railroad and shipper guaranteeing a rate basis for a specified volume or proportion of the shipper's business over a specified period of time under agreed-upon conditions are specifically made legal (subject to anti-trust law); not all aspects of the contract are public information.

- *Surcharges* may be applied by a railroad to a specific commodity or route or to its division of a joint rate to bring revenue up to the cost of handling the shipment, potentially eliminating the cross-subsidization of unprofitable traffic associated with the regulated rate structure evolved over the years.

Many other aspects of intramodal (railroad vs railroad), and intermodal competition and of common-carriage in general may be expected to change with implementation of this and probable subsequent Acts, in directions difficult to predict. Some of the principles illustrated in this chapter's discussion of the handling of a shipment will undoubtedly become inapplicable or at least different.

Equal Access

Since most rail shipments now represent fairly regular movements from quantity producers to their customers, they usually originate at private side-tracks. As common carriers, railroads are required to provide a track connection to any customer who wants it, unless it can be shown that it is physically impractical. The railroad can require financial arrangements appropriate for the volume of business involved, but the same rules must apply to all. The railroad will place a car for loading and pick it up as part of the freight charge, but since equal service to all is the rule, there must be a charge, specified by tariff, for intra-plant movements; a large company with its own network of track will probably do its own switching.

Public Loading Facilities

The railroad must also provide places where shippers and consignees who don't have their own sidings can load and receive carload freight. The simplest of these are "team" tracks, sidings located and spaced so that teams and wagons (now trucks, of course) can back up to the cars. More elaborate railroad-owned facilities range from a small gantry crane up to the huge port terminals handling coal, ore, grain and other bulk cargoes between car and barge or ship, with provisions for intermediate storage. For each service provided by these facilities a schedule of charges must be established by published tariff, subject to regulation to assure that the rates are not unduly discriminatory to those who do not opt for all services. Fig. 8-3 is an example of the "new look" in team-track facilities.

Short-line Railroading

Shippers who are some distance from a "line-haul" railroad may reach a line-haul road via a connecting line. If it is a plant-built and -owned facility only, the owner saves switching charges; if it is a common carrier, the short line receives a "division" of the freight rate (typically, considerably more than just the percentage of the mileage involved, since the costs of an originating or terminating carrier are recognized as being disproportionately high). In return, the short line must be prepared to accept freight from all comers, including competitors, and its divisions will be scrutinized closely to see that profits from them don't constitute, in effect, a rebate on the freight rate as compared to what's available to others.

The Commodities Clause

Since 1906 it has been illegal for a railroad company to transport any commodity (except timber and materials used in railroad operations themselves) which it owns. That is, a railroad cannot own a coal mine or a steel mill and transport its output for general sale. This act was intended to equalize the situation between producers by requiring the carriers to divorce themselves from subsidiaries which could profit by manipulating freight rates. By raising rates exorbitantly, the railroad with captive mines could presumably put the squeeze on its competitors while using the freight income to offset the price paid on its product.

The converse is not prohibited; a non-railroad company such as a big steel producer can build and own a railroad to serve its needs, but this line, as a common carrier, must provide equal service and charge equal rates to its parent's competitors. These are matters which, presumably, can be more readily controlled by the regulatory authorities.

Tariffs

What is the freight rate on a shipment? Unfortunately, that isn't an easy question for the friendly local freight agent. Tariffs are complicated, to say the least, when you multiply the thousands of stations by the dozens of routings by the hundreds of commodities, which results in millions of different combinations. Over the period of a hundred years, the tariff bureaus, acting for the "Trunk Line" (Eastern), Southern and Western lines, have developed a system of published tariff documents which, by cross-referencing against each other, reduce the problem of presenting all needed combinations from being hopeless to merely challenging. The answer is contained in those documents, but is derived only by tracking down, adding, subtracting, multiplying and dividing a number of different numbers which together reflect all the factors that go into a rate, factors far more numerous than simply how much the shipment weighs and how many miles it has to go. Examining a couple of these and hinting at the rest should give some insight into the system.

Class and Commodity Rates

One-of-a-kind or occasional shipments, such as a car of granite curbstones going to a small town in the midwest to surround its new fountain in the park, are covered by *class rates,* rates determined by finding the classification which includes "granite, rough finished" (with some other characterizations and qualifications) in a list of hundreds of other items of generally equivalent density, value and nature with respect to handling care required. Class rates have become so high that, in general, even for a single shipment, application will be made to quote a commodity rate, which is usually done. Class rates move less than one percent of the traffic. Commodity rates move the rest.

More or less regular shipments (the bulk of the business) are likely to be covered by *commodity rates,* rates for one particular commodity or item from one specific point or area to another, such as raw copper ingots from a smelter town in Arizona to a processing plant in Illinois or washing machines, boxed in accordance with another reference specification, from a plant in Kentucky to a distribution center in the state of Washington. These rates, lower than corresponding class rates, have been set up, for example, to let an area compete in various markets with sources elsewhere in the country or world, to make it economically possible for a particularly bulky commodity to travel that far, or to recognize economies possible from centralizing a particular manufacturing, processing or distributing function at one point.

"Ex Parte" Changes

All these class and commodity rates in turn may be changed (in inflationary times, raised) by the effects of across-the-board "Ex Parte" changes authorized from time to time by the ICC to recognize changes in costs affecting the whole level of rates. In turn, these are usually modified by "hold downs" on particular items for which raises are not requested for competitive or technical reasons.

Incentive Rates

To encourage shipments in amounts, forms or under other conditions which will make possible more economical handling by the railroads possible, "incentive" tariffs (merely one form of commodity rate) may be established in return for the acceptance of such requirements as loading cars to more than the minimum carload weight. These are discussed in a little more depth in connection with unit-train operations.

Processing-in-Transit Rates

While the general level of freight rates generates a great deal of discussion, controversy and litigation, the matter of freight rate comparisons between different sections of the country, different port cities, and even in different directions for the same commodity between the same areas is ever more controversial. Over the years thousands of such matters have been determined by Congress, the ICC and the courts, and are reflected in current tariffs.

In the case of our East-West System, for example, consider the matter of the farmers at A versus those on the branch leading west from U (both in the west-central area of Fig. 2-4). There is a flour mill at A, so grain processed there can go directly to the bakeries in the metropolitan area of J .

136

on the east coast. Wheat grown in the U area would be at a disadvantage as there is no mill in the area. It would have to be shipped as grain to the processor at F and re-shipped to J, at greater freight cost since two shipments are involved. The answer, so far as the miller at F and the wheat growers at U are concerned, is the "milling-in-transit" rate established many years ago which treats the two "legs" of the trip from U to J, with a stopover at F where the grain becomes flour, as a single movement, accorded a rate equal to the through A - J flour rate. The flour mill at F can stay in business despite dwindling local supplies as shopping centers and apartment developments take over the wheat fields.

Figure 8-3 Team-Track Loading Facility

9

CAR TYPES AND CARLOADINGS

To get any load from origin to destination, there has to be a suitable car. The technology or standardization, as previously shown, makes it possible for any car to go anywhere. But what kinds of cars are needed; who is going to buy them; how do you find the one you need; and how do the empties get back?

Freight Car Types

The fleet in the United States, according to recent data, consists of the following types of car:

Type	Total	Class I railroads	Other railroads	Car companies and shippers
Box cars:				
Plain..........	274,002	210,426	44,544	19,032
Equipped.......	179,217	169,220	9,771	226
Covered hoppers	268,919	164,959	5,317	98,643
Flat Cars........	151,377	99,342	4,649	47,386
Refrigerator cars	81,266	64,924	3,392	12,950
Gondola cars.....	178,979	154,629	7,150	17,200
Hopper cars......	356,504	325,479	13,267	17,758
Tank cars........	178,069	2,310	89	175,670
Other freight cars	31,977	25,790	3,248	2,939
Total..........	1,700,310	1,217,079	91,427	391,804

In addition to these revenue freight cars, Class I railroads in the U.S. own approximately 19,000 cabooses.

Traffic Distribution

For each principal class of commodity *going from one producer to one receiver,* there is one preferred freight car design to carry it. Many variables govern the type of car needed: available loading and unloading gear; the size, shape and nature of the commodity; its value and need for protection; and the customary unit quantity of shipment. All these variables make a difference, large or small, in how satisfactory a particular car can be. Since there can't be an infinite number of different types of car, the one actually used will represent a compromise between what's ideal and what is practical for the car builders, railroads and shippers.

Annual carloadings are reported in one ICC breakdown, in 18 major commodity groups and three general classifications. Following are these categories, with some idea of the amount of the traffic each represents and an illustration of the preferred or alternate type of car involved. Carloadings do not tell the whole story so far as revenue is concerned, since high-value commodities will typically travel farther and carry a higher freight rate than bulk materials (though usually loading at fewer tons per car), but do give a feel for the distribution of railroad business.

> Commodity Group: Grain
> Car Loadings per year: 1,550,000 (7.0%)
> Average Tons per Carload: 89
> Example of Preferred Car: "Jumbo" Covered Hopper.
> (AAR Mechanical Designation LO)
> Fig. 9-1

Figure 9-1 LO "Jumbo" Covered Hopper Car

Figure 9-1A Hopper Slope Sheets That "Funnel" Lading Out of Car

"Jumbo" covered hoppers are built with cubic capacities up to 5,700 cu. ft. to suit the density of the particular grain involved. They have superseded the boxcar (which must be equipped with temporary "grain doors" in its doorways to withstand the pressure and prevent leakage of the contents) as the principal carrier of grain, almost doubling tons per load and providing for direct loading and unloading by air or gravity.

Commodity Group: Other Farm Products
Car Loadings per year: 250,000 (1.1%)
Average Tons per Carload: 67
Example of Preferred Car: Mechanical Refrigerator
(AAR Mechanical Designation RP)
Fig. 9-2

Figure 9-2 RP Mechanical Refrigerator Car

The mechanical refrigerator car, with diesel-powered cooling unit and fuel capacity for as long as two weeks unattended operation, was developed to meet the sub-zero requirements of frozen food products which could not be met by the time-honored ice-and-salt-cooled cars. Now, most refrigerator car cooling systems are mechanical and are of general-purpose type, also capable of maintaining temperatures required by various fresh or frozen products. Most are also equipped with cushioning and load-restraining devices.

Commodity Group: Metallic Ores
Car Loadings per year: 1,500,000 (6.6%)
Average Tons per Carload: 80
Example of Preferred Car: Ore Hopper
(AAR Mechanical Designation HMA)
Fig. 9-3

Figure 9-3 HMA Ore Hopper Car

Ore is very dense, loading as heavily as 170 lb. per cu. ft., so cars used exclusively in this service are of small cubic capacity. Cars in processed taconite pellet service have an added collar to increase cubic capacity and carry the same tonnage of this lower density product.

Commodity Group: Coal
Car Loadings per year: 5,700,000 (25.0%)
Average Tons per Carload: 84
Examples of Preferred Car: Unit-Train Hopper
(AAR Mechanical Designation HT)
Fig. 9-4
Unit-Train Gondola
(AAR Mechanical Designation GT)
Fig. 9-5

Figure 9-4 HT Unit-Train Hopper Car

Figure 9-5 GT Unit-Train Gondola Car

Most coal tonnage goes to generating stations, to export docks and to steel mill coking plants, often in unit trains. Choice of bottom-dump hopper or high-side solid-bottom gondola depends upon unloading facilities at receiving point. Cars unloaded by overturning them in rotary car dumper may be equipped with rotary coupler at one end which allows emptying without uncoupling; bottom-dump cars, which may also be unloaded in rotary dumper, may be equipped with power-operated hopper doors for unloading in motion. Approximately 4,000 cu. ft. capacity is required for 100-ton load.

Commodity Group: Crushed Stone, Gravel, Sand
Car Loadings per Year: 750,000 (3.3%)
Average Tons per Carload: 78
Example of Preferred Car: "Aggregate" hopper
(AAR Mechanical Designation HM)
Fig. 9-6

Figure 9-6 HM "Aggregate" Hopper Car

Midway in density between ore and coal, crushed rock, gravel and sand require about 2,000 cu. ft. capacity for a 100-ton car. Where steady traffic is not expected, these commodities are often handled by partial loading of coal hoppers, but lower costs in regular service may warrant compact, quick-discharging cars of this type.

Commodity Group: Non-Metallic Minerals
Car Loadings per Year: 750,000 (3.3%)
Example ofPreferred Car: Small-cube Covered Hopper
(AAR Mechanical Designation LO)
Fig. 9-7

Figure 9-7 LO Small Cube Covered Hopper Car

Many minerals such as salt and phosphate require protection from the weather and cannot be shipped in open-top cars. Special car linings may be needed to protect contents from contamination; most minerals are dense and load to 70- or 100-ton car capacity in twin-hopper design of 2,500 to 3,000 cu. ft. capacity.

Commodity Group: Grain Mill Products
Car Loadings per Year: 900,000 per year (4.0%)
Example of Preferred Car: Food-Service Box Car
(AAR MechanicalDesignation XF)
Fig. 9-8

Figure 9-8 XF Food-Service Box Car Interior

XF cars have special seamless plastic linings to prevent contamination and "plug" doors which are forced inward by the operating mechanism after sliding into the closed position to provide a smooth interior. These cars are reserved for processed and packaged food service; carriers contaminating XF cars are subject to a special penalty charge.

Commodity Group: Food and Kindred Products
Car Loadings per Year: 950,000 (4.2%)
Average Tons per Carload: 44.9
Example of Preferred Car: Insulated Refrigerator Car
(AAR Mechanical Designation RB)
Fig. 9-9

Figure 9-9 RB Insulated Refrigerator Car

RB "bunkerless refrigerator" cars have the equivalent of at least 3-inch insulation of side and 3 1/2 inches on roof and floor but no cooling system. With plug doors, and usually load-restraining devices (designation RBL), these cars can maintain the temperature of many food products within satisfactory limits throughout an extended trip without the expense of mechanical temperature control.

Commodity Group: Primary Forest Products
Car Loadings per Year: 1,000,000 (4.4%)
Example of Preferred Car: Woodchip Hopper
(AAR Mechanical Designation HTS)
Fig. 9-10

Figure 9-10 HTS Woodchip Hopper Car

Largest of all hopper or gondola cars by far are those used in carrying woodchips from the forest to paper plants; it takes over 7,000 cu. ft. of some varieties to approach the 100-ton mark, so new cars built for this service are at the prescribed limit of height, width and length. "Shakeouts" (portable machines attached to the car which develop an oscillating force causing the car to vibrate on its springs) are often needed to encourage the load to flow out the hopper doors. Gondolas are used where suitable car dumpers are available.

Commodity Group: Lumber and Wood Products
(Except Furniture)
Car Loadings per Year: 500,000 (2.2%)
Average Tons per Carload: 54
Example of Preferred Car: Center-Beam Bulkhead Flat
(AAR Mechanical Designation FMS)
Fig. 9-11

Figure 9-11 FMS Center-Beam Bulkhead Flat Car

The bulkhead car is now used for transporting finished, packaged lumber because of the ease with which such lading can be handled by forklift trucks.

Commodity Group: Pulp, Paper and Allied Products
Car Loadings per Year: 1,100,000 (4.7%)
Average Tons per Carload: 40
Example of Preferred Car: Equipped Box Car
(AAR Mechanical Designation XL)
Fig. 9-12

Figure 9-12 XL Equipped Box Car

Rolls of newsprint are subject to flattening from impacts or shifting within the car, with subsequent problems in the printing press and damage claims. The cushion-underframe car equipped with load-restraining devices adaptable to its particular load is indispensable in handling such commodities. Paper products are also subject to damage if loaded in cars contaminated or roughed-up by previous loads.

Commodity Group: Chemicals and Allied Products
Carloads per Year: 1,380,000 (5.8%)
Average Tons per Carload: 67
Example of Preferred Car: Chemical Tank Car
(AAR Mechanical Designation T; Tank constuction and testing covered by numerous Department of Transportation (DOT) safety specifications for different commodity classes)
Fig. 9-13

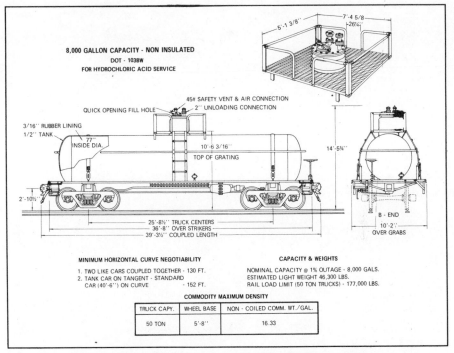

Figure 9-13 Non-Pressurized Chemical Tank Car

Tank car size has increased rapidly in recent years since elimination of requirements for running boards and use of tank itself as "center sill" strength member of car have allowed tank diameter to increase to clearance limit. Since many chemicals require special tank linings or materials, heater coils for unloading, etc., most cars are leased, owned by or assigned to individual shippers and carry only one class of product. Capacity ranges up to 150 tons (with six-wheel trucks) in some cars.

> Commodity Group: Petroleum Products
> Carloads per Year: 370,000 (1.6%)
> Average Tons per Carload: 56
> Example of Preferred Car: Pressure Tank Car
> (DOT Class 112A)
> Fig. 9-14

One of the principal petroleum products carried by rail is liquified petroleum (LP) gas, which must be kept under pressure to remain liquid at ordinary temperatures. Special restrictions apply to the construction, handling and equipment of cars in this "hazardous material" service. Capacity 33,000 gallons.

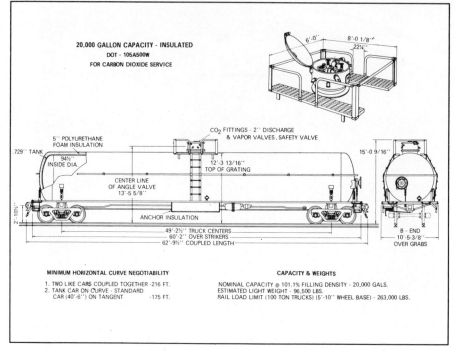

20,000 GALLON CAPACITY - INSULATED
DOT - 105A500W
FOR CARBON DIOXIDE SERVICE

5" POLYURETHANE FOAM INSULATION

.729" TANK

94½" INSIDE DIA

CENTER LINE OF ANGLE VALVE
13'-5 5/8"

CO_2 FITTINGS - 2" DISCHARGE & VAPOR VALVES, SAFETY VALVE

12'-3 13/16"
TOP OF GRATING

6'-0"   8'-0 1/8"
             22¼"

15'-0 9/16"

ANCHOR INSULATION

2'-10½"

49'-2½" TRUCK CENTERS
60'-2" OVER STRIKERS
62'-9½" COUPLED LENGTH

B - END
10'-5-3/8"
OVER GRABS

MINIMUM HORIZONTAL CURVE NEGOTIABILITY

1. TWO LIKE CARS COUPLED TOGETHER -216 FT.
2. TANK CAR ON CURVE - STANDARD
   CAR (40'-6") ON TANGENT   -175 FT.

CAPACITY & WEIGHTS

NOMINAL CAPACITY @ 101.1% FILLING DENSITY - 20,000 GALS.
ESTIMATED LIGHT WEIGHT - 96,500 LBS.
RAIL LOAD LIMIT (100 TON TRUCKS) (5'-10" WHEEL BASE) - 263,000 LBS.

Figure 9-14 Pressure Tank Car

<u>Commodity Group:</u> Stone, Glass and Clay Products
Carloads per Year: 800,000 (3.5%)
Average Tons per Car: 60
Example of Preferred Car: DF Boxcar (glass and clay
                          products)
                          Gondola (stone)
                    Fig. 9-15

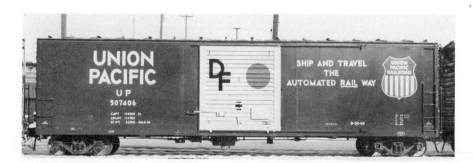

Figure 9-15 DF Box Car

Figure 9-15A Typical Load Restraining Device Used in DF Car

DF cars are box cars with special loading devices that prevent damage to the lading. Often, the cars are prominently marked with the letters "DF" to indicate their special purpose.

Commodity Group: Coke
Carloads per Year: 300,000 (1.2%)
Example of Preferred Car: Coke Hopper
(AAR Mechanical Designation HTC)

Coke, used primarily in blast furnaces in the smelting of iron ore, travels relatively short distances from coking plants to the steel mills. Much lighter than coal, coke is shipped in hopper cars built to larger cubic capacity or equipped with "coke" racks to accommodate its volume.

Commodity Group: Metals and Products
Carloads per Year: 850,000 (3.8%)
Average Tons per Carload: 64
Example of Preferred Car: Covered Gondola
(AAR Mechanical Designation GBSR)
Fig. 9-16

Figure 9-16 GBSR Covered Gondola Car

Finished steel in sheet or coil form requiring protection from the weather is shipped in gondola cars with removable covers allowing it to be loaded and unloaded from above by gantry cranes. The concentrated weight of coils requires heavy-duty load-securing devices, aided by sliding-sill or end-of-car cushioning. Structural shapes, pipe and other long products travel in open-top "mill gons" of 52 to 65 ft. length, with drop ends to allow overhang above an "idler" flat car for exceptionally long loads.

Figure 9-17 FA Enclosed Tri-Level Auto Rack

Commodity Group: Motor Vehicles and Equipment
Carloads per Year: 950,000 (4.2%)
Average Tons per Carload: 24
Example of Preferred Car: Enclosed Tri-Level Auto Rack
(AAR Mechanical Designation FA)
Fig. 9-17

The low rates made possible by carrying 12 to 18 automobiles per car not only regained the majority of this traffic for the railroads but have allowed the auto manufacturers to concentrate assembly of particular makes and models at single plants because of the greater distances over which shipping finished cars is economically attractive. Increasing vandalism and pilferage claims have caused the development and adoption of the enclosed rack car despite the additional investment, which may amount to as much as $900,000,000 for the 30,000 cars involved.

Commodity Group: Waste and Scrap Materials
Carloads per Year: 650,000 (2.6%)
Average Tons per Car: 51
Example of Preferred Car: Gondola
(AAR Mechanical Designation GB)
Fig. 9-18

Figure 9-18 GB Gondola Car

The relationship of freight rates for "recycling" materials to those for shipping ores, minerals, etc. used in the alternative process of meeting current needs by the use of new raw materials (and leaving the scrap to clutter up the environment) has become a considerable social issue in recent years. Scrap is not a time-sensitive commodity requiring expedited handling, but the volume fluctuates wildly with changes in price, tending to cause alternating shortages and surpluses in car supply, both of which are costly to the railroads. This gondola, suitable for scrap and other heavy loads, is also equipped with lading strap anchors for commodities requiring tie-down.

General Classification: All Other Carloads
Carloads per Year: 2,200,000 (9.8%)
Examples of Preferred Car Types:
    Unequipped "Free-Running" Box Car
    (AAR Mechanical Designation XM)
               Fig. 9-19
    Combination-Door Box Car
    (AAR Mechanical Designation XM)
               Fig. 9-20
    General-Service Flat Car
    (AAR Mechanical Designation FM)
               Fig. 9-21

Second only to coal in carloadings, this miscellaneous category includes merchandise and machinery of all types. So many more specialized cars have been assigned to specific services that the "plain Jane" XM box car has become in short supply at times.

Figure 9-19 XM "Free-Running" Box Car

Figure 9-20 XM Combination-Door Box Car

Figure 9-21 FM General-Service Flat Car

The "combination door" car is an example of a car intended to be more versatile by its suitability for handling both bulk commodities (using "grain doors" across the regular sliding center doors) and package or palletized items, easily loaded or unloaded through the wide opening provided by the extra set of "plug" doors. Unfortunately, the flexibility of the combination door car is not always realized. When the plug becomes inoperable, the car must be operated as a narrow door box car.

The general-service flat car has a wood deck for nailed-down blocking of the load, standard-size stake pockets and concentrated-load capacity to handle a wide variety of loads.

General Classifications: Forwarder and Shipper-Association
　　　　　　　　　　　　　　Traffic; Less-than-Carload (LCL)
Carloads per Year: Forwarder 600,000 (2.7%)
　　　　　　　　　　　LCL　　　　　20,000 (0.1%)
Average Tons per Carload: 19
Example of Preferred Car: TOFC (Trailer on Flat Car)
　　　　　　　　　　　　　　or "Piggyback" Flat Car
(AAR Mechanical Designation FC)
Fig 9-22

This traffic, formerly handled in box cars, is now almost entirely handled in piggyback trailers, as described in the later discussion on intermodal traffic. An additional 1,100,000 carloads of freight falling within other commodity classifications, mail, and express is handled in trailers or containers, making intermodal carloadings equal to more than 6% of the total.

Figure 9-22 FC TOFC/COFC (Piggyback) Flat Car

10

CAR OWNERSHIP AND DISTRIBUTION

Each railroad wants to have just enough cars available for the shippers on its line, not too few, since that sooner or later means lost business, and not too many because the cost of car ownership (interest, depreciation and maintenance) is (except for transportation labor) the largest single item of expense on the railroad, amounting to about 20 percent of revenues.

Some roads are primarily *originating* carriers, located in areas where more products are mined, grown or otherwise produced than are consumed; they will tend to be short of cars and under pressure to buy more. Predominantly *terminating* carriers can depend upon cars made empty on line as their supply for loading, to the extent that the cars are suitable for carrying the commodities they originate with reasonable efficiency. But they may have large, unfavorable balances of car rental payments, if they don't own their share of the fleet. Much traffic is seasonal; to make the best overall use of cars, all are essentially in a pool, from which roads draw extra cars during their periods of peak demand.

Car Rental Systems and Rates

The terms and amounts of payments for using another company's cars are a primary factor in ensuring an efficient level of supply of cars of needed types.

Railroad-owned cars, identified by a 2-, 3- or 4-letter assigned set of "reporting marks", usually the initials of the railroad's name, are "rented" on a basis which is still often referred to as *per diem*, although it is now on an *hourly* instead of daily time basis and also includes a charge for each mile run. For a great many years in the 1920's through the 1930's the charge was a flat "dollar a day". This charge was gradually raised after World War II; eventually, the prevalence of more specialized, productive and sophisticated cars and the disproportionate increase in new-car prices (which increased six-fold between 1950 and 1980) caused the rental to be based on the initial car cost less depreciation for age.

Under daily rentals, the road on which a car was physically located at midnight each day owed the fee to its owner; hourly car-hire rates were substituted in 1979 to remove any incentive for a mad scramble (perhaps resulting in inefficient scheduling and operations) to shove cars onto connections just before the daily deadline.

What Should the Rate Be?

The objective is to set the rate high enough that there will be a net return to the owner (to encourage an adequate total car inventory) and a strong incentive for railroads to keep "foreign" (rented) cars moving, but yet low enough to encourage a receiving road to hang onto an empty long enough to find a return load and thus improve overall car utilization.

The Interstate Commerce Commission has been involved in setting the rental rates, since car rental is part of the cost base on which a "fair return" level of freight rates is based. The ICC has also acted as guardian of the principle that a "commodity" (empty cars) in scarce supply is to be doled out to claimants in an even-handed, non-discriminatory way with small shippers receiving at least equal consideration. This principle has frequently been in conflict with the assignment of cars to high-volume, quick-turnaround (unit train) service which has the effect of doing the overall transportation job with fewer cars and thus decreasing the change of a shortage.

Car Service Rules

The flow of cars is regulated by "Car Service Rules" promulgated by the Car Service Division (CSD) of the AAR. By the terms of the Staggers Act of 1980, as part of the "deregulation" process, ICC control of car distribution was eliminated, leaving car service rules and their enforcement to the industry itself. Railroads are "subscribers" to the CSD, contractually agreeing to its rules under penalty of assessments (subject to arbitration) and to its direction of the flow of cars to areas where they are needed. Railroads are also free to make particular rental arrangements regarding specific cars or classes of cars and their handling directly with each other.

The most basic car service rules are Rules 1 and 2, which in effect require that a car made empty on a railroad terminating a shipment be loaded only in the direction of its home road. Car owners may (and in times of car surplus frequently do) choose to release some of their cars from Rules 1 and 2 so that they will have a better chance of moving freely around the country and earning rental rather than being sent home empty where they may have to be stored for some time before a load is available.

Typical rental charges vary from 12¢ per hour/+ 3.3¢ per mile for an elderly 40 ft. plain box car to 44¢ per hour + 4.7¢ for a relatively new, expensive 89 ft. piggyback flatcar at 1980 rates.

How Does an Empty Get Back?

General-purpose railroad-owned cars made empty will be loaded "toward the home district," an area including lines of the owning road, if possible. Fig. 10-23 shows car utilization regions into which the United States and Canada have been divided. This heads them in the direction of their owning line, though they may not get there on the first bounce. If no load is likely to be available, they will be sent home "via the service route" (Fig. 2-5), retracing the route they took on the loaded trip. Thus, the roads that got a piece of the revenue will bear the burden of the empty mileage.

However, if the demand for cars is building up in an area beyond that supplied by normal return movements, the CSD will issue "Car Service Directives" requiring that empties be sent there instead, for example, diverting grain cars from the northern transcontinental railroads to the Southwest in anticipation of the winter-wheat harvest.

Private-Owner Cars

Privately owned cars, shipper-owned or leased from a freight car company, are identified by reporting marks ending with "X". They are paid for on the basis of the miles run. In effect, the railroads compensate the owner for getting his business without the expense of providing a car for his shipments. This rate is not intended to be high enough to cause a big stampede into the car-owning business, but it does provide a way for the shipper to ensure himself of cars of the types and in the level of supply that's best for his business.

Assigned Service Cars

Cars in "assigned service" (or any car required to protect a regular movement) are returned via the service route; they are in effect in a pool making regular trips from one plant to another via a specific route, with car ownership usually shared by railroads making up the route in proportion to the mileage. This may result in an empty owned by the terminating railroad being hauled back empty to a "foreign" line for loading, but the rentals will balance out. These cars are usually ones which are specially equipped or suited for the item being transported.

Private-owner cars operate in much the same way. There is an advantage, of course, to an owner who can so arrange his business as to provide loads in both directions and obtain twice as much transportation for the same car costs.

The increase in specialized cars has brought about an increase in one-way loading of cars, helping to drive down the load/empty ratio, with hopefully offsetting benefits in shipper satisfaction due to the specialized handling of their needs.

"Free-Runner" is the term used by transportation people to describe cars that may be loaded toward home in accordance with the Car Service Rules, rather than be returned empty reverse route.

Railbox-Railgon

To provide access to a fleet of cars of types not otherwise available in sufficient quantity, subsidiaries of the Trailer-Train Corporation (itself owned cooperatively by 32 railroads) were established to acquire large fleets of "Railbox" and "Railgon" standardized plain box cars and gondolas, which are available as free-runners to railroads upon demand at charges generally below the ICC car-hire rates. Trailer Train itself owns and leases out a fleet of about 50,000 piggyback flat cars, 25,000 multi-level automobile-shipping flats and 12,500 special service flat (e.g. farm implement) cars.

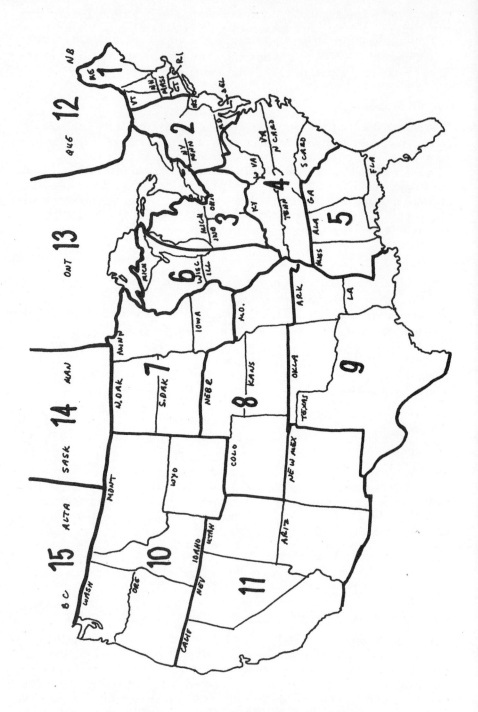

Figure 10-1   Regional Car Utilization Map

How Do You Find an Empty?

In filling the order of a shipper for cars to load, the traffic department of the railroad has its own records (most are now computerized) of its own and foreign cars on line. For major movements of traffic to be handled in non-assigned cars, however; it's not good enough to be seeking out suitable empties *after* the orders have been placed; the cars needed should already be moving toward the loading points. Several major data processing, communication and display systems aid the CSD and the railroads in doing this.

UMLER

The Universal Machine Language Equipment Register is a data file, updated daily by the car owners to reflect car availability, added, retired, bad order. The data include the reporting marks, number, capacity, dimensions and so on for all cars in interchange service and for most of the trailers and containers used in piggyback service. It's a self-policing system; if a car isn't in UMLER, its owner won't get per diem.

Car distribution is directly controlled by the Operations Department, in most cases. Car orders are placed through agents, who are operating employees, and filled by yardmasters, dispatchers or transportation officers. Each individual railroad's computer system takes care of, perhaps, 90 percent of the car distribution job and 100 percent of the job of matching cars to actual shipper orders.

Train II

This second-phase version of the "Telerail Automated Information Network," in operation since June, 1975, receives information from railroads involved in 98 percent of the interchanges in the United States and Canada. Most of the information is received no more than one day after the event, and is used to update hourly the data bank on the location and status of every freight car. Besides data on such events as time of placement for loading, release for movement, crossing of zone boundaries, interchange, arrival and release after unloading, it has information on the commodity being carried (important in determining what the car can be used to haul on its next trip) and serves as an automatic message routing system to send information from the originating road's computer to bridge and terminating lines' machines so they can plan its handling.

Car Tracing

Shippers are even more interested in the location, status and time of arrival of cars loaded with their goods, and railroad traffic departments have long maintained communication and office systems for providing such information on a timely basis. Increasing computational capability has extended and automated the process; starting in 1980 the AAR has provided a SAM (Shipper Assist Message) service whereby a shipper with high-speed data communication capability can direct a query to the AAR's computer in Washington and automatically receive data on any of the cars carrying his shipments from the computers of all participating railroads. "Third-party" agents will provide such service (for a fee) to shippers who do not have such message-transmission capability.

11

TERMINAL OPERATIONS

The first step in the actual rail movement of our shipment occurs when the switch or local freight crew, which also brings and sets out incoming loads and empties for loading, picks up the car. The actual operation of picking up a load is simple and quick, though there are some important things to be remembered (such as closing the derail and releasing the hand brake). Often the car to be picked up will be sandwiched between partially loaded or unloaded cars which will have to be re-spotted. As Fig. 11-1 shows, it does make quite a difference which way the siding is connected to the main track.

In total, however, the switching involved in originating, terminating and interchanging shipments is a very expensive part of railroad operations. Industries outside of terminal limits are served by road crews, and much yard switching is in connection with forwarding trains through intermediate yards. The fact that 75,000 of the 160,000 train crew personnel on U.S. railroads in a recent year were *in yard service* doesn't mean that precisely that proportion of transportation labor costs goes for picking 'em up and setting 'em out. It does indicate that terminal operations are expensive and that the ability of the trainmaster to provide reliable, timely service with a minimum number of switch and local crews and engines has a lot to do with whether the railroad makes money or not.

The Switching District

For a simplified but representative bird's-eye view of some of the ways such operations may be arranged, consider our East-West System's situation in the metropolitan/port area of J. Fig. 11-2 shows the principal trackage in the "J Switching District," an area within which a shipper located on any one railroad is in effect served by all. The basic rate to "J" applies for shipments (from all points beyond a certain minimum distance) to any point within the area, whether it's directly on one of the line-haul railroads such as the E-W System or can only be reached via the J Terminal and a car-float trip across the harbor to Port Island.

The tangle of trackage in Fig. 11-2 looks complicated, and it is, but it's not even in the same league as the actual situation in such areas as New York, Chicago or Minneapolis-St. Paul. It will serve to illustrate some typical arrangements for getting freight into the line-haul system.

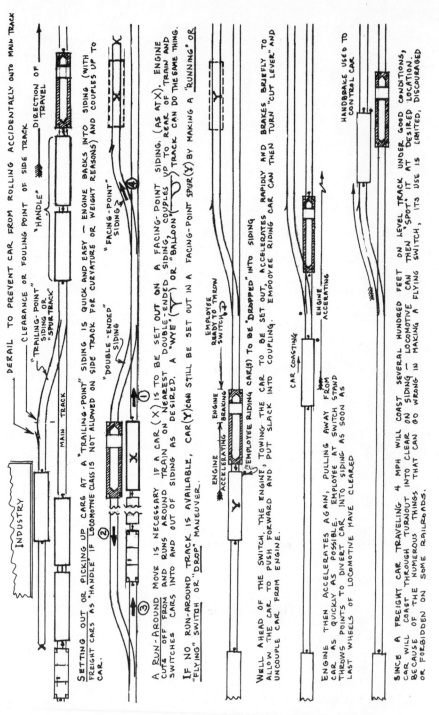

Figure 11-1 Set-Outs, Pick-Ups, Run-Arounds and Drops

The Base of Operations

The East-West System's principal operating base in J is its "77th St. Yard", (1) in Fig. 11-2. Trains to and from the west start and end their runs here, and most switching crews working within the J district work out of 77th St., where complete servicing facilities for locomotives are available.

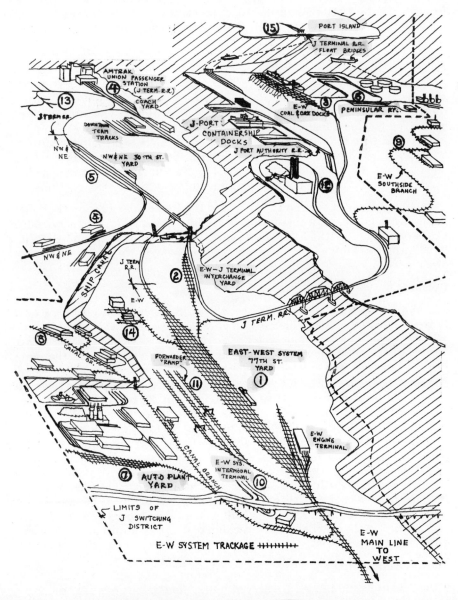

Figure 11-2 The J Switching District

Switching and Terminal Companies

Much of the trackage in the J area is owned and operated by the J Terminal Railroad, which as we noted in connection with the system network map (Fig. 11-2) is a "joint facility" owned by the line-haul railroads serving J. The E-W System "interchanges" cars for points on the "J-T" at a small yard (2) switched directly by 77th St. yard crews. To reach its huge export-import coal piers at (3), the E-W has trackage rights over the J-T and its key bridge across the harbor. Intercity passenger trains operated for Amtrak by the line-haul railroads continue without pause onto J-T trackage and into the "Union Station" downtown at (4).

Interchanges Large and Small

As our E-W System map (Fig. 2-4) shows, the E-W and the NW & NE are mostly competitors in the J area, but there is some freight originating on one of them destined for points on the other which will be interchanged at J. This traffic, a few cars each way a day, is handled by the J-T crews which pick it up at (2) and deliver it to the NW & NE's principal J yard at "30th St." (5). This, unfortunately, is not likely to be a quick process since there isn't enough business to make it a principal factor in scheduling the various trips that make up the short cross-town connections.

The interchange between the E-W and the Peninsular Ry., on the other hand, is a big one, with many cars of feed for the farming country south of J coming in on the E-W. Interyard "transfer runs" from (1) to (6) handle this traffic on schedules closely tied to the arrival and departure of connections at both ends.

Reciprocal Switching

A shipper on the E-W "Canal Branch" at (8), one on the J-T downtown in the congested old warehouse area at (13), and one on the NW & NE at (5) with something to ship to the west can all choose either E-W or NW & NE for its initial segment of its line-haul routing, and they'll get the same rate. In one case, the E-W will: order an empty from the NW & NE, to be delivered to them via the J-T; place it for loading; pick it up when released by the shipper; and deliver it to the J-T for transfer to the NW & NE for the road haul. In the other case, the situation is reversed. Within the switching district where these reciprocal arrangements apply, the originating line-haul road will "absorb" the switching and "per diem reclaim" charges payable to the other lines involved, giving up a chunk of its "division" of the through line-haul rate in exchange for being able to compete for the traffic from shippers not located on its tracks. Much of this balances out, of course, and the extra moves involved make it likely that service, speed and reliability will cause the shipper to tend to route his freight via the line he's on. "Freedom of choice," uninfluenced by *rate* differences, is preserved.

Marine Railroading

Port Island's industries are served by *car floats*, barges with tracks on their deck which receive strings of cars pushed aboard over "float bridges," mating sections of track arranged to rise and fall with the tide.

A tug then moves the float across the channel where its cars are offloaded and moved by switch engines to industry and dock trackage. Once a widely used method of serving harborside industries and of bridging gaps in the mainline rail network, this flexible but expensive method of reaching across the water is now limited to a few operations in ocean and Great Lakes port areas. As here at J, services by individual line-haul railroads have been consolidated into joint operations.

Shifters, Locals and Turns

The huge automobile plant at (7) is the principal source of traffic on the E-W "Canal Branch" that extends to (8), serving numerous industries within the J switching district. Auto plant traffic requires serveral trips a day from 77th St. to the small Auto Plant Yard, where the plant's own locomotives and crews take over for the extensive intra-plant rail operations.

Names for a particular crew assignment tend to have a strong local flavor, and what one line calls a "shifter" might well be dignified by an entirely different title on another railroad. All these crew assignments extending outside a yard but within a switching district have the common goal of picking up and delivering loads and empties as efficiently as possible, considering the constraints of long-standing work agreements, difficult physical track arrangements, congestion, grade crossing and drawbridge interfernce.

Thus, what the E-W employees mean when they refer to the "docks shifter" is not a single 1,000 hp switch engine puttering around the waterfront but a set of up to five six-axle diesel units which leaves 77th St. with a massive train of coal which it hauls over the J-T to the docks and exchanges for equally heavy loads of ore, also rearranging loads and empties at the pier that may be required to let the giant ship/car/stockpile stacker/unloader do its work.

Local Freights

Outside of yard limits, local freight crews handle industry switching as they work their way along the line. Since the E-W's "Southside Branch" (9) extends beyond the J switching district, its daily switching is accomplished by such crews. The branch is short but so busy that two crews are often used, one leaving 77th St. and working its way out to the far end, where a second crew takes over its locomotive, caboose and papers for the trip back.

Out on the main lines (Fig. 2-4), local freight crews are assigned segments of line long enough so that normal levels of traffic can be readily handled in a day's work, and occasional overtime. One such run is from H to K, a fairly long distance but with relatively few plants to be switched; it is worked westbound on Monday, Wednesday and Friday, eastbound on the alternate days.

Turns

Branches such as that from T to S may be handled by "turns," runs which go out to the end of the line, turn, and come back. Through lines, such as between H and P, may be run as two shorter turns; one crew will work from H to M and back; meeting its counterpart (which is doing the same thing starting from P) at the midpoint and exchanging trains. This gets everybody back to the home terminal at the end of the shift, and the meeting point can be changed as necessary to equalize the time required on the two turns if the relative amount of business changes.

12

CLASSIFICATION AND BLOCKING

The next step in the terminal operation is to assemble the cars from various sources into *blocks* (blocks of cars, not to be confused with track "blocks" in the signal system) headed for individual destinations; these blocks will then be combined into trains for the line haul. There are two principal ways the switching can be done -- flat and gravity—and the E-W, like most of the larger railroads, uses both.

Flat Switching

Fig. 12-1 is a condensed and shortened diagram of the E-W's 77th St. Yard at J. In actuality, a yard serving this large a metropolis would have many more tracks, but the operating scheme would be the same. Locomotive and car movements in any yard on a railroad are much the same, but the pattern and purpose of the operation is part of the railroad operating scheme as a whole, and each yard may be distinctly different in that respect.

Yards, Sub-Yards, Tracks and Leads

In reality, yards of this size and complexity are also located in areas as sparsely populated and seemingly remote as J is densely populated and strategically situated. The logic for this is the FRA-mandated 500 mile inspection. All trains, regardless of commodity, terrain or climate, must be thoroughly inspected every 500 miles for safety-related defects by qualified railroad personnel. It is also quite convenient to perform major switching operations at these yards.

Within any major yard, the tracks will be arranged in several sub-yards, each with a somewhat more specific purpose. At 77th St. there is an engine terminal with tracks where hostlers: fuel, sand and water the diesels; separate and rearrange units into new combinations making up suitable locomotives for outgoing runs; and move engines into and out of the diesel shop for inspection, running repairs and heavier maintenance work by the mechanical department's specialists. Car repairs are performed on the rip track, in the car shop and in the car shop yard on freight cars found to need it. To the east is the E-W System, J Terminal R. R. Interchange Yard, arranged so that cars placed by one road's switching crew can easily be picked up, after acceptance by the car inspector, by the other road's crew.

There are two classification yards in the 77th St. complex, Tracks 1 through 4 being known as the "Forwarding Yard" and Tracks 10 through 16 as the "Main Yard." Each consists of a group of parallel body tracks connected by ladders (Fig. 3-7) at each end to switching leads extending from each end. Crossovers connect the switching leads to main tracks (the main line to the west and to downtown, the auto plant branch) leading to the outside world. These are all hand-throw switches, operated by the switch crews themselves or, in the case of trains entering or leaving the yard in completing or starting their runs, by switch tenders. Some tracks, designated as thoroughfare tracks, are normally kept free of standing cars so that yard and road engines can use them to get from one end of the yard to the other freely without fouling the main tracks.

Shuffling the Deck

To take one example of all the car-flows in which 77th St. is involved, consider the matter of getting empty cars to industries along the E-W's main line between J and I. There are plenty of cars available which have come into the J area from the west under load, and consigned to team tracks, distribution terminals and consuming industries all over the J Switching District. They come back into 77th St. from various switch runs, directly and via the J-T interchange and will be found on tracks in the Main Yard assigned as "arrival tracks" by the yardmaster.

The Switch List

Yard and computer generated data received on all empty cars entering the 77th St. yards is analyzed by the division's car distributor who will identify suitable empties (in regard to ownership, type, special equipment, etc.) to match against empty car orders received from agents on the line. Based on this information, the yard office will generate a switch list which tells a yard crew on which tracks and in what order cars currently sitting on other tracks are to be placed.

The objective in this particular case is to make up the today's "I Peddler," the local freight which runs from J to I, serving the lineside industries en route. In the process, of course, the switch crew, a yard conductor or foreman, engineer, and several yard brakemen or switchmen, will handle many cars as part of their travels in other directions on other missions. When the I Peddler is complete, it will have both empties and loads for its industries, including cars that have come from the Peninsular, from the docks on Port Island and even from *eastbound* trains. It may be quicker to bring a car destined for a point just west of J into 77th St. on a fast freight from the west and then take it back on the local rather than having it come all the way east from I in local service.

Station Order

To speed up the local's work, its train will be arranged in "station order," with cars to be set out at the first station at the head end followed by those for the next station and so on. Blocking cars by station order is particularly important in the case of through freights which make setouts and pick-ups at only a few specified points and whose schedules aren't compatible with any additional manipulating en route.

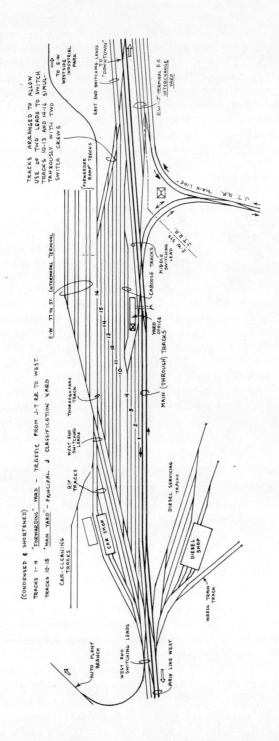

Figure 12-1 East-West System — J 77th St. Yard (Condensed and Shortened)

Batting 'em Out

To carry out the work put on paper by the switch list, the engine takes a cut of cars from one of the yard tracks, hauls it back onto the switch lead, and then proceeds to shove or "kick" the cars into their assigned tracks. A capable, experienced crew will often have several cuts of cars moving at one time, coasting slowly toward the cars already on the body tracks after being cut from the string attached to the engine. The brakemen will think ahead so as to be in the right position to line up a switch for the next cut or to ride the car and work the uncoupling lever to cut it loose, all with a minimum of lost time and a maximum of riding rather than walking. The crew will kick cars with due regard for their weight, the distance to be traveled, and any grades in the yard (yard leads are sometimes just a bit higher than the center of the body tracks so that a slight grade helps keep the cuts rolling) so that they do not impact at more than walking speed (4 mph or less). Cars with especially sensitive loads are moved all the way into coupling with engine attached, and other cars are not dropped onto them, as called for by the rules.

Nevertheless, flat switching is a relatively slow and consequently expensive process if there is a lot of rearranging to be done. After the cars are in the proper tracks for their destination, they probably will not be in station order, so it will be necessary to pull back out and shuffle them again. In flat-switching a long train, the switch engine may take short cuts of cars and classify them, moving rather snappily in the process but having to go back several times to get more, or take longer cuts and have to accelerate sluggishly in making each move. Either way, the engine will move the equivalent of many train-lengths in getting all cars into their assigned positions.

Gravity Switching

Because of the time and money consumed by flat switching, the E-W System (like most fairly large railroads) does as much of its classification as possible by gravity. It has built what it likes to call "electronic classification yards," often simply known as "hump" or "retarder" yards, at D and H. The yard at H, on the basis of system traffic-flow studies, provides hump classification of westbound cars only, while D Yard, located between the two main tracks, has separate gravity yards for handling eastbound and westbound traffic.

System-Wide Effects

Due to the capability for thorough classification of westbound trains at H, the J 77th St. Yard simply places into trains in any order all westbound cars arriving from every connection, branch and station in the area (except for those going out in the I local) and sends them off to H. Cars coming into H from the west are already blocked for the various connecting railroads, docks, yards and major industries in the J area. As a result, about half the trackage in the main 77th St. classification yards was removed to make room for the new Intermodal Yards handling the E-W's steadily increasing piggyback traffic.

Very little eastbound traffic comes onto the E-W between D and H, so trains are blocked at D so thoroughly that they can go to their destinations without further classification and by-pass the H yard; what little eastbound work must be done there can better be done by flat switching.

The Hump Yard

Fig. 12-2 shows a gravity yard arrangement typical of that built by the E-W System at H. The basic idea, of course, is to push the cars being sorted over an artificial hill or "hump" and let gravity push them into the classification tracks. It is the most efficient classification method if the traffic pattern is such that most of the cars passing through are headed in different directions from their neighbors in the incoming trains. Running the whole train over the hump just to get one or two groups of cars headed in the right direction would not be worthwhile. But where the cars are really scrambled, the hump comes into its own; the hump locomotive need travel only one train length in classifying the entire consist.

Receiving Yard

Incoming trains stop in the *receiving* or *arrival* yard, which must have enough tracks to accommodate trains coming in from all principal lines over a period of a few hours. Road locomotives and cabooses are removed, and the humping engine, often a six-axle unit with a slug attached, couples up to the rear of the cars on one track.

Other hump yard facilities include an inspection pit, often provided on the single track approaching the hump itself so that each car's running gear can be thoroughly inspected for defects, which will get in-train or rip-track attention depending on the nature of the problem. Receiving yards may also be set up with track spacing and runways so that inspectors can examine cars from small utility vehicles.

Before being pushed over the hump, air must be bled from brake cylinders so that the cars will roll freely. A switch list is provided to the "pin-puller" standing at the right side of the hump so he will know where the cars are to be separated. The upgrade leading to the hump insures that the slack is in so the cut lever can be operated.

The Classification Bowl

The classification tracks themselves, often called the "bowls" because of their concave profile, fan out from the base of the hump in groups of five to nine tracks; the total number depends on the size and function of the yard and available land but may be as many as 60 to 70.

Coming over the hump, the cuts of one or more cars first encounter a steep grade, which quickly accelerates each cut so that there will be enough space between it and the next one for switches to be thrown. There is usually a "weigh-in-motion" scale which automatically takes care of the requirement that each car loaded on-line must be weighed before it enters interchange or reaches its destination.

Car Retarders

Electric or electro-pneumatic car retarders regulate the motion of the car during its descent; it is the computerized control of the switches and

170

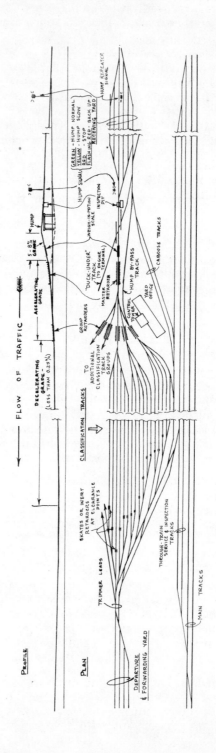

Figure 12-2 Gravity Classification Yard

retarders that gives the modern hump yard its "electronic classification yard" title. The retarder itself is a set of powerful jaws on each side of and a few inches above the railhead which grasp the car wheels slowing the car to the computed exit speed. This process produces loud squealing, and some yards located in populated areas now must meet environmental requirements by providing noise baffles alongside the retarders to reduce, to an acceptable level, noise radiated sidewise.

The retarders are arranged so that each car passes through only two, a master retarder at the foot of the hump and one group retarder on the track leading into each group of classification tracks. Through the group retarders, the tracks are on enough of a grade to accelerate the cars and make sure that they will move through the turnouts into the classification tracks. Beyond that point, they flatten out to a grade that isn't quite enough to keep a free-rolling car moving at the speed at which it enters the track.

At the far end of the classification tracks there is usually a slight upgrade which will tend to slow cars as they approach the turnouts and tracks leading to the departure tracks. Skates (wedge-shaped shoes placed atop the rail by a remote-controlled skate-placing machine) or inert retarders (spring-loaded versions of the master or group machines) are used to keep cars from rolling too far and fouling the exit trackage.

Retarder Control

In the most modern electronic yards, the retarder and switch control system accepts "switch list" data telling it which track each cut is to take, along with waybill information on the weight of each car, and a count of the cars already in each track. Its memory includes such information as the length, grades and curvature of each track and its approaches. It gets individual data on the speed and "rollability" of each cut -- on both curved and straight sections -- from trackside radar devices, and keeps track of the wind velocity affecting car movement.

On the basis of this computerized information, the retarders are controlled to cause each car to leave the group retarder at a speed which will let it roll just far enough up the track to which it is being sent to couple with the cars already there. The hump tower operator monitors the whole operation from his vantage point where, day or night, he can watch each cut roll down into the bowl. He can override or modify the automatic operation should any problem threaten to develop.

Trimming

At the lower end of the yard, one or two trimmer engines takes care of such chores as pushing cars together if they didn't quite come together, rearranging cars within a classification and re-humping any misclassified cuts.

Cars go over the hump at a rate of about 3 mph, which works out to one 50 ft. car every ten seconds or 300 cars per hour. With two hump locomotives on the job so that a second train can start over the hump as soon as the first has cleared, and with a reasonable allowance for trimming and other delays, a single hump can classify up to 1,500 cars per 8-hour shift. Traffic is rarely distributed evenly around the clock to fully utilize hump capacity on all three shifts, but processing of 3,000 to 3,500 cars per day is often achieved.

High-Capacity Yards

Since all the cars being classified into a single bowl must go over one track, yards which must handle more cars than this must either have two hump tracks which — at least during some times of the day — can function as two separate sub-yards, each distributing cars into the tracks on its side of the bowl, or the speed over the hump must be increased. This can be done by providing a third set of *tangent-point* retarders (located at the point where the cars enter the individual classification tracks) making the final speed reduction. Cars can then travel through the turnouts and group retarder area at higher speeds, increasing the rate at which the train can go over the hump without having the cuts too close together.

Departure

In some hump yards trains leave directly from the classification tracks, but in most cases classified cuts are pulled forward into a departure and forwarding yard. Here they are combined into trains in station order and receive road motive power and cabooses.

13

LINE-HAUL OPERATION

Everything discussed to this point is just the prelude to the primary railroad operation that must bring in all the revenue to support the whole system, moving trains along the line, from one point to another. The average mile of line in the United States operated in freight service carries 5.4 trains per day, which doesn't sound like much activity. However, since 67 percent of the ton-miles are concentrated on less than 20 percent of the mileage, the typical main line will see several times that many trains. As we have seen, traffic will tend to concentrate itself at certain times of the day, so planning, scheduling and dispatching trains so that each uses its "track space" to generate its share of transportation is important.

Scheduled, Advertised and Extra Trains

Fig. 13-1 is a highly condensed "schedule" of westbound through-train operations on our East-West System for part of one particular day. There is no official timetable that shows all these train movements on one page; "employees' timetables" show only trains operating on the particular division which they cover. Also, in the E-W scheme of things (typical but by no means the way it is done on all railroads), only First Class trains appear in the timetable with schedules which actually confer timetable authority for their operation.

First Class schedules include only Train Nos. 17, 19, 151 and 153 westbound. In accordance with standard practice, trains that are west- or southbound by timetable have odd numbers, while east- or northbound trains have even numbers. On the E-W, all trains are either east or westbound; the timetable arbitrarily designates that H to K, K to F and T to D are westbound directions.

Nos. 17 and 19 are passenger trains operated by the E-W System for Amtrak; Nos. 151 and 153 are piggyback freights permitted to run at passenger train speeds and also accorded first-class status. On the E-W, all other trains are technically "extras," which must be given specific authorization to run each trip and are designated by the number of the locomotive unit leading the consist and the direction of operation (Extra 5411 East, for example). Thus, it is possible for any employee to tell immediately the direction of a train's movement. One exception to this is a "work extra," usually a maintenance-of-way train performing duties which may require moving back and forth over a section of track more than once. Work extras are given authority by train order to work between two designated points for a period of time and do not have a specified direction.

Advertised Freight Service

At another point in the employees' timetable are the "Advertised Freight Service" schedules, accompanied by a note that "the times shown convey no timetable authority." Nevertheless, these trains are usually the backbone of the railroad's service, and their schedules are the ones that the traffic department's freight solicitors publicize. They are variously known as "symbol" or "manifest" trains, often given formal or informal "name train" status reflecting their speed, purpose or other attractive attribute. Their operation, particularly in making connections with other trains, is closely watched. Taken as a whole, the advertised freight service constitutes the network of services which can move a car to any point on the main lines of the system in reasonably predictable fashion.

Fast and Not-so-Fast Freights

Each advertised freight, often identified by a symbol including the initials of its origin and destination, has certain functions to perform and will be so scheduled. In general, the more business a line has, the more specialized the purpose of its "hotter" freight trains. If there is only one sizeable train-load of through freight moving over a particular route per day, the daily fast freight on that line will have to make stops at each operating point to set out and pick up cars for and from the local freights working the area; it will probably do some "work" at major industries as well. Its average speed may not be impressive, but if it can receive most freight loaded by the end of the work day and move it to its destination in time to catch the first available connection, it has done its job.

Other trains may have to be provided with extra horsepower, skip major stops and accept only high-rated traffic to their connections, hundreds of miles farther on, to reach principal destinations at the most desirable time, very early in the morning, so that cars may be placed for unloading at the start of the business day. A closer examination of Fig. 13-1's schedules (shown in "24-hour" time to save space here, although "A.M. Lightface -- P.M. Boldface" is more likely to be used in timetables in the United States) will show examples of both fast and not-so-fast freights.

Extra Trains

Also shown on Fig. 13-1 are examples of the extra trains which will normally handle much of the traffic. Many of these, which run only when the business is there, are on just as fast and exacting schedules as the advertised or timetabled trains; the dispatchers, yardmasters and trainmasters know what treatment each warrants and will act accordingly. An ore extra is going to take a long time to get up the big hill between F and E and back down to fairly level ground again (Fig. 7-1), so all the more nimble trains will be allowed to run ahead of it at this point. But its overall time may not be much longer than that for some arranged trains which do intermediate work and are reclassified at the major yards.

Keeping the Line Moving

Other extras, such as "Advance JD-1," are just that, additional trains run to handle the periodic overflow of traffic which would otherwise clog up the railroad. When it becomes apparent that JD-1 will not be able to handle all the traffic available by its scheduled 0330 departure from J and still be able to pick up its cars originating at I, an extra, unofficially known as its "advance section," will be created at I, to run ahead of JD-1 and relieve it of enough tonnage and work so that it can maintain its schedule and make connections at D. In the process, Advance JD-1 will "fill to tonnage" with any westbound empties which may have accumulated. Running the advance in the same "time slot" as JD-1 from H to D affects other trains less than if it were sent out at some intermediate time.

Balancing Power

Then there are those extras that no one really wants to run but which may actually improve productivity overall. There will often be periods in which traffic is much heavier in one direction than the other and the normal method of "balancing motive power" -- simply adding the extra diesel units to the locomotives heading back in the slack direction with their trains -- will not get enough units back fast enough to handle tonnage in the heavy direction. Since locomotives running "light" (without train) can make much better time, in traveling over a heavily-graded line such as this one over the mountain, there may be no alternative but to run groups of units back to the other end of the railroad from time to time.

Moving Those Blocks

The job of the advertised freight service is to move quickly and efficiently the blocks of cars assembled in the various yards by the classification process to their destinations in train-size lots. This process becomes a matter of scheduling, taking into account not only the cars, but motive power, train and yard crew, yard space and main-track availability as well. For a brief look at a little bit of what's involved, consider one group of one day's trains on the schedule of Fig. 13-1 --specifically, OH 5, PMH, PRH, HB 5, and a "Unit Coal Mty Extra."

PRH is a key schedule; it is the principal carrier of through traffic which has come up from BB and CC and intermediate points on the Peninsular Railway, leaving in the evening and arriving at the Peninsular's J Yard early in the morning. "Normal" interchange at this point would call for a transfer run taking the cars for the E-W over to its 77th St. Yard, where they would be classified and put into the next train west. This process would take the better part of a day, so the two line-haul railroads have set up a "run through" arrangement.

TRAIN / FREQUENCY	STATION: MAIN LINE	STATION: BRANCH		SCHEDULED (FIRST CLASS): ATK 17	ATK 19	FWDR 151	TTX 153	ADVERTISED FGT. SERVICE (EXTRAS ON TIMECARD): JD1	HA1	JH3	HD3	HSW	OH5	PMH	PRH	TA-1	HB-5	DDD	EXTRAS (EXAMPLE): ORE XTRAS	UNIT COAL MTY	JH PICK UP	ADV JD-1	GRAIN MTY	MINI-BR'GE	AUTO PTS.
FREQUENCY				DAILY	DAILY	DAILY EX SUN	DAILY EX-MON	DAILY	DAILY EX. SUN-MON	DAILY EX SUN-MON	DAILY EX SUN-MON	DAILY EX. SUN-MON	DAILY	DAILY	DAILY	DAILY	DAILY	DAILY EX. MON.	8 TRAINS 2/WK	10/WK	2/WK	AS REQ'D	5/WK	2/MO	4/WK
ATLANTIC DIV.	J	TERMINAL 77TH. ST.	LV. LV.	1800 —	0900 —	— 2000	— 0100	— 2300	(DAILY FROM D)	— 0315	— —	— —	— —	— —	PEN, RY YARD 0600	— —	— —	— —	ORE PIER 0400	COAL DOCK 0900	0330	— —	— —	— 0045	— 1900
	I	—	LV.	1915	1115	PASS 2200	PASS 0315	0215	—	0615	—	—	—	—	0930	—	—	—	PASS 0800	PASS 1130	0700	0015	—	PASS 0245	PASS 2200
	—	P	LV.	↓	↓	↓	↓	↓	—	↓	—	—	—	0800	↓	—	—	—	↓	↓	↓	↓	—	↓	↓
	—	O	LV.	↓	↓	↓	↓	↓	—	↓	—	—	0600	↓	↓	—	—	—	↓	↓	↓	↓	—	↓	↓
	—	L	LV.	↓	↓	↓	↓	↓	—	↓	—	—	↓	LV. M 0945	↓	—	—	RUN THRU	↓	↓	↓	↓	—	↓	↓
	H	—	AR LV	2100 2110	1330 1340	0001 0015	0500 0520	0430 0530	— 0900	0915 ↳	1230	1245	1115	1130	1145	— →	1400	FROM S.E. R.R.	1400 1430	1300 1315	1030	0300 0515	— FROM	0445 0500	0130 0200
ALLEGHENY DIV. EASTERN STD. TIME	—	K	LV	↓	AR 1600	↓	↓	↓	↓	—	↓	↓	—	—	—	—	↓	0800	↓	↓	—	↓	SW&AA R.R.	↓	↓
	G	—	LV	2340	—	PASS 0300	PASS 0810	PASS 0830	1330	—	PASS 1500	1515	—	—	—	RUN—	PASS 1610	↓	PASS 1800	PASS 1545	—	0840	PASS 1000	PASS 0750	PASS 0450
	F	—	LV	0040	—	PASS 0415	0950	1050	1500	—	PASS 1930	PASS 1900	—	—	—	THRU FROM AA	PASS 1935	1800	2200	1915	—	1130	1250	0940	0650
	E	—	LV	PASS 0430	—	PASS 0900	PASS 1440	PASS 1800	PASS 2300	—	0030	PASS 0100	—	—	—	(NW & NE R.R.)	PASS 0115	PASS 2400	PASS 0630	PASS 0300	—	1845	PASS 1850	PASS 1430	PASS 1330
	—	T	LV	↓	—	↓	↓	↓	↓	—	↓	TO HH	—	—	DV-1	0100	↓	↓	↓	↓	—	↓	↓	↓	↓
	D	—	AR LV	0645 0700	—	1115 1130	1750 1830	2230 ↳	0300 0350	—	0415	AND STU	—	— →	0750	0500 0800	0430 0515	0400	1030 TO	0700 0830	=	2315 —	0100 0215	1730 1800	1650 2000
WESTERN DIV. CENTRAL STD. TIME	—	V	AR	↓	—	↓	↓	—	↓	—	—	RR PTS.	—	—	1530	↓	↓	—	STEEL MILL R.R.	↓	—	—	0915	↓	↓
	C	—	LV	0745	—	PASS 1230	PASS 1930	—	0650	—	—	—	—	—	—	PASS 1000	0730	—	—	PASS 1045	—	—	SET OUT	PASS 1900	PASS 2245
	—	W	AR	↓	—	↓	↓	—	↓	—	—	—	—	—	—	↓	↓	—	—	PASS 1245	—	—	AT U;	↓	↓
	B	—	AR	0925	—	1415	2115	—	0900	—	—	—	—	—	—	1201	0900	—	—	TO MINE	—	—	MNO R.R.	2050	0100
	A	—	AR	—	—	RUN-THRU TO PDQ R.R.	2300	—	1200	—	—	—	—	—	—	1500		—	—	—	—	—	CONN. TO A	2250	

Figure 13-1 East-West System — Westbound (Partial Schedule, Local Freight Runs Not Shown)

Pre-Blocking

The Peninsular "pre-blocks" cars for the E-W interchange in three classifications -- a block for I, a block of cars for points in the Southwest via the E-W and the SW & AA to HH, and all other cars for points on the E-W; this is about all the classifications it can make without delaying its overnight train. The E-W, in turn, runs PRH out of the Peninsular yard in J rather than 77th St. and inspects and accepts the cars from the Peninsular at that point.

Motive power and cabooses are not pooled on this particular run-through because changing them loses no time, and the utilization would not be improved. But PRH, once its inspection is complete, moves out over the J Terminal RR with a J-T "shuttle" train crew. As it passes 77th St. the E-W crew climbs aboard, the J-T crew drops off, and the train continues on its way to H. At I the Peninsular block is set out, and any cars from I which have accumulated since JH 3 left are picked up.

Synchronized Arrival

OH 5 (from O), PHM (from P and M) and PRH all arrive at the westbound receiving yard at H within a thirty-minute period; JH 3 has finished going over the hump, so tracks are available. The Southwest block from the PRR is immediately cut off the rear of PRH, run over the hump first to put its cars into the proper blocks of cars from earlier trains which are to go out in HSW, and within an hour they are on their way. HSW is the hottest train off the E-W to the Southwest; it is pre-blocked and runs through to the STU RR intact from H. A one-hour connection including some classification is not normally possible, but the traffic pattern is such that the Peninsular cars almost always go into no more than three different blocks of HSW. With this special attention, the transfer is made, saving a day's time.

Cars from OH 5, PMH and the rest of PRH go over the hump in normal fashion, and priority cars are blocked and in HB 5 for its 1400 departure. The hump classification process at H on these three trains is sufficiently thorough so that HB 5 need not go into the yards at D or B. Its cars have not just been blocked as those for C, for B, and connections west from B, but rather into cuts for particular major industries at B, for particular locals working out of C, and for individual cities and yards all along the PQR.

Assigning Motive Power

Between H and D are the Alleghenies. While considerable poetic license was used in the energy-per-ton discussions of Fig. 2-6 in making this eastern railroad go over a pass 5,000 feet high, they are still a formidable obstacle. The E-W has some 20 miles of 2.0 percent (compensated) grade going up the Big Hill on the westbound track and long stretches of 0.3 percent in approaching the mountains. Fast freights, such as HSW, carry very few empties and run about 90 cars, usually grossing about 80 tons a car, for a trailing tonnage of 7,200.

To make the schedule, the train will have to run up to 60 mph on the level stretches and not less than 30 on an 0.3 percent adverse grade. Fig. 4-10 shows that about 1,800 tons can be assigned to a 3,000 hp unit on that basis, so four such units will provide enough power until the train reaches the mountain. What will happen then? At 1,800 tons per unit on 2.0 percent, a four-axle unit simply won't hack it; speed will fall below 22 mph. To prevent slipping, its power-matching circuitry will reduce horsepower output. There won't be enough tractive force, and the train will stall.

Three six-axle 3,000 hp units will have sufficient tractive force to lug the consist up the grade at about 10 to 12 mph, but the continuous tractive force rating of the traction motors will be exceeded unless they are low-geared, with 65 mph maximum speed. Experience has shown that scheduling train speed so close to the locomotives' rating results in high traction motor maintenance, since there will be occasions when speed will briefly exceed the established limit by a few mph. Twenty miles at 10 mph will take a very long two hours. Now what?

Helpers and Doubling

On lines where a single grade is the problem and very few trains are run, a standard practice is to "double the hill." The crew takes half the train to the summit, sets it out and goes back for the rest, too slow a process for main line trackage. Maintaining 20 mph up a 2 percent grade required reducing the load to about 900 tons per unit. This would require eight units to haul the 7,200 tons over the route. If there were several such grades along the line (a very unfavorable situation, fortunately found on only a few main lines), reduced tonnage or the use of radio controlled units would be the best solutions. Most doubles are unplanned, due to such factors as locomotive failure.

As it is, the E-W uses helper units to assist its fast freights over the Alleghenies between F and E. Four on the rear end plus the four road locomotives "on the point" will provide the required one unit per 900 tons; as Fig. 4-10 shows, at the required 20 or 22 mph speed, either 4-axle or 6-axle units will do about equally well. Since the west slope of the Big Hill is almost as steep and even heavier tonnage moves eastward, helpers (if that is the solution chosen) will be needed eastbound in even greater numbers. Therefore, HB 5 might keep its helpers all the way to E so that their dynamic braking power will allow the train to descend more rapidly without overheating the train wheels. The pushers will then be in position to help the next eastbound.

Heavy Freight Service

As our schedule sheet shows, a "Unit Coal Mty" extra left H just 45 minutes ahead of HB 5. This is a train similar to the one considered in Figs. 2-7 and 2-8, 100 empty gondolas weighing only 25 tons each, rolling back toward the mines at 45 mph. Eastbound the train weighs 12,500 tons with its load and is powered to make 35 mph on level track, which takes only 5,300 hp. It rates just two 3,000 hp units. It's on an exacting schedule in each direction, since the whole operation depends on the train's making a round trip every 72 hours.

Westbound up the hill the empty train has 1,250 trailing tons per unit. Fig. 4-10 shows that two six-axle 3,000 hp units can maintain about 14 mph with that load; it can get up and over without assistance. With adroit dispatching, HB 5 with its helpers will overtake and pass the empty train on the hill west of F where there is a second westbound track (Fig. 7-1) for just such maneuvers.

Right behind HB 5 leaving H is one of three westbound Ore Extras carrying a shipload of iron from the docks at J to the steel mills of D. Grossing 13,000 tons each, they are powered by three 3,000 hp six-axle units and can make 35 mph on level track, hogging down to about 18 mph on a long 0.3 percent grade. What will they need to get up the hill?

Locomotive Selection

The ore trains *can* take the time to lug up the hill at 10 mph, so they can be loaded to 1,800 tons per unit, which means a total of 7.22 units. Since 0.22 of a unit is not available, in practice the E-W will add five units to the two already on each extra and expect to make it. Train dynamics analysis is very appropriate in determining how many units can be put on the head end and how many on the rear end without exceeding the coupler or center-sill strength of the cars or approaching a hazardous L-V ratio (Fig. 6-5) on any of the curves on the hill.

From this sampling of motive power assignment problems on the E-W, at least two factors are apparent that will determine the types of locomotive the railroad should have on its roster. For pusher service, it will have six-axle units; they are essential for the ore drags and will do as well as four-axle units in assisting fast freights. For fast-freight, over-the-road service, the E-W will prefer four-axle units. They're lighter and cheaper to maintain and, even with fast-freight gearing, will do well pulling their share of the load up the mountain because the speed is not allowed to drop too low.

Computerized Scheduling

From this sample, which doesn't begin to cover all the little interactions between trains, tracks, signals, laws and people that must be considered in figuring out the best way to run the railroad, it should be clear that scheduling is a complicated process. A standard way of handling it, particularly on single-track lines where trains can only meet each other where there are passing tracks, has been with string. Strings stretched across a board marked out with the hours of the day on two sides and with mileage and station locations at its ends represent the train schedules. The strings are then shifted until they cross each other only at passing points, keeping the slope of each string correct at all points since it represents the speed of the train.

Today, computer programs, including individual train performance routines, offer a way of refining the process of working out the best pattern of traffic, making quick changes in conditions, and trying out new ideas before disrupting the railroad itself.

Car Scheduling

The nuances of train scheduling are important to the railroad, but the shipper couldn't care less how the trains move. The important thing is when will the carload be delivered at the consignee's plant. Therefore, a considerable effort is going on to utilize the computer to tell the railroads how each car should be moved to do the best overall job, with consideration to cost, speed and (particularly) reliability of service. Then the railroad must pass the word to each employee concerned so the cars can be handled accordingly.

14

UNIT-TRAIN OPERATIONS

From the earliest days of railroading there have been large-scale movements of single commodities from one point of origin, a mine, for example, to a single destination, such as a port or processing mill. In effect, trains have shuttled the same cars back and forth in handling the traffic, and the relative efficiency of handling a non-breakable item at economical speeds in heavy trains has been reflected in the rate established.

Multi-Car Rates

However, as a matter of public policy, the railroads were for many decades prohibited from establishing any rates or rules which provided lower rates in return for requiring that a commodity be shipped in quantities larger than a carload at a time. This was on the basis that such rates would favor large shippers. This consideration became increasingly unrealistic, since unregulated bulk barge operators on the government waterways were under no such restrictions. The fact that the big shipper had no incentive to ship or receive in large lots did not encourage working with the railroad to explore lower costs possible with an integrated large-scale loading/transporting/unloading system.

The Unit Train

Over the last twenty years, a gradual change in Congressional opinion on the matter, eventually enforced by various court decisions, has permitted multi-car or trainload rates. The *unit train*, a system including efficient, rapid loading and unloading facilities matched up with trains of cars and locomotives assigned to the service, has resulted. A long-term contract for transportation under specified train-load conditions assures a high degree of equipment utilization and thus allows an attractive freight rate with benefits to all concerned.

While the primary application of this principle has been in the movement of coal from mine to power plant (over 50 percent of which is now on a unit-train basis), it is also used in handling such commodities as semi-finished steel coils, orange juice, hot liquid sulfur, grain, crude oil and fertilizer. Fig. 14-1 shows a typical coal train being "flood loaded."

Equipment Specialization

The amount of money and the long-term commitments involved require extensive study of each unit-train system. As a result there is con-

Figure 14-1 Unit Coal Train Being "Flood Loaded"

siderable specialization in particular equipment used. Coal-carrying cars, for example, may be owned by the mining, railroad or power company, or may be leased. They may be unloaded by overturning the cars in a dumper (without uncoupling the cars if one end of each is equipped with a special rotary coupler) or by manual or automatic bottom-dump, depending to a considerable extent on the space available at the receiving end of the movement. Motive power may be shipper- or railroad-owned and may be all at the head end or include mid-train remote-control units if the route profile makes that work out best.

Equipment Utilization

The utilization of dedicated cars achieves mileage-per-day averages from 3 to 20 times that of the general-service car. The train travels directly from origin to destination on a single waybill without being switched at intermediate points. At its destination, it is immediately unloaded and started back for a similarly-quick reloading. Turnaround-cycle time may range from 1 1/2 hours (for some automated within-plant operations covering a few miles) to 96 hours for a 2,000-mile round trip which may include crossing major mountain ranges.

Mini-Trains

A related system possibility brought about by multi-car ratemaking is the point-to-point "mini-train" carrying a commodity such as crushed rock or grain in five- or ten-car units directly from a loading to a delivery point. They operate under tariffs requiring special "while-we-wait" loading and unloading and work rules allowing a reduced-size (two-man, for example) train crew not restricted by normal divisional or yard/road limits.

The mini-train becomes, in effect, a 500- or 1,000-ton truck which can take grain from a country elevator to a terminal on demand without tying up expensive covered hoppers for days in the "normal" local freight set-out/load/pick-up/classify/road haul/yard/switch crew/set-out/unloaded-and-return .cycle. The unit train has rapidly become dominant in the large-scale bulk-material transportation field, with low rates making producers competitive over distances previously impossible; the degree to which mini-trains can get short-haul traffic back on the rails remains to be seen.

15

INTERMODAL TRAFFIC

In 1885 the Long Island Railroad established a short-lived service in which loaded farm wagons, horses and farmers were carried into Long Island City on flatcars, boxcars and a passenger coach, respectively, thus saving two transfer operations in getting the produce to market. This was by no means the earliest "piggyback" operation, so the idea of intermodal through shipments without reloading is not new. After long periods of little activity, however, the idea really started to catch on in the early 1950's, sparked by several factors: improved rail equipment for carrying more than one trailer per car was developed; the ICC decided that a railroad wouldn't have to obtain a truck-route certificate to carry freight over its own rails in its own trailers; and containerization of ocean freight began to change the shape of the merchandise-carrying fleets of the world.

COFC/TOFC Traffic Levels

What is most widely called piggyback, technically labeled TOFC/COFC (Trailer on Flat Car or Container on Flat Car), has continued to expand, to the point where it now represents over 6 percent of the car loadings and about 9 percent of the revenues of U. S. Class I railroads. Recent yearly revenue trailer and container loadings have totaled more than 2,000,000 per year, representing more than 1,400,000 flatcar loadings.

The Intermodal Transfer

The unique feature of intermodal traffic is the transfer from one mode --rail, sea or highway -- to another. Where rail is involved, there are three principal methods in use.

Circus Loading, so named for its use for over a hundred years in getting the wagons of traveling shows (or the vehicles of an Army group) on and off the flatcars taking them from town to town, requires only an end-of-track ramp. Fold-down bridge plates on the ends of the flatcars (Fig. 15-1) form a temporary roadway over which the trailers (or containers on chassis) are backed -- ramp-to-car and car-to-car -- in loading a string of cars. Ramp loading is the only suitable method for use at locations where only a few transfers a day are made, but becomes slow, inflexible and expensive where volume is high.

Gantry Loading, suitable for either containers or trailers, uses a traveling overhead crane straddling roadway and track to make the transfer or "lift." Gantries have become bigger, faster, more versatile and more expensive as the business has developed. Since loaded containers must be lifted by the top corners while trailers must be supported from below during the lift, a crane handling both must be equipped with two types of adapter slings.

Side Loading of containers involves sliding the box from road chassis to flatcar, originally with specialized gear peculiar to the particular container/car system in use. Its chief problem has been the failure of any one system to achieve wide enough acceptance to become standard. Potentially, side loading can be the quick, flexible and low-capital way for handling containerized movements.

A currently popular system avoiding the container vs. trailer decision is the mobile side-loader -- an enormous, relatively high-speed "forklift" which simply picks up trailers or containers bodily, drives over to the appointed spot and sets them down on roadway, flatcar or chassis.

Intermodal Terminals

While the largest number of intermodal transfer points (commonly called "ramps" whether or not circus loading is the method used at the particular point) are simple ramps (fixed or portable) which can circus-load only trailers or containers on chassis, the large-volume terminals accounting for most of the business now use gantry or mobile-lift transfer.

The E-W System's 77th St. Intermodal Terminal (Fig. 12-1) illustrates some of the points necessary for a sucessful facility. Its tracks connect directly with the main line so that incoming and outgoing TOFC/COFC trains, the hottest on the railroad, do not have to work their way through the yards. Since its gantries can place the trailers and containers directly on flatcars designated to go to their destination, there is no further "classification" of the rail cars necessary after loading. Within the metropolitan area it serves, the terminal is located for easy highway access (Fig. 11-2) but west of the Ship Canal drawbridge which could seriously interfere with reliability.

Piggyback Equipment

Fig. 15-1 shows some of the dimensions and characteristics of intermodal components as they have become standardized in the mid-1970's. International containerized freight uses "boxes" built to the International Standards Organization (ISO) standard dimensions and weight limits; the 20 ft. container is used as the measuring unit for traffic, although shorter and longer units, in 5 and 10-foot increments up to 40 ft. are in use. The 89 ft. flatcar, usually carrying two 40 ft. trailers, dominates the railroads and Trailer Train Corporation-owned intermodal flatcar fleet, but actually comes in a variety of sub-classes equipped for various combinations of trailer and/or container lengths.

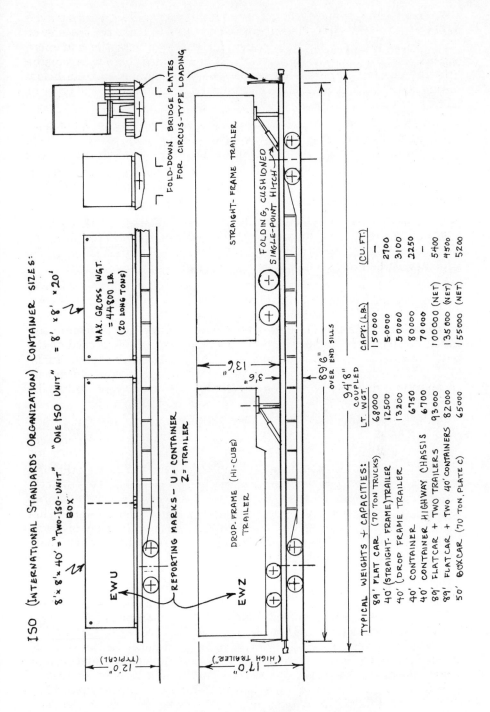

Figure 15-1 TOFC/COFC Equipment

Trailer vs. Container vs. Boxcar

Compared to boxcar traffic, TOFC traffic is more expensive to move over the road because of the extra tare weight represented by the trailer and its wheels, greater wind resistance of the high cars, and (sometimes) restrictions associated with the high center of gravity. Terminal expenses are greatly reduced, as the cost and delay of moving individual cars through crowded switching trackage and classifying for linehaul is replaced by one-man/one-trailer movements which can be taking place simultaneously all over town as the time for train loading and departure approaches.

COFC avoids the height, wind resistance and extra-weight problems of TOFC at the cost of the logistic problems of having chassis available when and where needed; a great many containers travel piggyback on chassis for this reason, diluting the potential savings.

In general, the intermodal transfer costs require a trip length of 300 to 500 miles to make the three-to-one fuel consumption saving of rail movement and the labor saving of carriage in trains competitive with road haulage. Improvements in terminal operations, such as concentrating traffic at large-scale, well-located points served by fast, frequent, high mileage trains, are considered to have the greatest potential for capturing more short-haul business.

Intermodal Plans

Once the capability for through freight movement on an intermodal basis has been established, the number of combinations of "who does what for whom" rapidly expands. As a common carrier, a railroad cannot simply start hauling trailers. There must be approved tariffs, and as a business organization the railroad must consider the effectiveness of the tariffs and services in generating profitable traffic that doesn't disproportionately hurt its existing business.

Seven TOFC/COFC "plans" now in use account for practically all of the business. Fig. 15-2 shows the different parts of an intermodal shipment and their ownership or responsibility under each of these plans, with the percentage distribution among them, based on the total number of rail-originated carloadings.

Truck Freight by Rail

Plan II represents one end of the spectrum. Here, a railroad essentially goes into the trucking business, since the unit of shipment becomes a truck-trailer load rather than a carload (which fits in with the desire of many businesses for a smaller unit), and railroad personnel are directly involved with shipper and consignee. It has the advantage of rail linehaul economies in setting its rates.

Engines and Rails Only

The other extreme is Plan IV, widely used by freight forwarders, in which even the job of getting the trailers or containers aboard and providing the flatcar is "farmed out," and the railroad does what it should be

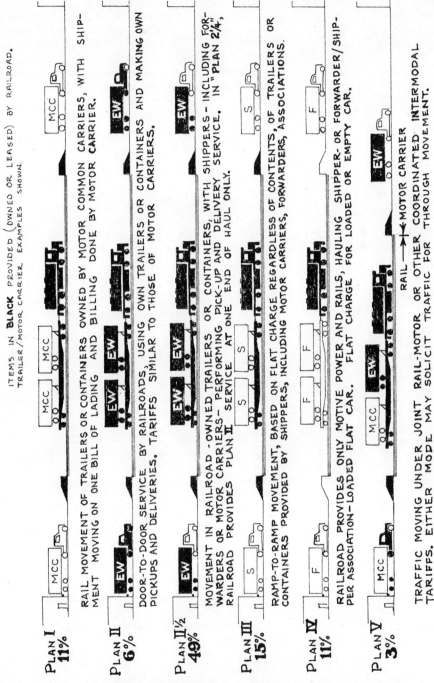

ITEMS IN **BLACK** PROVIDED (OWNED OR LEASED) BY RAILROAD. TRAILER/MOTOR CARRIER EXAMPLES SHOWN.

PLAN I **11%** RAIL MOVEMENT OF TRAILERS OR CONTAINERS OWNED BY MOTOR COMMON CARRIERS, WITH SHIP-MENT MOVING ON ONE BILL OF LADING AND BILLING DONE BY MOTOR **CARRIER.**

PLAN II **6%** DOOR-TO-DOOR SERVICE BY RAILROADS, USING OWN TRAILERS OR CONTAINERS AND MAKING OWN PICKUPS AND DELIVERIES. TARIFFS SIMILAR TO THOSE OF MOTOR CARRIERS.

PLAN II½ **49%** MOVEMENT IN RAILROAD-OWNED TRAILERS OR CONTAINERS, WITH SHIPPERS - INCLUDING FOR-WARDERS OR MOTOR CARRIERS - PERFORMING PICK-UP AND DELIVERY SERVICE. IN "**PLAN 2¼**," RAILROAD PROVIDES PLAN **II** SERVICE AT ONE END OF HAUL ONLY.

PLAN III **15%** RAMP-TO-RAMP MOVEMENT, BASED ON FLAT CHARGE REGARDLESS OF CONTENTS, OF TRAILERS OR CONTAINERS PROVIDED BY SHIPPERS, INCLUDING MOTOR CARRIERS, FORWARDERS, ASSOCIATIONS.

PLAN IV **11%** RAILROAD PROVIDES ONLY MOTIVE POWER AND RAILS, HAULING SHIPPER- OR FORWARDER/SHIP-PER ASSOCIATION-LOADED FLAT CAR. FLAT CHARGE FOR LOADED OR EMPTY CAR.

PLAN V **3%** TRAFFIC MOVING UNDER JOINT RAIL-MOTOR OR OTHER COORDINATED INTERMODAL TARIFFS. EITHER MODE MAY SOLICIT TRAFFIC FOR THROUGH MOVEMENT.

RAIL ——— RAIL →← MOTOR CARRIER ——— MOTOR CARRIER

Figure 15-2 TOFC/COFC Plans (Items in Black Provided — Owned or Leased — by Railroad. Trailer/Motor Carrier Examples Shown.)

best at -- hauling cars over the rails, with payment provided whether they're loaded or empty. Between these two plans is a wide choice, of which Plan II 1/2 has become most popular, within which a railroad may seek its fortune.

International Services

The huge shift of overseas merchandise traffic to container-ships and the concomitant saving of time in transit has led to the establishment of the "land bridge" and "mini-land-bridge" (Fig. 15-3); traffic moves on water-carrier tariffs at water rates based on carriage via the Panama Canal; the water carrier pays for the transfers and the rail haul from the money it saves by reducing the turnaround time for its vessels. The containers travel across the United States in "unit trains" on reliable and relatively fast schedules. This is primarily "Plan III" traffic.

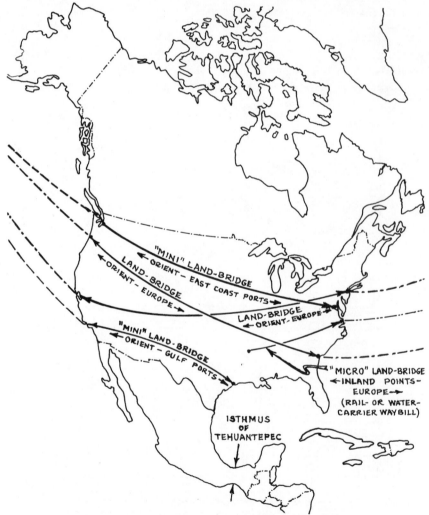

Figure 15-3 Rail Hauls on All-Water Tariffs

"Micro" land-bridge operations in which containers loaded at inland points move piggyback to ports for overseas water shipment are also becoming important, with railroad or water carrier originating the shipment waybilling it for the entire trip.

Other water-competitive intermodal routes of increasing importance include containerized shipments via Canadian and U.S. Atlantic ports to and from Great Lakes ports. The Mexican government is reconstructing and upgrading an existing rail line across the Isthmus of Tehuantepec and ports at each end for land-bridge traffic.

Reduced-Tare Intermodal Technology

The further increases in fuel costs affecting all modes of transportation have resulted not only in increased interest in rail intermodal operations but also in the introduction of "third generation" equipment aimed at major decreases in the tare weight per trailer or container associated with the intermodal option. The general shift to 45 ft. trailers (which can be loaded on the maximum-length 89 ft. piggyback flat only in connection with a 40 ft. companion) has also spurred the search for alternatives. Fig. 15-4 illustrates some of the new arrangements being used.

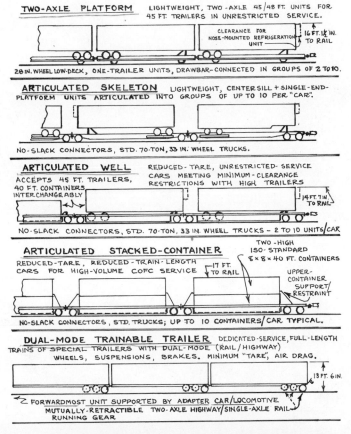

Figure 15-4 Low-Tare Intermodal Equipment

16

SPECIAL FREIGHT AND PACKAGE SERVICES

The primary business of the railroads in North America is now, as it has always been, the transportation of freight in standard carload lots. Nevertheless, the transportation of LCL (Less than Carload) and express package shipments has always had a relatively higher degree of public visibility because of the sheer number of customers directly concerned and the perceived dependence of big vs small-business competitiveness upon the relative shipping costs in large vs small lots. The handling of loads too large or heavy for other overland transport modes also focuses attention on the rail network.

Large and Heavy Loads

Standard clearances and load limits are included by reference as a part of railroad freight tariffs, indicating the size and weight of shipments which can be handled in regular service. Most routes provide at least AAR "Plate B" clearance and 220,000 lb. weight on rail for eight-wheel cars. Many main lines have been modified to be able to handle piggyback and auto-rack traffic without restriction, to the extent that typical limits, beyond which special arrangements are required, are 20 ft. above rail, 11 ft. 6 in. wide and 125 tons net weight.

High-Wide Load Coordination

Nevertheless, about 100,000 oversize shipments per year on U. S. railroads require special coordination. Railroads maintain special offices for this purpose, to work with shippers in finding routes (sometimes unbelievably roundabout) which will by-pass close clearances, bridge load-limitations and other bottlenecks. Railroad limits may actually determine the largest size to which bridge girders, pressure vessels or generators may be designed and what provisions must be made for piecemeal shipment and on-site assembly. Finally, the operating department of the railroad is involved in determining and observing any special restrictions necessary en route: low-speed travel by local freight or special train; scheduling to avoid trains on adjacent tracks; inactivating uncoupling levers on multi-car shipments; etc.

Special Equipment

Railroads owning special depressed-center, well-hole or high-capacity flat cars for oversize or overweight loads (AAR Mechanical Designations

FD, FW, FM) receive a special payment of $100 to $300 each time one is loaded, as a partial inducement for owning an adequate number of these expensive cars which can't expect steady use.

For the very largest power-generating machinery, "Schnabel" cars (AAR Mechanical Designation LS) in which the load forms the central part of the car structure (Fig. 16-1) and can extend to the very limits of the clearance diagram have been built. Some include special jacking devices to shift the load a few inches in any direction to clear specific obstacles. Maximum capacity is about 500 tons for a 20-axle car. Since most mainline tracks are spaced on 14-ft. centers, the disruption involved in moving an object 20 ft. in diameter can only be overcome with the best in advanced planning.

LCL Traffic

With the general availability of over-the-road truck service handling less-than-carload shipments on a regulated common-carrier basis, most railroads have been permitted to discontinue handling LCL traffic, which has traditionally been unprofitable. However, several million tons per year in small freight shipments ride the rails in forwarder- and shipper-association traffic.

Forwarders

A *forwarder* accepts LCL and LTL (less than truckload) shipments for transportation at a package rate and puts them together in carload lots for the long haul. The railroad has a carload to haul, the forwarder makes his profit from the difference between the two rates, and the quantities involved allow the dispatch of cars on regular schedules which individual shippers could not support.

Most forwarder traffic is now handled in piggyback service, giving the forwarder reduced terminal and handling costs and making him more competitive with the common-carrier or contract trucker. On the East-West System, the forwarder traffic on his own leased and loaded Trailer Train flatcars (Plan IV) is enough to warrant running Train 151, a first-class schedule, as the first leg of a run-through train to the West Coast. Accepting only TOFC/COFC traffic, 151 is allowed 70 mph and provided enough horsepower to climb the mountain only slightly less vigorously than the passenger runs.

Shipper associations organized on a cooperative, non-profit basis to perform similar functions to forwarders in obtaining carload rates and the advantages of larger-scale and more regular traffic flows for their members were specifically exempted from regulation at the time (1940) that forwarders were brought under the purview of the ICC. With the advent of piggybacking these organizations, although forbidden from advertising their services commercially as a condition of non-regulation, have grown rapidly and are a major factor in the handling of small shipments. *Shipper agents* or *consolidators* handle shipments at established common carrier rates, charging a fee for the services they provide their customers by maintaining regular patterns of service and handling details of the shipping process.

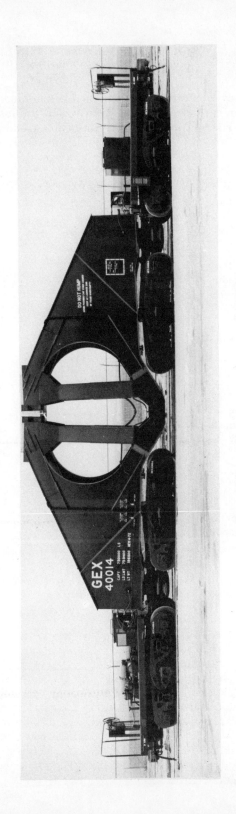

Figure 16-1 LS (Schnabel) Car for Transporting Large Power-Generating Machinery.

With the deregulation of many aspects of both rail and truck transportation in 1980, many aspects of these relationships may be expected to change.

17

RAIL PASSENGER SERVICES

As indicated in Fig. 18-2, less than three percent of U.S. railroad revenue is from passenger services, and in North America throughout railroading history passenger traffic has been a relatively minor segment of the business. Since these services involve direct contact with millions of customers, however, public awareness of the size of the railroad iceberg that doesn't show up above the water is often limited, to the extent that the importance of freight railroading is little appreciated.

Passenger Service

When does a system with two rails and guiding wheels stop fitting the classification of "railroad"? To avoid answering this question directly, Fig. 17-1 lists a spectrum of rail passenger-carrying systems ranging from light rail (space age terminology for yesterday's streetcar) through what is still labeled in ICC records as "steam railroad" passenger train service, and beyond. Omitted on the left is the San Francisco cable-car system, which probably deserves inclusion since it has the distinction of being the only mass transit system in which the weight of the passengers in, on and clinging to the cars often exceeds the empty weight of the vehicle.

Terminology used is generally that used by the U. S. Department of Transportation, with a separation of railroad commutation service into two categories: primary, where the line exists because of the passenger service and ancillary, where other traffic predominates, at least on a revenue basis. Typical characteristics of the different passenger systems are listed as a means of showing similarities and differences. Several existing systems don't fit any mold in all respects, and technical developments will undoubtedly result in further obscuring the picture. Taken as a whole, the train consist, accommodations, fare, schedule, right-of-way and performance characteristics lay out the differences between rapid transit, railroad commuter and intercity systems.

Heavy Rapid Transit

Heavy rapid transit systems usually involve a considerable proportion of subway mileage and an exclusive right-of-way, leading to the choice of third rail electric propulsion to keep tunnel size and cost to a minimum. Older systems are receiving intensive upgrading with higher performance, air-conditioned equipment; new systems being built or perfected in several cities use centralized "computer" control of the operation of individual trains, with the operator on board primarily in a monitoring and emergency manual control role. The 90-second headway achievable, with 8 to 12-car trains, offers the promise of moving people during rush hour without the "crush loads" which the cars are capable of carrying, but which also discourages lots of potential customers.

With approximately 7,000,000 riders per day, the rapid transit concept in North America is definitely a "going concern" whose impact will continue to grow; the extremely high costs of tunnel-building in existing urban areas, however, is tending to favor a return to the old "elevated" --with a much less claustrophobic, single-column supporting structure.

Railroad Commuter Service

Most primary and ancillary commuter services have not been self-supporting in recent years and are now either owned or subsidized by municipal, regional or state authorities. Practically all routes have received new rolling stock within the last decade; electric M.U. equipment is of significantly higher performance, while most equipment on diesel lines is now operated in push-pull fashion and of double-deck design wherever clearances permit. Current traffic amounts to about 500,000 round-trips per day, with an average journey of 18 miles.

Intercity Passenger Service

The National Railroad Passenger Corp. (Amtrak) was created by act of Congress effective May 1, 1971 to operate a nationwide passenger service over a skeleton network of routes designated by the Secretary of Transportation. In return for contributions of rolling stock, facilities and cash related to the amount of the deficits they had been incurring in operating intercity passenger service, railroads joining Amtrak were allowed to terminate operation of their existing passenger runs.

Amtrak Routes and Operations

Subsequent events, including provisions of the Railroad Revitalization and Regulatory Reform Act of 1976 related to the restructuring of the bankrupt northeastern railroads into the Consolidated Rail Corp. (Conrail), have resulted in Amtrak ownership of 750 miles of primarily passenger railroad routes. This includes the "Northeast Corridor" line between Washington and Boston which is being upgraded to provide frequent, high-speed service under a federal program jointly managed by the FRA and Amtrak.

Under successive Congressional authorization acts and with the participation of several states under Section 403b of the basic Act (requiring Amtrak operation of trains partially subsidized by the local jurisdictions), the Amtrak network generally expanded in the extent and frequency of service despite elimination of various less-patronized routes; in 1980, some 22,000,000 passengers (half of them on the Northeast Corridor) were carried over more than 25,000 miles of line, serving 500 stations. With passenger fares at this point covering between 40 and 50 percent of operating costs, the extent of the corporation's operations is dependent upon legislative appropriation actions year by year, although authorization actions looking toward continuing capital and operating support of well-patronized routes within a national rail passenger system on a multi-year basis were taken in 1979.

Train crews and some en-route equipment-servicing personnel are employees of the railroads over which Amtrak trains operate; passenger service personnel are Amtrak, as are equipment servicing and maintenance personnel at points where Amtrak has established shop facilities. Ticket agents and station personnel are Amtrak unless part-time or shared services are provided by the railroad on a contract basis.

Amtrak owns all passenger-train cars and locomotives used in regular service. All passenger motive power, (gas turbine, diesel and electric) has been built new since the start of operations, as have approximately three-fourths of the passenger-carrying cars; the remainder have been extensively rebuilt to include conversion to head-end power (HEP) for heat and air-conditioning. Long-haul trains west of Chicago have been re-equipped with double-deck equipment.

Railroad Service Contracts

Amtrak contracts with railroads over which its trains operate are on the basis of reimbursement of direct costs, plus performance incentive payments. On-time performance above 80 percent earns up to a maximum of 27.5 percent above costs, depending upon train performance, ridership, reliability or making connections, etc.

Other Passenger Services

Railroads in the U.S. which did not join the Amtrak system have continued to operate passenger services under jurisdiction of the ICC; only one such route had not been taken over by Amtrak or discontinued by 1980 (Denver & Rio Grande Western — Denver/Salt Lake City).

VIA Rail Canada was established by the Canadian Government as a Crown Corporation in 1976 to take over intercity passenger operations of the Canadian National and Canadian Pacific in an arrangement generally similar to Amtrak. Including both "Corridor" short-haul routes in the Windsor-Toronto-Montreal-Quebec area and transcontinental trains, VIA traffic reached a level of over 6,000,000 passengers in 1980.

The *Auto-Train Corporation*, a privately-owned company operating without subsidy under a specific exemption in the original Amtrak authorization act, has operated an auto-ferry service between Virginia and Florida in which passenger and their automobiles are transported overnight between end-points of the route. All rolling stock is owned and maintained by Auto-Train, only train crews and trackage rights being provided by railroads over which the trains operate. Fully-enclosed bi-level and tri-level auto transporter cars and refurbished low-density coaches, dining, sleeping and lounge cars have been operated in consists as long as 50 cars.

| | MASS TRANSIT | | | RAILROAD | | | | |
| | LIGHT RAIL | HEAVY RAPID TRANSIT | | COMMUTER | | INTERCITY | | |
		URBAN	COMMUTER	PRIMARY	ANCILLARY	CORRIDOR	LONG-HAUL	AUTO FERRY
TYPICAL TRAIN CONSIST	SINGLE OR TWO-CAR ARTICULATED LIGHT-RAIL VEHICLES	SELF-PROPELLED MULTIPLE-UNIT PASSENGER CARS	SELF-PROPELLED MULTIPLE-UNIT CAB & MID-TRAIN PASSENGER CARS	SELF-PROPELLED MULTIPLE-UNIT PASSENGER CARS	LOCOMOTIVE-HAULED (PUSH-PULL) OR SELF-PROPELLED PASSENGER CARS	LOCOMOTIVE-HAULED OR SELF-PROPELLED (MULTIPLE-UNIT OR FIXED-CONSIST) PASSENGER & SNACK CARS	LOCOMOTIVE-HAULED PASSENGER & NON-REVENUE CARS	LOCOMOTIVE-HAULED AUTOMOBILE-TRANSPORTER, PASSENGER & NON-REVENUE CARS
TYPICAL PASSENGER ACCOMMODATIONS (LOW-DENSITY + STANDEE = 40 PASSR/CAR; MEDIUM-DENSITY = 70 PASS/CAR; SINGLE-DECK COMMUTER = 100/CAR; DOUBLE-DECK COMMUTER = 160/CAR)	SINGLE-DECK, LIMITED SEATING + STANDEES	SINGLE-DECK, LIMITED SEATING + STANDEES	SINGLE-DECK, FULL SEATING + LIMITED STANDEE	SINGLE OR DOUBLE-DECK + LIMITED STANDEE	SINGLE OR DOUBLE-DECK + LIMITED STANDEE	MEDIUM-DENSITY COACH, SNACK,+ LIMITED 1ST CLASS (LOW-DENSITY)	SINGLE & DOUBLE-DECK, LOW-DENSITY COACH, LOUNGE, SLEEPING, DINING	SINGLE AND DOUBLE-DECK, LOW-DENSITY COACH, LOUNGE, SLEEPING, DINING
FARE STRUCTURE, SALE & COLLECTION (TYPICAL)	FLAT-FARE, SINGLE-OPERATOR OR MACHINE-ISSUED, FAREBOX ON CAR	FLAT OR ZONE, SINGLE-OPERATOR MACHINE-ISSUED, TURNSTILE COLLECTION	GRADUATED SINGLE-TRIP FARE MACHINE-ISSUED, TURNSTILE COLLECTION	MULTI-RIDE, ZONE-FARE, AGENT-SOLD, FLASH TICKET	MULTI-RIDE, ZONE FARE, AGENT SOLD, OR ON-TRAIN TICKET COLLECTION	SINGLE-TRIP, AGENT-SOLD, UNRESERVED, ON-TRAIN COLLECT	SINGLE-TRIP, RESERVED, ON-TRAIN COLLECT	SINGLE-TRIP, RESERVED-ACCOMMODATION, CHECK-IN
SCHEDULES: TRIPS/DAY (EACH WAY, PER LINE) (TYPICAL)	50-150	100-200	25-150	25-75	2-25	4-40	1/2-4	1
MINIMUM HEADWAY (RUSH HOUR, PER TRK.)	5 MIN.	1½ MIN.	3 MIN.	3 MIN.	5 MIN.	15 MIN.	N.A.	N.A.
HOURS OF SERVICE	DAY, EVENING, LIM. WEEK-END	DAY, EVENING, WEEK END	WEEKDAY, LIM. EVENING	RUSH HOUR-LIM. OFF-PEAK, EVE	RUSH-HOUR WEEKDAY	DAILY, DAY & EVENING	DAILY OR TRI-WEEKLY, OVERNIGHT(S)	DAILY OVERNIGHT
MILES BETWEEN PASSENGER STOPS (AVERAGE, TYPICAL)	0.2	0.5 (LOCAL), 1.5 (EXPRESS)	1.5	2.5 (LOCAL), UP TO 15 (EXPRESS)	3.0	35	80	800
LENGTH OF ROUTE-MILES (TYPICAL)	10	15	20	30	40	60-300	300-2500	900
SPEED - AVERAGE INCL. STOPS	10	25	35	25 (LOCAL), 40 (EXPRESS)	30	70	55	55
M.P.H. MAXIMUM	40	75	80	80	70	105	79	79
RIGHT-OF-WAY: PRINCIPAL LOCATIONS, EXCLUSIVITY	SURFACE-STREET OR PRIVATE RIGHT-OF-WAY (WITH GRADE CROSSINGS)	TUNNEL, ELEVATED, SURFACE- (NO GRADE CROSSINGS)	ELEVATED, TUNNEL, SURFACE- (NO GRADE CROSSINGS)	SURFACE, TUNNEL (NO GRADE CROSSINGS)	SURFACE- (SOME GRADE CROSSINGS)	SURFACE- (FEW GRADE CROSSINGS)	SURFACE- (MANY GRADE CROSSINGS)	SURFACE- (MANY GRADE CROSSINGS)
OTHER NON-PSGR. RAIL TRAFFIC	NONE	NONE	NONE	LIMITED FREIGHT	FREIGHT	FREIGHT	FREIGHT	FREIGHT
No. OF TRACKS	2	2 to 4	2	2 to 6	2	2 to 4	1 to 2	1 to 2
SIGNALING/CONTROL (TYPIC. RL) (ABS = AUTOMATIC BLOCK SIGNALS; ATC = AUTOMATIC TRAIN CONTROL; CTC = CENTRALIZED TRAFFIC CONTROL)	ABS (ON PRIVATE R/W)	ABS/ATC	ABS/ATC	ABS/ATC	ABS	ABS/ATC	CTC/ABS	CTC/ABS
STATION PLATFORMS	LOW	HIGH	HIGH	HIGH	LOW	HIGH & LOW	LOW	LOW
TRAIN CHARACTERISTICS: PROPULSION/POWER DISTRIBUTION/VOLTAGE (LOW VOLTAGE = 600-750V; HIGH V. A.C. = 11,000-25,000V)	ELECTRIC- OVERHEAD TROLLEY WIRE, LOW V. D.C.	ELECTRIC- THIRD RAIL, LOW V. D.C.	ELECTRIC- THIRD RAIL, LOW V. D.C.	ELECTRIC- OVERHEAD CATENARY- HIGH V. A.C., LOW V. D.C.	DIESEL-ELECTRIC, DIESEL/HYDRAULIC	ELECTRIC- OVERHEAD CATENARY HIGH V. A.C./ DIESEL-ELECTRIC	DIESEL-ELECTRIC	DIESEL-ELECTRIC
CARS/TRAIN	1-4	2-12	4-12	2-12	3-16	4-12	4-18	20-45
TRAIN WGT/PASSENGER	300 (WITH STANDEES)	450 (WITH STANDEES)	700	800	1000	2000	5500	8000
ACCELERATION: MAX/SEC @ BOTTOM STEP	4.5	3.5	3.0	3.0	1.0	1.5	0.3	0.3
ACCELERATION CONTROL	OPERATOR	AUTOMATIC	COMPUTER	AUTOMATIC	OPERATOR	OPERATOR	OPERATOR	OPERATOR
BRAKING	DYNAMIC/AIR/MAG.	ELECTRIC-PNEUMATIC, DYNAMIC, E-PNEU.	DYNAMIC, E-PNEU.	ELECTRO-PNEUMATIC	AUTOMATIC AIR	DYNAMIC/E-PNEU.	AUTOMATIC AIR	AUTOMATIC AIR

Figure 17-1 Rail Passenger Systems

Mail and Express

With the discontinuance of in-transit mail sorting by the U. S. Postal Service, visibility of mail traffic by rail has virtually disappeared. However, some 175,000 trailer or container loads of mail and express are carried each year in piggyback service on expedited freight or, where business is sufficiently concentrated, mail and express trains.

18

THE RAILROAD ORGANIZATION

Railroads come in all shapes and sizes, from less than one to more than 20,000 miles of line and with usually proportional annual revenues. On the smallest of lines, the general manager and a clerk may constitute the entire office force, and a road that's close to ICC Class I status (gross revenues of $50,000,000 per year or more) will still have many of its employees taking care of multiple duties that might be handled in disparate parts of the organization on a large railroad. The fact that all use tracks and trains as part of a continental transportation system, however, means that the same things have to be done, and the essentials of the organization are much the same, whatever the size. Names and titles may vary, as well as the ways some of them may be linked together on the organization chart. But a look at the corporate structure of one of the larger systems, one with 20,000 employees and revenues in 1980 of about $1.6 billion per year, will show one way in which a railroad corporation can be organized to successfully carry on its business of the wheel, which comes from the heavy force-fit used to keep the wheel in place.

Corporate Structure

Railroads are corporations, with a board of directors headed by its chairman, who is sometimes also designated as the chief executive officer, responsible for long term plans and practices. The railroad president, who also may be designated as the chief operating officer, is directly responsible to the board for running the railroad by making decisions on a shorter-term basis.

Railroad Regulation

Railroad corporations are subject to numerous rules, in addition to those applying to all corporations. For example, since 1906 it has been illegal for a railroad to own mines or factories producing products (other than timber or materials needed for the railroad's own use in producing transportation) to be shipped over its tracks. This law was passed to break up such combinations as coal mining and railroad companies, which were judged to represent unequal competitors for independent producers. A mining or metals company can still own a railroad, but if it is a common carrier, its rates and operations are regulated by the ICC. It must serve all shippers, particularly its owner's competitors, on an impartial basis.

204

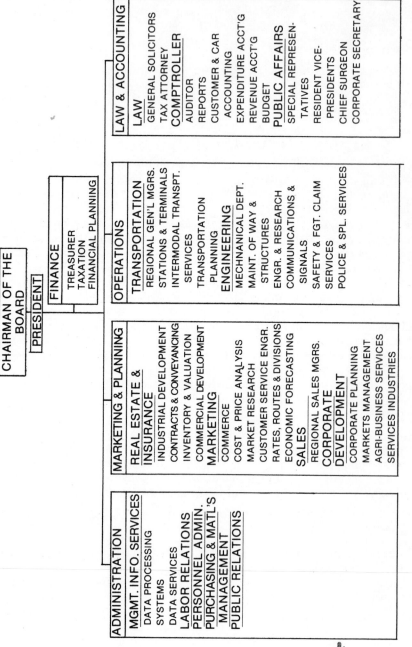

Figure 18-1 Railroad Corporate Structure Example

CHAIRMAN OF THE BOARD

PRESIDENT

FINANCE
TREASURER
TAXATION
FINANCIAL PLANNING

ADMINISTRATION
MGMT. INFO. SERVICES
DATA PROCESSING SYSTEMS
DATA SERVICES
LABOR RELATIONS
PERSONNEL ADMIN.
PURCHASING & MATL'S MANAGEMENT
PUBLIC RELATIONS

MARKETING & PLANNING
REAL ESTATE & INSURANCE
INDUSTRIAL DEVELOPMENT
CONTRACTS & CONVEYANCING
INVENTORY & VALUATION
COMMERCIAL DEVELOPMENT
MARKETING
COMMERCE
COST & PRICE ANALYSIS
MARKET RESEARCH
CUSTOMER SERVICE ENGR.
RATES, ROUTES & DIVISIONS
ECONOMIC FORECASTING
SALES
REGIONAL SALES MGRS.
CORPORATE DEVELOPMENT
CORPORATE PLANNING
MARKETS MANAGEMENT
AGRI-BUSINESS SERVICES
SERVICES INDUSTRIES

OPERATIONS
TRANSPORTATION
REGIONAL GEN'L MGRS.
STATIONS & TERMINALS
INTERMODAL TRANSPT. SERVICES
TRANSPORTATION PLANNING
ENGINEERING
MECHANICAL DEPT.
MAINT. OF WAY & STRUCTURES
ENGR. & RESEARCH
COMMUNICATIONS & SIGNALS
SAFETY & FGT. CLAIM SERVICES
POLICE & SPL. SERVICES

LAW & ACCOUNTING
LAW
GENERAL SOLICITORS
TAX ATTORNEY
COMPTROLLER
AUDITOR
REPORTS
CUSTOMER & CAR ACCOUNTING
EXPENDITURE ACCT'G
REVENUE ACCT'G
BUDGET
PUBLIC AFFAIRS
SPECIAL REPRESEN-TATIVES
RESIDENT VICE-PRESIDENTS
CHIEF SURGEON
CORPORATE SECRETARY

As a result of this restriction, some railroad corporations have been set up as subsidiaries of railroad holding companies ("East-West Industries," for the East-West Railroad Co.). The holding company can then own and operate other non-railroad businesses without the particular restrictions.

Railroad Accounting and Finance

Fig. 18-1 is the corporate-level organization chart for our billion-a-year railroad operating company. Attached directly to the president's office is the finance staff office, including the treasurer who is legally responsible for the corporation's funds, income and tax liabilities. The financial planning office is there both to keep the company from running out of cash and to manage its investments and borrowings, so the overall cost of meeting its obligations is as low as possible. This includes maintaining as good a financial rating for the railroad's financial paper, and as low an interest rate, as its operating results can support.

One of the theories behind railroad regulation is the determination of a level of rates that will not result in profits beyond a rate of return considered "reasonable." Since the way in which a company's books are kept can have a big effect on its reported profits, the law requires that railroad accounting and financial reports to the ICC follow very specific rules. The financial community which rates and handles railroad securities wants its reports in accordance with "generally accepted accounting principles," which change from time to time and are not always similar to ICC rules. The ICC "Uniform System of Accounts" which went into effect in 1978 in some ways narrowed the differences but it has made it difficult or impossible to compare current results with those from prior years in some other accounts important in judging railroad finances.

Railroad Financial Results

Over the years, a few specific terms such as "operating ratio" and "ordinary net income" have become well established in talking about railroad operations. Before going into the rest of the railroad organizational structure, it will be useful to look at just what these terms mean and also to get some feel for what are the large and small items in railroad income and outgo.

Fig. 18-2 shows where the railroad operating dollar comes from and where it goes, summing up *all* Class I freight railroads in the U.S. as reported to the ICC for 1980, a year of moderate recession at the start of the "deregulation era". Since the 60 companies included range in health from vigorous to bankrupt, items relating to profitability for any particular railroad may vary greatly from (and generally will be somewhat better than indicated by) these industry-wide totals. Major items of income and expense, however, will not be too far from these percentages.

Leverage

A large portion of railroad expenses, such as interest on long-term borrowed money, office expenses and real estate taxes, don't vary with the amount of business being done. Therefore, the level of traffic has a great "leverage" on the net profits of the railroad. Fairly small seasonal or

206

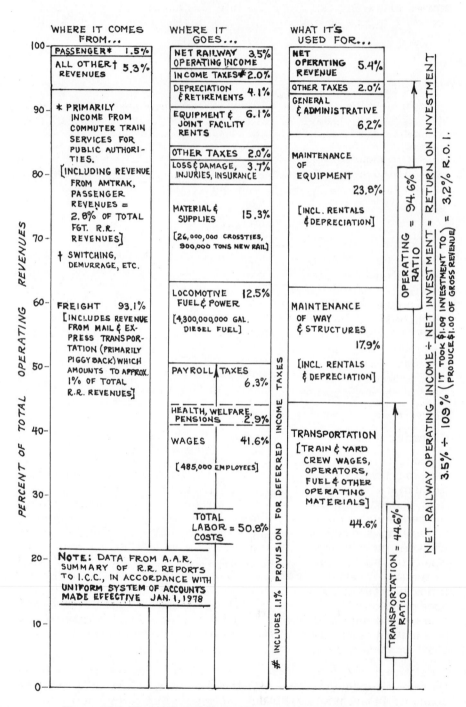

Figure 18-2 The Railroad Dollar (U.S. Class I Freight R.R.'s)

business-cycle changes tend to cause much bigger changes in its earnings. Also, operating revenues have been greatly affected by rate increases following years when the rate of inflation has been high. It is necessary to look at longer-term trends to get a good feel for the situation.

Operating Revenues

As Fig. 18-2 shows, the vast bulk of railroad revenues comes from hauling freight. This has always been true for North American railroads, even in the days before the automobile and improved highway.

As some measure of the size of the industry, operating revenues in 1980 amounted to approximately $27,500,000,000. Note that all items in Figs. 18-2 and 18-3 are in percentages of the total operating revenues.

Who Gets the Money

As the second column of Fig. 18-2 shows, railroading is a labor-intensive business, about half of its revenue going directly into wages and fringe benefits. The major recent change in distribution of expenses is the further doubling of the percentage of revenues going into fuel costs which occurred between 1975 and 1980, following the first big "oil shock" increases of 1974 — fuel costs in 1970 were only 3.5% of revenues. Items such as taxes, loss and damage, depreciation and fixed charges are now small relative to fuel costs though still large in comparison with net income. Some of these will be discussed further in connection with the parts of the organization that have to deal with them.

Operating Ratio

The third column of Fig. 18-2 shows what the operating revenues were used to accomplish: maintenance, transportation, overhead, etc. A traditional overall measure of a railroad's performance has been the *operating ratio*, defined as the proportion of the revenues received which is required to operate and maintain the railroad. The definition of the *net operating revenue* upon which it is based was changed considerably under the U.S.O.A. rules by including in expenses several additional items, principally taxes (other than income taxes) and net equipment and joint facility rentals. It is therefore meaningless to compare pre-1978 operating ratios directly with current figures — a railroad which was able to bring a good profit down to the "bottom line" of *net ordinary income* in previous years would have to achieve an operating ratio no higher than the low 80's in most cases; under U.S.O.A. rules, an equally health railroad may show an operating ratio as much as ten points higher.

Relative differences in operating ratios from railroad to railroad or for the same company from year to year under the same rules tell a good deal about its financial situation, but analysts trying to fully appreciate a road's prospects must also look at some additional factors.

Deferred Maintenance

The nature of railroad track is such that it can go for quite some period of time without major repairs or much apparent deterioration. Thus, should management want to present a favorable-looking operating ratio, it can make major cuts in the maintenance-of-way account. In periods of reduced traffic, of course, the track is receiving less wear, and some reduction in maintenance expense would not result in a net decline in track condition. Beyond this point the track is accumulating "deferred maintenance." To look for this, rail and crosstie replacement figures may be studied and compared to past years.

To some extent, the same is true for maintenance of equipment, though this will usually show up in the "bad order ratio", the percentage of cars and locomotives in unserviceable condition. A conscientious management, of course, wants to have a good estimate of any deferred maintenance it may be incurring, but changes in technology make this somewhat difficult at best; a good estimate of the life of improved rail or of a new type of crosstie may not be available until a dozen years after installations in quantity may have begun. Since the ICC has, in some cases, required that the proceeds from rate increases be used only to reduce deferred maintenance, whether and to what extent it exists has become a lively topic, and one of great importance to the railroad's financial planners.

Transportation Ratio

The costs of making up and moving trains over the roadway, excluding maintenance, determine the "transportation ratio," typically somewhat less than 40 percent for a reasonably healthy railroad. Improved equipment and operating practices will tend to bring this ratio down. The extent to which the ratio fluctuates with changes in traffic level may well be more a matter of the railroad's traffic mix than of management efficiency. If most of the line's business is in mineral traffic which can be handled satisfactorily by running proportionally fewer trains of the same length, the ratio may go down with reduced traffic because the latest, most efficient equipment can do the whole job. On the other hand, if most of the traffic is time-sensitive freight handled in trains which must run on schedule, reduced business will rapidly raise the ratio.

Net Railway Operating Income (NROI)

This figure, which has not changed much under U.S.O.A. rules, represents the money available from the operation of a railroad *after* income taxes, paid or deferred by investment credits and accelerated depreciation under IRS and tax regulations, but *before* paying the "fixed charge" interest on bonds or other money it has borrowed.

The NROI is available to pay interest to the bondholders who have loaned money to the railroad and to the stockholders who own it, so the ratio of NROI to the net investment in the railroad is the rate of return for the investors. The net investment in Class I railroads in the United States is about $30,000,000,000. The return on investment in recent years for the railroads as a whole has never approached the 5.75%

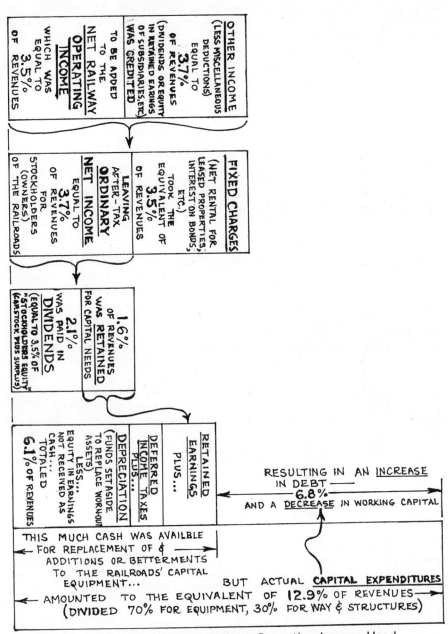

OTHER INCOME
(LESS MISCELLANEOUS DEDUCTIONS)
EQUAL TO
3.7%
OF REVENUES
(DIVIDENDS OR EQUITY IN RETAINED EARNINGS OF SUBSIDIARIES, ETC.)
WAS CREDITED

TO BE ADDED TO THE
NET RAILWAY OPERATING INCOME
WHICH WAS EQUAL TO
3.5%
OF REVENUES

FIXED CHARGES
(NET RENTAL FOR LEASED PROPERTIES, INTEREST ON BONDS, ETC.)
TOOK THE EQUIVALENT OF
3.5%
OF REVENUES

LEAVING AFTER-TAX
ORDINARY NET INCOME
EQUAL TO
3.7%
OF REVENUES
FOR STOCKHOLDERS (OWNERS) OF THE RAILROADS

1.6%
OF REVENUES WAS **RETAINED** FOR CAPITAL NEEDS

2.1%
WAS PAID IN
DIVIDENDS
(EQUAL TO 3.5% OF "STOCKHOLDERS EQUITY" (CAP. STOCK PLUS SURPLUS))

RETAINED EARNINGS PLUS...
DEFERRED INCOME TAXES PLUS...
DEPRECIATION
(FUNDS SET ASIDE TO REPLACE WORN-OUT ASSETS)
LESS...
EQUITY IN EARNINGS NOT RECEIVED AS CASH...
TOTALED
6.1% OF REVENUES

RESULTING IN AN <u>INCREASE</u> IN DEBT——
6.8%
AND A <u>DECREASE</u> IN WORKING CAPITAL

THIS MUCH CASH WAS AVAILBLE
← FOR REPLACEMENT OF & →
ADDITIONS OR BETTERMENTS
TO THE RAILROADS' CAPITAL
EQUIPMENT...
BUT ACTUAL **CAPITAL EXPENDITURES**
← AMOUNTED TO THE EQUIVALENT OF **12.9%** OF REVENUES →
(DIVIDED 70% FOR EQUIPMENT, 30% FOR WAY & STRUCTURES)

Figure 18-3 How Was Net Railway Operating Income Used

established by the ICC (in 1920) as a "fair rate of return" and is even farther below the 8 to 12% return allowed most public utilities by regulatory authorities. The return has been higher than the average for the Southern and Western Districts, and negative for the Eastern District.

Distribution of Net Income

Fig. 18-3 shows what became of the NROI. Other income (interest and dividends on investments, earnings of subsidiaries, and the like) added to the NROI, less various minor miscellaneous cost items, resulted in a total income of over 7 percent of gross revenues. "Fixed charges" represent primarily the share of the railroad's earnings which must go to pay interest on its borrowings to arrive at the ordinary net income available to the owners of the business.

About two-thirds of the ordinary net income was paid in cash dividends. However, since about one third of railroad stock is owned (with the consent of the ICC) by other railroads, quite a bit of this apparent return to the owners is actually an internal transaction, which has already showed up in the "other income" item. Since the rate of return on railroad investments is not usually enough to attract new investors, the other third of the net income was plowed back into the business as retained earnings. Here it was joined by the depreciation and retirement cash set aside from revenues (at rates prescribed by the ICC) to replace the property as it wears out. As is the case in most industries in recent years, rapidly rising prices for all such items meant that to acquire enough equipment to handle the traffic (which in general has been increasing) took an additional amount equivalent to 6.8 percent of revenues beyond that available. This money, about $1,900,000,000 had to be borrowed, which explains: how the net investment in railroads is increasing despite the poor rate of return; why much equipment is leased; and why a great deal of importance is attached to improving car utilization, so that more traffic can be handled without further increasing the investment.

Equipment Trusts

The relatively unattractive rate of return in recent years has meant that most improvements in the physical plant, such as the new multi-million dollar "electronic" classification yards, are paid for out of retained earnings from current operations. Since rolling stock can be "repossessed" and re-sold if necessary, money is more readily available to help pay for cars and locomotives. In the most common arrangement, called the "Philadelphia Plan," equipment trust notes covering about 80 percent of the cost of specific equipment are issued by a financial institution, with the railroad making a down payment of 20 percent. The notes are paid off in installments by the railroad, with the bank retaining title to the rolling stock until the last notes are retired, usually in 15 years.

Leveraged Leases

Railroads need so much capital investment to continue operations that even relatively prosperous companies may not have enough net income to obtain full tax benefits from credits for investing in all the equipment they must have. Therefore it may be less costly to lease rolling stock from an investor who can realize major savings from the depreciation write-off and tax credit from buying and owning rolling stock applied against taxes on his other income and can therefore afford to rent the equipment to the railroad at a rate in effect sharing these benefits. Such leases are secured only by the underlying value of the equipment and involve risk to the owner should business conditions result in a surplus of the particular type of equipment. Lease terms vary widely, with some including eventual railroad purchase/ownership of the equipment as an option.

Depending upon terms of these long-term leases, value of the equipment may have to be shown as part of the railroad's capital account in accordance with accounting principles.

What's "Addition or Betterment?"

When parts of the track or some cars are repaired, the cost is a business expense which reduces net income for the year, and therefore, no income taxes are involved. In theory, a car wears out at the rate for which "depreciation" is allowed by the ICC and could be replaced at the end of its life for the original cost. The money which had been set aside (tax-free) in the depreciation account during the car's lifetime would purchase another. The railroad would be right back where it started, with a new car and no money in the depreciation account.

But what's a repaired car and what's a new car? A car that is in need of major repairs, may be rebuilt into something bigger, better and suitable for some entirely different lading that has become important in the railroad's traffic mix during the car's lifetime. If it is determined to be a repair and replacement-in-kind job, it is done with tax-free money. If it is a retirement of one car and purchase of a new one, the increase in value is made with "retained income" money (on which income tax has been paid) or by borrowing money to be paid back over a period of years, with interest. Since the income tax rate for large corporations can be as much as 50% or more, a good part of the net income of the railroad can rest on these rules and decisions. The car body may be virtually replaced at one time and the trucks and couplers at another, resulting in a car that is nominally 50 or more years old but which actually contains no parts that are anywhere near that ancient.

In maintenance of way, the rules can be fairly clear: when 90 lb. rail is replaced with 132 lb., 42/132 of the rail is an "addition and betterment," while the replacement steel for the first 90 pounds per yard is chargeable as an expense. The cost of boring a tunnel or building an embankment to efficiently run the trains through the mountains has been a tough question for the tax accountants and lawyers -- do such things depreciate? Since it's literally nothing, the hole through the hill will never "wear out." But it must be expected that with the passage of time, it may become less useful as traffic patterns and the relative power, weight and cost of trains change. The hole will be as good as ever, but in the wrong place or, perhaps, not quite big enough.

Deferred Taxes

Several tax decisions in recent years on such subjects as tunnel and grading cost depreciation and temporary or regular changes in the tax laws intended to encourage industrial investment in production facilities and produce jobs have had the effect of allowing companies to set aside money for depreciation at a faster-than-normal rate and thus pay less income tax during the early years of the life of the facilities. Since you only can depreciate anything once, depreciation in later years will be less,and the taxes then will be higher. Initially, however, money representing deferred taxes is available (Fig. 18-3) to help meet the railroad's capital requirements. U.S.O.A. requirements include provisions to bring this aspect of railroad financial reporting in line with generally accepted accounting principles.

19

ADMINISTRATION, LAW, ACCOUNTING

The many corporate functions not directly involved in attracting and handling traffic or operating and maintaining the railroad may be arranged in as many different ways as there are railroads. In the example of Fig. 18-1, they are grouped into two major departments called *Administration* and *Law and Finance*, each headed by an executive or senior vice president. Many of the matters under the various titles within these areas are reasonably self-explanatory and what would be expected in any organization of this size, with appropriate adjustments for railroads' singular characteristics. Some offices are found only on a railroad and are worth some discussion.

Management Information Services (MIS)

Digital computers which can talk to each other over long-distance wire or microwave links have been as important to the railroads as to any other industry. So many different parts of the railroad organization (operations, sales, accounting, purchasing and materials management, personnel) use the computers that it is now usual to have a special group responsible for developing, maintaining and operating an integrated central system and the computer programs used to receive, process and display the data for all. If the railroad does not have its own computer facility, leased or owned, it will still need people who can handle the company's input/output data exchange with the UMLER and TRAIN II systems of the AAR Car Service Division.

Labor Relations

While the railroad industry is not a closed shop, its operations in almost all aspects are governed by contracts with a relatively large number of separate unions, often referred to as "The Brotherhoods," representing both railroad-only occupations (such as train and yard service or car maintenance) and general trades. While the railroad managements are represented in industry-wide bargaining by the National Railway Labor Conference Organization, local agreements govern actual operations on each railroad.

Personnel Administration

The personnel department of a railroad, similar to that found in general industry, makes sure that the company has complied with all applicable laws, regulations and interpretations of the FSLC, EEO, IRS, NLRB and not a few other agencies plus their counterparts in the various states where the railroad has employees. In addition, railroad operations are subject to the Federal Hours of Service Law which provides extremely severe penalties for allowing any employee concerned with train operation from being on duty more than 12 hours at a stretch.

Training program coordination is of increasing importance with the continual rise in the complexity of technology, both railroad and non-railroad, which employees must be able to handle. Most railroaders will continue to learn the critical aspects of their work on the job, but many skills are being developed through more formal training programs and facilities.

Purchasing and Materials Management

"Purchases and Stores," as it is known on many roads, is often set up as a separate department, though on the smaller railroads it may be located within the operating department. It is responsible for spending almost one quarter of all the railroad's revenue.

Inventory carrying costs are now so high and the volume and variety of materials and supplies used so great that a railroad's net income can practically be consumed if the purchasing organization consistently buys items too far in advance of need or in quantity not closely related to need.

Running out of critical items can be even more serious, and buying competitively and in quantity can also lead to major savings, so the purchasing organization has the clear-cut job of handling its affairs so that its "customers" throughout the railroad have confidence in its responsiveness and reliability. Otherwise, every operating group will squirrel away material in a thousand scattered hideaways, and the road may be buying items it already has in surplus. Most purchasing and materials management departments are computerized to some degree, but the storekeeper out in the field is still very much a key person.

Public Relations

Beyond its specific assignments of handling the railroad's advertising, generating press releases and publishing whatever newsletter or employee's magazine management authorizes, "PR" has the job of keeping the company's image as positive as possible throughout its territory. PR is truly everybody's business, and an undamaged shipment delivered on time every time counts more than a catchy slogan. There is no way the public relations staff can offset the effects of a sloppy railroad with disgruntled employees. What it can do is help keep the record straight with timely, correct, well-phrased information about the capabilities and accomplishments of a good railroad and help the president or the chairman of the board make each employee a plus rather than a minus in establishing the railroad's identity in all the many communities through which it passes.

Law and Public Affairs

As public utilities regulated by federal, state and local authorities, railroads are in need of legal counsel to a degree beyond that typical of most businesses of the same size. The impact of changes in laws and court rulings on the railroad is such that many lines, including our example, find it worthwhile to have officers of high rank located at key points in the various areas served whose main duties are concerned with such "public affairs" matters.

Accounting

The various money matters handled by the office of the comptroller or accountant on a railroad include those such as billing the customer and paying the company's bills, plus the extra complexities of auditing inputs from dozens or hundreds of agents, conductors or collectors and keeping track of the charges and revenues resulting from the wanderings of all those freight cars. There are also certain ICC rules, dating from the days when preventing illegal rebates to favored shippers was its principal concern, prohibiting handling freight charges on a credit basis; these must be observed.

Traffic

The direct interface with the railroad's customers is the Traffic Department, the agents who quote rates, receive and receipt shipments, make out shipping papers, notify consignees their goods are in, and (on occasion) try to find out why the goods haven't arrived. Using the more modern and general terminology for such functions, our example railroad has a Marketing and Planning Department, which includes two functions (corporate development and real estate) often located in the law or administration areas of the corporate structure.

Corporate Development

On a small railroad, the chairman of the board or the president may be the only person specifically planning ahead in terms of the direction the company should follow in enhancing its future. It helps to have everyone in the organization working today to make tomorrow better, but studying the company's choices is a top management function. In this structure, since the main opportunities are in developing new transportation needs which the railroad can profitably meet, a corporate planning staff is located in the marketing/planning area.

Real Estate and Insurance

All railroads own at least one long, narrow piece of real estate, the right of way. Additionally, most companies have adjacent land which they own which is zoned for industrial or commercial use and can be used to help induce important shippers and receivers of freight to locate where the railroad can readily serve them. Thus, real estate management, contracts, insurance and related functions find a logical home in the department charged with developing the market for freight service.

The *industrial development* organization's success in convincing companies planning new or expanded plants that the best location is at some available site along the railroad (or accessible to its piggyback service) will have a lot to do with what the company's income looks like years from now. A good "plant hunter" makes it his business to know more about plant sites, zoning laws, water supply, labor availability, tax rates and possible new-business concessions than anyone else in the area, as well as respecting the confidential nature of such inquiries.

The *insurance* organization of the railroad is concerned with providing appropriate protection against major loss. In general, a railroad's property is so spread out or relatively indestructible that all but the most major catastrophes are more economically handled by relying upon self-insurance rather than by taking out insurance. The insurance manager's job is to study these trade-offs. On a smaller line, particularly with respect to public liability, the answer may be considerably different.

Markets Management and Development

In this organization, the development of particular types of business, including some that may not exist at present (for example, the hauling of compacted trash collected in a city to a distant disposal site) is promoted by offices attached directly to the chief of marketing and planning.

In a railroad tradition, this line continues to foster the development of agriculture and forestry practices suitable for its territory through its agri-business agents; many important products which are quite literally "growth industries" can be traced back to improved species, fertilizers and crop-management schemes pioneered by such experts.

The *services industries* office works on a long-term basis to develop auxiliary services, such as warehousing, which the railroad can provide as add-ons to its basic transportation to: increase its overall profitability; attract more business; or create a function that makes money itself.

Marketing -- Longer-Range Sales

In accordance with most present-day terminology, the longer-range aspects of getting the freight onto the trains are the responsibility of the "marketing" organization. The job of making up a package of rates and service, often including innovations in loading, unloading or railroading technology, which will capture, increase or retain traffic has several essential parts.

Cost and Price Analysis will consider the price the railroad must charge to be better off handling the traffic than not; it must cover the out-of-pocket costs and make some contribution toward the overhead costs of the railroad. It will also calculate how much the transportation is worth to the customer, taking into account his costs and alternatives, such as decentralizing his plants so that less transportation is required, or shipping via the competition.

Market Research generates information on the amount of prospective traffic. In general, goods aren't produced just because a wonderfully low freight rate may become available but rather because somebody has a use for the item, though a favorable transportation situation may make a new producing area become competitive.

Customer Service Engineering develops concepts for hardware which will cut costs, reduce damage or otherwise significantly improve the total process of getting the goods from where they are to where they're needed.

Rates, Routes and Divisions considers: the various routes over which the traffic can be moved; the rates which can be established legally, considering their relationships to others in effect; and the division of the revenue between the carriers involved.

All of this must be done in collaboration with the operating department, of course, before the *Commerce* organization can put together a marketing program that goes after the business. A major change in the rate structure may keep the law and public affairs people busy for a long time overcoming tariff suspensions, rate appeals and other roadblocks. Aggressive, imaginative and precise work in marketing is the key to railroad prosperity, though, so there is nothing else to do but keep after the matter.

Economic Forecasting

To handle the business, the railroad still has to have the cars, locomotives and track capacity. If new or different traffic is forecast, there may be lead time of anywhere from six months to two years or more for ordering new equipment. As much as anything, the general level of business activity at this future date will determine whether or not the railroad should commit its capital funds to be in position to make money later. The railroad thus finds it advisable to have an economist on its staff to provide as informed a basis as possible for making the necessary preparations.

Sales -- The NOW of Marketing

The direct contact with the customer occurs mostly through the sales organization. Headed up by regional sales manager, agency sales offices are located in all the major shipping and receiving localities on the railroad. The outposts of the system are the *off-line agencies* -- in 25 cities in 12 states in the case of the E-W -- soliciting and making arrangements for interline traffic. Since over 75 percent of all railroad freight shipments travel over more than one line, such agencies are maintained by most roads, and several have agencies in foreign countries as far off as Japan.

Much of the push for marketing actions originates from the sales organization, which also has the job of making sure that customers are made aware of what a new rate, schedule or service can mean in terms of their traffic.

Since familiarity with the customer's particular product, processes and needs is often the key to effective sales and marketing, individual sales agents will specialize in one or more commodity groups. On some railroads, the entire traffic organization is set up on this basis, with its major groupings by coal, merchandise, forest products, grain or other traffic elements. Railroad expenses charged to "traffic" as a whole amount to less than two percent of revenues, but it's a vital function if there is to be enough for the operating department to haul to keep the railroad in the black.

20

OPERATIONS

About 85 of every 100 railroaders work in the Operations Department. Fig. 20-1 is a typical organization chart for this department of a large railroad, condensed by leaving out many important staff and support positions attached to officials at various levels and by listing only examples of the many employee classifications at the working level throughout the department. On a smaller railroad -- say one with 300 to 2,000 miles of track, grossing up to $100,000,000 a year and with perhaps 3,000 employees -- some consolidation of positions and simplification might occur.

Operations is headed up by a vice-president or senior vice-president, to whom report the vice-president (or general manager) in charge of transportation and the vice-president of engineering (or chief engineering officer) in charge of the maintenance-of-way and mechanical (motive power and car) organizations. Two other organizations are usually supervised directly by the head of the Operations Department; since the safety and freight claims group and the railroad security force are concerned with both train operations and maintenance and facilities, they logically report to the person in charge of all the railroad's facilities and their use.

Safety and Freight Claims

These two elements are often placed in one organization because technology, training and discipline to minimize personal injury and equipment damage also contribute toward reducing damaged shipments. Pilferage and vandalism, increasingly serious causes of freight claims, come under the jurisdiction of the railroad police force which also comes directly under the chief of operations.

Railroad Safety and Accident Reporting

Over a period of time, railroad travel remains the safest mode, but the hazard potential of train and railroad maintenance operations must be respected. Since 1910, railroads have been required to report, under oath, all collisions, derailments, and accidents resulting in a personal casualty or in damage to equipment or track exceeding a specified dollar amount. Results reported only by totals can be quite confusing, so Fig. 20-2 elaborates a bit on the principal sources and classifications of all accidents and casualties connected in any way with railroads. Figures are

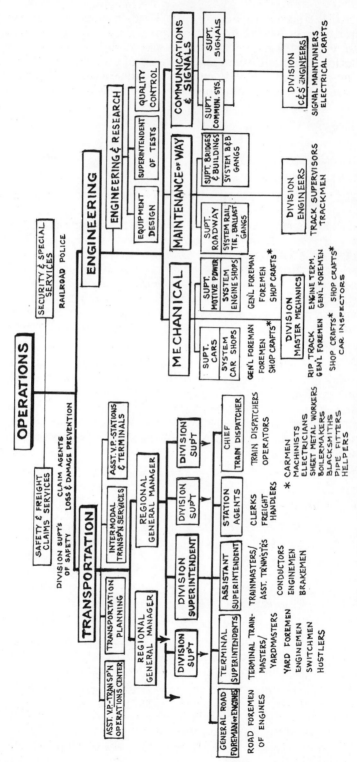

Figure 20-1 Condensed Organization Chart — Operating Department

from the FRA annual report for 1979. While the number of casualties in the rarer categories, such as passenger deaths, will vary greatly from year to year, the larger categories show rather stable trends. The distribution of casualties among the types of accident and the categories of persons involved is steady enough to indicate the main problem areas and where safety program efforts are most needed.

Train Accidents/Incidents

Major changes in railroad accident and casualty reporting took place in 1975 and in 1979, primarily to bring the reporting of injuries into agreement with that for other industries, data for which are collected by the Occupational Safety and Health Administration (OSHA). This makes comparisons between current figures and those for prior periods difficult or impossible; in general, with all injuries requiring medical attention counted as casualties, rather than those involving lost work days, the total number of "incidents" *appears* to have more than trebled although railroad fatality and major injury rates have generally decined. Illnesses considered related to conditions in the workplace are also now included in the statistics.

Nomenclature has also changed significantly: the current distinction between train wrecks — involving significant damage to railroad rolling stock and track — and such casualty-producing eventualities as unanticipated severe slack run-ins or highway grade-crossing accidents not resulting in a derailment is between *train accidents* and *train incidents*. The threshold dollar damage, starting in 1981, is adjusted annually to reflect inflation and thus maintain some degree of comparability over longer periods of time. For 1979, it was $2900.

Train accident reportable damage is limited to that to railroad property — equipment and track — and thus is only a portion of the total cost, which of course includes loss and damage to lading, liability claims, disruption of operations and cost of clearing wrecks. Even so, the direct damage of $314 million in 1980 is sufficient to justify the emphasis on safety throughout the railroad organization. During the 1970's, a steadily increasing proportion and number of train accidents were associated with track defects; this trend appears to have been reversed toward the end of the decade as track design and maintenance/rehabilitation have begun to catch up with the suddenly increased stresses associated with the widespread introduction of the 100-ton capacity freight car.

Train incidents not involving major damage to railroad equipment account for over 85 percent of all fatalities associated with railroad operations. Half of all deaths occur from highway grade crossing accidents while an additional 35 percent involve trespassers on railroad property. Installations of gates, flashers and other safety improvements at grade crossings, along with the joint railroad/public authority educational program "Operation Lifesaver" in states where it has been established have resulted in a reduction of more than one third in fatalities nationwide over the last decade.

TRAIN ACCIDENTS / CAUSE & TYPE

CAUSE / TYPE	OPERATING PRACTICES	EQUIPMENT FAILURE	TRACK DEFECTS	OTHER	TOTAL NO. TRAIN ACCIDENTS	TOTAL DAMAGE TO R.R. PROPERTY
COLLISIONS	1163	82	74	106	1425	$42 M
DERAILMENTS	1332	1542	3946	662	7482	$254M
OTHER	165	191	30	199	585	$10 M
HIGHWAY GRADE XING	–	–	–	248	248	$8 M
TOTAL NUMBER TR. ACCIDENTS	2660	1815	4050	1215	9740	→
TOTAL DAMAGE TO R.R. PROP.	$80M	$77M	$111M	$46M		$314M

CASUALTIES

	EMPLOYEES ON DUTY		PASSENGERS		NON-TRESPASSERS		TRESPASSERS		TOTAL	
	K	I	K	I	K	I	K	I	K	I
TRAIN ACCIDENTS (DAMAGE TO R.R. EQUIPMENT/TRACK ABOVE THRESHOLD — $2900 IN 1979)	15	265	–	351	–	8	–	–	15	642
	7	366	–	50	–	3	–	1	8	433
	–	36	–	1	–	2	–	–	–	39
	8	74	–	–	61	96	8	9	77	179
TOTAL, ACCIDENTS	30	741	–	402	61	109	9	13	100	1275
TRAIN INCIDENTS										
GETTING ON/OFF TRAINS	6	2694	4	31	1	11	11	77	22	2815
FLYING/FALLING OBJECTS	–	1540	–	24	–	11	–	6	–	1581
OPERATING LOCOMOTIVES	–	882	–	–	–	1	–	–	–	883
STRUCK/RUN OVER	12	149	–	–	48	202	382	395	442	751
COUPLING INCIDENTS	3	692	–	–	–	–	–	–	3	692
HIGHWAY GRADE XING	1	90	–	2	662	3555	83	196	746	3843
ALL OTHERS	19	4504	1	251	4	44	8	33	32	4832
TOTAL, TR. INCIDENTS	41	10551	5	308	715	3824	484	707	1245	15414
NONTRAIN INCIDENTS										
MAINT. WAY & STRUCTURES	6	18870	–	–	2	48	–	–	8	19028
MAINT./SERV. EQUIPMENT	8	16916	–	–	1	17	–	–	9	17055
STUMBLING/FALLING	3	4984	1	105	2	245	5	20	11	5755
GETTING ON/OFF EQUIPMENT		2462	–	132	1	19	–	7	–	2648
OPERATING SWITCHES		2481	–	–	–	–	–	–	–	2485
ALL OTHERS, MISC.	13	9918	–	54	24	261	18	58	56	10466
TOTAL, NONTRAIN	30	55632	1	291	29	591	23	85	84	57437
TOTAL CASUALTIES	101	66924	6	1001	805	4524	516	805	1429	74126

EMPLOYEE FATALITY & INJURY/ILLNESS RATES

	FATALITIES PER 10,000 EMPLOYEES	INJ./ILL. PER 100 EMPLOYEES
RAILROAD:		
EXECUTIVES, OFFL'S.	–	0.9
PROF., CLERICAL, GEN'L	–	2.4
MAINT. WAY & STRUCT.	–	20.4
MAINT EQUIP. & STORES	–	15.6
TRANSPT., NON-TRAIN	–	4.8
TRAIN & ENGINE SERV.	–	13.3
RAILROAD, TOTAL	1.9	12.0
TRUCKING, W'HOUSING	N.A.	15.7
WATER TRANSPORT'N	N.A.	13.9
TRANSPORT'N BY AIR	N.A.	13.4
CONSTRUCTION	3.1	16.0
ALL MANUFACTURING	0.6	12.8
ALL PRIVATE-SECTOR EMPLOYMENT	0.86	9.2

1979 DATA; RAILROAD - FRA; OTHER INDUSTRIES - OSHA.

Figure 20-2 Annual Accident Summary — All U.S. Railroads

Nontrain Incidents

The innumerable combinations of function, location, occupation, equipment and time associated with personal-injury accidents are reported and cross-indexed by the FRA with a detail probably exceeded only by the compilation of statistics for professional sports. Fig. 20-2 includes totals for a few of the largest classes of incidents; the importance to railroaders of learning the right way to get on and off trains is evident.

Under a recent reporting rules change, casualties from getting on or off, striking or otherwise being injured in connection with operating or maintaining railroad rolling stock are classified as train incidents *only if the equipment is moving at the time*; otherwise, they show up in the "nontrain incident" category. Nontrain incidents, which account for more than 80 percent of all employee injuries, are essentially similar to those resulting from the hazards to which workers in any heavy industry are exposed. Railroad industry fatality and injury rates (for all classifications of reportable accidents) for employees in the principal categories are given in Fig. 20-2, along with comparable rates for related industries and the U.S. workforce in other major sectors where available. The complexity, mass and energy of railroad hardware will always require great respect, but the long tradition of "Safety First" has made the railroad a reasonably safe place to work.

Freight Claims

The ratio of loss and damage (L & D) claims to freight revenue bounces around in the range between 1.2 and 1.6 percent, which puts it in the hundreds of millions of dollars a year range. Individual roads and the Freight Claim and Damage Prevention Division of the AAR endeavor to pinpoint the places where prevention efforts, including new packaging and load-securing car designs and intensified training efforts on the part of railroad and shipper personnel, will pay off. On any particular commodity, cooperative work on the part of equipment suppliers, railroad damage prevention and operating people and the industry involved have been able to reduce L & D, whether the principal problem is primarily impact, environmental control, handling, vandalism, pilferage or some peculiar combination not immediately apparrent.

Complicating the campaign to continue reducing L & D payout by fixing specific problems is the diverse nature of the beast — over half the damage in recent years is in the "All damage not otherwise provided for" category. Other major line items: include train accident (about 25 percent of total L & D and also equal to about 25 percent of the direct damage to track and equipment from those same accidents), and robbery, theft and pillage (8 percent).

21

TRANSPORTATION

Somewhat over half of the railroad's employees are in the transportation segment of the operation organization, which, to put it as simply as possible, runs the trains. To keep the operation manageable, a railroad of more than a few hundred miles will be organized into a number of segments, traditionally known as divisions. Since the traditional day's work for road train crews was 100 miles or ten hours in freight service or 150 miles in passenger service, a railroad's main line was likely to have its division point yards at about these intervals, unless there was some reason (an established city or a marked change in the terrain, as in going from prairie to mountain country) to dictate otherwise. With faster trains, better communications and less short-haul business, most railroads have combined these segments into longer divisions, which may include 500 miles of line or more. Within these divisions, lines will be divided into sub-divisions or districts for operating purposes. Large railroads, those with several thousand miles of line or more, may group their divisions into regions or areas. On the other hand, if a railroad has several main lines coming together in one city, it may set up all its tracks and yards in the area as a terminal division, with only a few miles of line but hundreds of miles of track to manage.

Transportation Headquarters Organization

The Transportation headquarters organization will be staffed to take care of those system-wide functions which cannot logically be handled on a regional or division basis, such as through and interline train scheduling and system freight car distribution. In the example of Fig. 20-1, the Vice-President-Transportation has four staff offices. The Assistant Vice-President-Transportation is in charge of a "control center" located in the railroad's operating headquarters city from which, with the aid of several status displays, CTC panels, data read-outs and other modern pieces of management information gear, the trains of the system are controlled. With information as detailed as the temperature of each journal bearing on every train passing any one of more than 50 wayside hot-box detectors located at intervals on all the railroad's main lines, and a microwave/radio system which can communicate with each train, the minute-by-minute operation of the system is literally controlled from one point. This makes it possible to consider, almost instantly, what any person, office, locomotive, car, or piece of track on the system can do to correct any problem that threatens to disturb the scheduled operation or to provide quick response to any opportunity for improved service.

Transportation Planning looks ahead to work out the future schedules and operating practices that will most efficiently produce the system's basic product. Additionally, a special office has been established to coordinate intermodal (piggyback) service. Both of these offices are heavily involved in run-through services with connecting railroads. The Assistant-Vice-President-Stations and Terminals is a trouble-shooter, bringing a system-wide approach to improved ways of running these expensive parts of the railroad.

Similar positions at the transportation headquarters level are often set up to manage other operating areas of special importance to a particular railroad, passenger train service, unit train service, merchandise transportation, and so on.

The Division

In our example, the railroad is set up on what is sometimes known as the "departmental" form of organization. The officers of the mechanical, maintenance of way, and communications and signal organizations at the division level, the division master mechanic, division engineer and division C & S engineer, report to their respective organization heads at the system or regional headquarters. Some railroads are set up on the "divisional" basis, with these officers reporting to the division superintendent while carrying out the functions of their departments. In practice, of course, all the officers of the division must work closely together, and there is little essential difference in the way the work of the railroad gets done.

Division Transportation Functions

The division head, the superintendent, has five main transportation functions to supervise, reflected in those reporting to him:

Trainmasters, usually reporting to the assistant superintendent and responsible for specific districts within the division, determine (within the limits established by the system schedules) how the traffic is arranged in specific trains, scheduling and supervising the train crews to move them over the line.

Terminal Trainmasters, usually reporting to a terminal superintendent in the case of major terminals, supervise yardmasters, yard crews, switch tenders and hostlers in making up trains, getting locomotives to them, switching cars to local industries and moving road trains into and out of the terminal within yard limits.

Station Agents are responsible for the local agencies and their facilities at which business with customers is transacted, and for the supervison of the clerks, freight handlers, porters, and others on the railroad's property.

Chief Train Dispatchers are responsible for authorizing and directing all movements of trains over the railroad, through dispatchers transmitting instructions to train crews, via operators at stations, offices and interlocking towers and via the signal system within CTC territory.

Road Foremen of Engines supervise the operation of locomotives in moving the traffic of the division, instructing and qualifying enginemen and representing the mechanical department of the railroad in seeing that motive power is used efficiently.

Who's In Charge Here?

Perhaps the single most important fact affecting the railroad organization, particularly in the transportation department, is that *most of its employees must carry out their work away from their supervisor*; yet the railroad is a system whose parts must all work together in precise timing. This high level of individual responisbility has made railroading a proud profession, and it has also meant that the limits of individual initiative in carrying out duties must be established by written rules. In practice, rules are bound to conflict with each other and also to fall short of covering many situations. To keep reliance on rules alone from tying the railroad in knots, the operating department (the only one that runs trains) established a series of documents, in levels of increasing authority in case of conflict, with authority to deviate delegated to the level of supervisor issuing the document.

For train operation, a typical arrangement is illustrated in Fig. 21-1. Many railroad employees are responsible to different chains of command for various parts of their duties. The station agent is the person on the scene for the traffic or sales organization in his dealings with the customers, but usually reports to the division superintendent. To clarify the situation on the road, trainmen and most others report to the trainmaster; in the case of operators who actually give train orders to the conductor and engineer, a typical Rule 839 states:

> Operators report to the trainmaster and receive instructions from the chief train dispatcher. In matters pertaining to agency work they receive instructions from the agent.

Conductors

The conductor is in charge of the train, but the engineer runs it! Conductors' responsibilities are specified by rules such as:

> 886. The general direction and government of a train is vested in the conductor and all other persons employed on the train must obey his instructions except when such instructions imperil the safety of train or persons, or involve violations of rules... Should there be any doubt as to authority or safety of proceeding, from any cause, he must consult with the engineer and be equally responsible with him for the safety and proper handling of the train...

Engineers

Engineers report to and receive instructions from the trainmaster. Their responsibilities with respect to the machine they are running and in train operation are spelled out in rules 1000 and 1001:

> ...They must comply with instructions of the "road foreman of engines (known as the "transporation engineer" on some roads). In mechanical matters, they must comply with

DOCUMENT	EXAMPLES OF CONTENTS:	ADDRESSED TO/GOVERNS:	TYPICAL TIME SPAN:	ISSUED UNDER AUTHORITY OF:____ BY:____ VIA:
TRAIN ORDER	 "NO. 25 TAKE SIDING AND MEET EXTRA 3342 EAST AT G"	CONDUCTOR AND ENGINEER OF AFFECTED TRAINS	FROM ISSUE ("COMPLETE") UNTIL FULFILLED [MINUTES TO HOURS]	SUPERINTENDENT → CHIEF TRAIN DISPATCHER → OPERATORS
CAN SUPERSEDE:	SIGNAL INDICATION RIGHT BY CLASS OF TRAIN SCHEDULE			
BULLETIN ORDER	 TEMPORARY SLOW ORDER LOCATIONS SCHEDULE MODIFICATIONS	TRAIN SERVICE EMPLOYEES	FROM ISSUE UNTIL TERMINATION OR INCORPORATION IN TIMETABLE [DAYS-WEEKS]	SUPERINTENDENT → TRAINMASTERS
BULLETIN NOTICE	NOTICES TO EMPLOYEES	ALL DIVISION EMPLOYEES		
CAN SUPERSEDE:	SPECIAL INSTRUCTIONS SCHEDULES			
EMPLOYEES TIMETABLE	 SCHEDULES TIME & CLASS OF TRAINS SPECIAL INSTRUCTIONS SPEED RESTRICTIONS SPECIAL SIGNAL INDICATIONS DESIGNATION OF SUPERIOR DIRECTION	ALL DIVISION EMPLOYEES CONCERNED WITH TRAIN OPERATIONS	FROM EFFECTIVE DATE & TIME UNTIL NEXT TIMETABLE. [3 TO 6 MONTHS]	GENERAL MANAGER OF TRANSPORTATION → SUPERINTENDENT
CAN SUPERSEDE:	BOOK OF RULES			
BOOK OF RULES	 GENERAL RULES (A THRU X) CONDUCT OF EMPLOYEES OPERATING RULES (1 THRU 1100) TIMETABLE/TRAIN ORDER OPERATION STANDARD SIGNAL ASPECTS/ INDICATIONS HAND, WHISTLE SIGNALS DUTIES OF EMPLOYEES	ALL EMPLOYEES IN OPERATIONS DEPARTMENT	UNTIL MODIFIED [DECADES]	V-P OR GENERAL MGR IN CHARGE OF OPERATIONS

Figure 21-1 The Priority of Operating Documents

instructions of proper officers and supervisors of that department... They are under the direction of the conductor of the train with respect to its operation and must comply with his instructions, except when such instructions imperil the safety of train or themselves or involve violations of rules.

22

ENGINEERING AND EQUIPMENT

In our example, the Vice-President-Engineering has charge of organizations responsible for building and maintaining both the railroad's cars and locomotives and its track, roadway and structures. On many lines, these organizations (usually known as mechanical and engineering, respectively) report directly to the official in charge of operations. In either case, their task is to provide the rolling stock and right of way which transportation uses to haul the traffic.

In the organization shown in Fig. 20-1, the Vice-President-Engineering has three staff groups responsible, system-wide, for: engineering design of equipment to meet the railroad's requirements; planning and conducting tests of track and rolling stock in the field and in the railroad's research laboratory; and methods for quality control of materials and items used by the railroad.

Maintenance of Way (M/W) (Engineering)

The M/W organization responsibility is actually broader than indicated by its title, since it's in charge of both maintaining and building tracks, bridges, buildings and other structures.

When railroad construction began, there were only two types of engineering, military and civil, so the title "chief engineer" on the railroad continues to refer to the man in charge of its roadway and structures, while his counterpart in charge of the mechanical department is usually known as the "chief mechanical officer."

The M/W organization shown is typical of that which has evolved with the high degree of mechanization of most track work in recent years. Most rail laying, tie replacement and track surfacing operations are done by large gangs equipped with highly specialized equipment enabling one or, at the most, a few of them to take care of the entire system. These gangs, and the system M/W engineering and planning office (not shown) come under the Superintendent of Roadway, who also has a single shop maintaining all the track maintenance equipment for the system. A similar organization takes care of system bridge and building work.

Division Engineers

The M/W organization located at each division point is headed by the division engineer, with his staff to handle design and minor construction projects on the division. Track supervisors, or foremen, and their gangs, assigned segments of track, handle all maintenance not accomplished by the system gangs, and have the field responsibility for the quality and safety of the railroad's most basic item, its track.

Communications and Signals

Communication and signaling system responsibilities are usually combined organizationally, since both are primarily electronic and electrical. In our example, each area has a superintendent at the system level, sharing a common organization out in the field at the division level where signals, microwave terminals and relay stations, hump-yard car retarders, grade crossing gates and hot box detectors are installed, maintained and modified. Signalmen are responsible for the entire job of installation of these items, including a variety of both light and heavy work.

Mechanical Department (Motive Power and Cars)

Like the M/W organization, the mechanical department is responsible not only for the maintenance and servicing of the items under its care but also for selecting or designing and obtaining them. While diesel locomotives are basically designed by their manufacturers rather than by the railroad, there is still a strong "do it yourself" tradition and capability. The superintendent of cars and the superintendent of motive power typically have strong design and industrial engineering staffs to develop specifications for equipment and procedures for its servicing and maintenance (not shown on the chart).

In recent years the cost-saving from certain mechanized maintenance operations has tended to result in more centralized repair facilities, such as automated wheel shops capable of turning out all the freight car wheelsets needed on an entire railroad system or locomotive heavy-repair shops rebuilding all the engines of one manufacturer for the system on a production line-basis. These system shops come directly under the system superintendent's organization, though they may not all be located at the same terminal.

The heavy cranes and other equipment necessary to lift and position cars and locomotives for heavy repair work can do the same thing in a manufacturing operation. Therefore, some railroads, of all sizes, make use of their shops for car building programs (often using "kits" supplied by car builders) and major locomotive rebuilding and upgrading (modernizing) work. The organization for these shops, with general foremen and foremen of the various trades required, along with planning and quality control elements, is not unlike that in a production-line manufacturing business.

Division Master Mechanics

Heading up mechanical department organizations at the divisional level are the master mechanics. Each division will have several points at which the mechanical department will operate: maintenance, service and inspection facilities; "rip tracks" for running repairs to cars; heavy repair car shops; engine terminals, varying in capability from simple fueling and sanding to major repairs; and interchange points where cars received from connections are inspected.

The employees performing the maintenance and inspections tasks in these facilities include: carmen (specialists in a variety of inspection and maintenance operations peculiar to railroad cars); machinists and electricians concerned primarily with locomotive maintenance and check-out; members of the metal-working trades (sheet metal workers, boilermakers, blacksmiths and pipefitters) who can repair, rework or rebuild car, locomotive and shop structural and accessory parts; along with storekeepers, equipment operators and helpers to make up a team matching the job, which must be expected, particularly in isolated areas, to include the unexpected.

Task Forces

It is clear from the inter-related nature of the responsibilities of the organizational units discussed in these four chapters that the degree of success of the railroad in selling and producing transportation depends not only on how well organized, staffed, equipped and trained the individual segments are but even more on how effectively they work together. This shows up particularly if a railroad — whose operations are by nature day-by-day, repetitive and likely to get into a comfortable rut — is to enter a transportation market in which it has been inactive.

For example, suppose a railroad wishes to take advantage of partial rate deregulation to compete with agriculture-exempt trucking of produce by establishing guaranteed-schedule intermodal trains carrying traffic at rates varying with the "spot market" for such transportation — business which can only be profitable if pricing can quickly vary both down and up in accordance with the demand/supply situation and be backed up by efficient train operations and effective marketing filling up empties on the backhaul.

It is clear that almost every part of the organization, from motive power to law, will be involved. In such cases, a special organization is needed, whether it be called a "creativity team," a task force or some other term devised to stay away from the odious title of "committee." A good measure of the strength of the railroad's management is its ability to get it all together, on a temporary or continuing basis, and produce the results which can only come from the coordinated efforts of people with all the necessary experience and responsibility working as a team.

SUGGESTED READINGS

Accounting and Finance

Railway Accounting Rules. Mandatory and Recommendatory Interline Accounting Rules and Forms. January 1, 1974, edition. Accounting Division, Association of American Railroads. 364 pages. LC No. A36-407.

Railway Statistical Manual. Accounting Division, Association of American Railroads, 1970. 288 pages. LC No. A53-9998.

Recommended Railway Treasury Procedure Respecting Treasury Agency Relations. Treasury Division, Association of American Railroads, corrected to 1967. 157 pages.

Economics

American Railroads, by John F. Stover. University of Chicago Press, 1961. 302 pages. (In hard and paper editions) LC No. 61-8081.

American Railroads and the Transformation of the Ante-Bellum Economy, by Albert Fishlow. Harvard University Press, 1965. 452 pages. LC No. 65-22068.

Domestic Transportation: Practice, Theory and Policy, by Roy J. Sampson and Martin T. Farris. 2nd Edition. Houghton Mifflin, 1971. 493 pages. LC No. 71-141287.

The Economics of Competition in the Transportation Industries, by John R. Meyer, Merton J. Peck, John Stenason, and Charles Zwick. Harvard University Press, 1959. 359 pages.

Economics of Transportation, by D. Philip Locklin. 7th Edition. Richard D. Irwin, 1972. 925 pages. LC No. 76-187057.

Enterprise Denied: Origins of the Decline of American Railroads, 1897-1917, by Albro Martin. Columbia University Press, 1971. 402 pages. LC No. 71-159673.

Issues in Transportation Economics, by Karl M. Ruppenthal. Charles E. Merrill, 1964. 349 pages. LC No. 64-66237.

Modern Transportation Economics, by Hugh S. Norton. 2nd Edition. Charles E. Merrill, 1970. 463 pages.

National Transportation Policy, edited by Hugh S. Norton. McCutchan, 1969. 255 pages.

Railway Pricing and Commercial Freedom: The Canadian Experience, by T.D. Heaver and James C. Nelson. The Centre for Transportation Studies, The University of British Columbia.

Transportation Century, edited by George Fox Mott. Louisiana State University Press, 1966. 279 pages. LC No. 67-29273.

Transportation Economics, edited by National Bureau of Economic Research. Columbia University Press, 1965. 464 pages. LC No. 65-11221.

Transportation: Economics and Public Policy, by Dudley F. Pegrum. 3rd Edition. Richard D. Irwin, 1973. 612 pages. LC No. 72-90533.

Transportation Law, by John Guandolo. 4th Edition. Wm. C. Brown, 1973. 1184 pages.

Transportation Subsidies—Nature and Extent, edited by Karl M Ruppenthal. University of British Columbia, 1974. 125 pages. LC No. 73-93911.

Engineering and Maintenance

Car and Locomotive Cyclopedia—1980. Simmons-Boardman, 1980. 1047 pages. LC No. 76-2145.

Fundamentals of Transportation Engineering, by Robert G. Hennes and Martin I. Ekse. McGraw-Hill, 1955. 520 pages.

An Introduction to Transportation Engineering, by William W. Hay. John Wiley, 1961. 505 pages. LC No. 61-5671.

Track Cyclopedia—1978. Simmons-Boardman, 1978.

Transportation Engineering–Planning and Design, by Radnor J. Paquette, Norman Ashford, and Paul Wright. Ronald Press, 1972. 760 pages. LC No. 79-190209.

Geography

Geography of Transportation, by Edward J. Taaffe and Howard L. Gauthier, Jr. Prentice-Hall, 1973. 226 pages. LC No. 72-8995.

A Geography of Transportation and Business Logistics, by J. Edwin Becht. Wm. C. Brown, 1970. 118 pages. LC No. 70-11884.

Guide to Industrial Site Selection, by M.J. Newbourne and Colin Barrett. The Traffic Service Corp., 1971. 37 pages.

Labor Relations

Collective Bargaining and Technological Change in American Transportation, by Harold M. Levinson, Charles M. Rehmus, Joseph P. Goldberg and Mark L. Cahn. The Transportation Center at Northwestern University, 1971. 723 pages. LC No. 71-154981.

Labor in the Transportation Industries, by Robert Lieb. Praeger, 1974. 125 pages.

Technological Change and Labor in the Railroad Industry, by Fred Cottrell. D.C. Heath, 1970. 160 pages. LC No. 71-114364.

Logistics, Traffic or Distribution Management

Business Logistics--Appraisal and Prospects, edited by J. L. Heskett. Stanford Transportation Series, 1965. 146 pages. Available from The Transportation Management Program, University of British Columbia. LC No. 65-24649.

Business Logistics in American Industry, edited by Karl M. Ruppenthal and Henry A. McKinnell, Jr. Stanford Transportation Series, 1968. 403 pages. Available from The Transportation Management Program, University of British Columbia. LC No. 68-14352.

Business Logistics--Physical Distribution and Materials Management, by J. L. Heskett, Robert M. Ivie, and Nicholas A. Glaskowsky. 2nd Edition. Ronald Press, 1973. 789 pages. LC No. 73-78570.

Cargo Containers: Their Stowage, Handling and Movement, by Herman D. Tabak. Cornell Maritime Press, 1970. 386 pages. LC No. 78-100658.

Case Problems in Transportation Management, by George P. Baker and Gayton E. Germane. McGraw Hill, 1957. 540 pages. LC No. 56-13388.

Container Service of the Atlantic, by John R. Immer. 2nd Edition. Work Saving International, 1970. 396 pages. LC No. 69-20211.

Developments in Business Logistics, edited by Karl M. Ruppenthal. Stanford Transportation Series, 1964. 129 pages. Available from The Transportation Management Program, University of British Columbia. LC No. 64-24264.

Distribution and Transportation Handbook, by Harry J. Bruce. Cahners Books, 1971. 393 pages. LC No. 76-132669.

Elements of Business Logistics, by E. Grosvenor Plowman. Stanford Transportation Series, 1964. 176 pages. Available from The Transportation Management Program, University of British Columbia. LC No. 63-16759.

The Essentials of Distribution Management, edited by Herschel Cutler. Distribution Economics Educators, 1971. 311 pages. Accompanying workbook, *Freight Classification, Rates and Tariffs.*

Freight Rate Retrieval and Freight Bill Payment, by Herbert S. Rush. The Traffic Service Corp., 1974. 88 pages.

Industrial Logistics--Analysis and Management of Physical Supply and Distribution Systems, by John F. Magee. McGraw-Hill, 1968. 353 pages. LC No. 67-23845.

Integral Train Systems, by John G. Kneiling. Kalmbach, 1969.

Logistics Management, by Grant M. Davis and Stephen W. Brown. D.C. Heath, 1974. 441 pages.

Management of Transportation Carriers, by Grant M. Davis, Martin T. Farris and Jack J. Holder. Praeger, 1975. 289 pages.

Management of Physical Distribution and Transportation, by Charles A. Taff. 5th Edition. Richard D. Irwin, 1972. 534 pages. LC No. 78-187060.

Model Legal Forms for Shippers, by Stanley Hoffman. Transport Law Research, Inc., 1970. 508 pages. Available from The Traffic Service Corp. LC No. 73-114997.

Modern Transportation: Selected Readings, by Martin T. Farris and Paul T. McElhiney. 2nd Edition. Houghton Mifflin, 1973. 466 pages. LC No. 72-6891.

New Dimensions in Business Logistics, edited by Karl M. Ruppenthal. Stanford Transportation Series, 1963. 173 pages. Available from The Transportation Management Program, University of British Columbia. LC No. 63-11549.

Physical Distribution Case Studies, by Jack W. Farrell. Cahners Books, 1973. 489 pages. LC No. 72-91987.

Physical Distribution Forum, edited by Jack W. Farrell, Lowell E. Perrine and Stephen Tinghitella. Cahners Books, 1973. 266 pages. LC No. 72-91981.

Physical Distribution Management, by Donald J. Bowersox, Edward W. Smykay and Bernard J. LaLonde. Macmillan, 1968. 469 pages. LC No. 68-15264.

Practical Handbook of Industrial Traffic Management, by Richard C. Colton and Edmund S. Ward. 5th Edition revised by Charles H. Wager. The Traffic Service Corp., 1973. 640 pages. LC No. 72-95464.

Principles of Logistics Management, by James A. Constantin. Prentice-Hall, 1966. 623 pages. LC No. 66-12570.

Railroad Management, by D. Daryl Wyckoff. D.C. Heath, 1976.

Readings in Physical Distribution, edited by Hale C. Bartlett. 3rd Edition. The Interstate Printers and Publishers, 1972. 576 pages. LC No. 72-075080.

Readings in Physical Distribution Management, by Donald J. Bowersox, Edward W. Smykay, and Bernard J. LaLonde. Macmillan, 1969. 376 pages.

Traffic Management, by Kenneth U. Flood. 3rd Edition. Wm. C. Brown, 1974. 505 pages.

Transportation and Traffic Management, by William J. Knorst and E. Albert Owens. College of Advanced Traffic, 1972-1973. 4 volumes.

Volume 1 - 13th Edition (1972)
Volume 2 - 10th Edition (1973)
Volume 3 - 8th Edition (1973)
Volume 4 - 10th Edition (1973)

Transportation-Logistics Dictionary, The Traffic Service Corp. 459 pages.

Transportation Mangement, by Henry B. Cooley. Cornell Maritime Press, 1946. 224 pages. LC No. 46-8300.

Rates and Regulation

Competition and Railroad Price Discrimination, by Jordan Jay Hillman. The Transportation Center at Northwestern University, 1968. 168 pages. LC No. 67-26548.

Criteria for Transport Pricing, edited by James R. Nelson. The American University, 1973. 320 pages. Available from Cornell Maritime Press. LC No. 73-4373.

The Dilemma of Freight Transport Regulation, by Ann F. Friedlaender. Brookings, 1969. 216 pages. LC No. 69-18820.

Economic Considerations in the Administration of The Interstate Commerce Act, by Marvin L. Fair. The American University, 1972. 182 pages. Available from Cornell Maritime Press.

The Economics of Loyalty-Incentive Rates in the Railroad Industry in the United States, by Robert F. Lundy. Bureau of Economic and Business Research, Washington State University, 1963. 144 pages. LC No. 63-63114.

Freight Transportation: A Study of Federal Intermodal Ownership Policy, by Robert C. Lieb. Praeger Publishers, 1972. 225 pages. LC No. 79-168341.

A Glossary of Traffic Terms and Abbreviations. 8th Edition. The Traffic Service Corp., 1972. 37 pages.

Miller's Law of Freight Loss and Damage Claims, by Richard R. Sigmon. 4th Edition. Wm. C. Brown, 1974. 425 pages.

New Techniques in Railroad Ratemaking, by George E. McCallum. Bureau of Economic and Business Research, Washington State University, 1968. 148 pages.

Prinicples of Public Utility Rates, by James C. Bonbright. Columbia University Press, 1961. 512 pages. LC No. 61-6569.

Public Regulation of Business, by Dudley Pegrum. Revised Edition. Richard D. Irwin, 1965. 787 pages.

Railroad Revitalization and Regulatory Reform, ed. by Paul W. MacAvoy and John W. Snow. American Enterprise Institute for Public Policy Research.

Regulated Industries–Cases and Materials, by William K. Jones. Foundation Press, 1967. 1283 pages. Separate Statutory Supplement, 121 pages.

Tariff Guide No. 9, by E. Albert Owens. The Traffic Service Corp., 1973. 20 pages.

Transport Competition and Public Policy in Canada, by H.L. Purdy, University of British Columbia, 1972. 327 pages. LC No. 72-81827.

The Railroad Dictionary of Car and Locomotive Terms. Simmons-Boardman Publishing Corporation, 1980. 168 pages.

The Transportation Act of 1958: A Decade of Experience, by George W. Hilton. Indiana University Press, 1969. 272 pages. LC No. 78-85086.

Transportation Regulation, by Marvin L. Fair and John Guandolo. 7th Edition. Wm. C. Brown, 1972. 608 pages.

Statistics

Moody's Transportation Manual-Railroads, Airlines, Shipping, Traction, Bus and Truck Lines-American and Foreign, edited by Robert P. Hanson. Published annually by Moody's Investors Service.

Transport Statistics in the United States. Published annually by the Bureau of Accounts, U.S. Interstate Commerce Commission. U.S. Government Printing Office.

Urban Transit

Beyond the Automobile: Reshaping the Transportation Environment, by Tabor R. Stone. Prentice-Hall, Inc., 1971. 148 pages. LC No. 72-140266.

Readings in Urban Transportation, edited by George M. Smerk. Indiana University Press, 1968. 348 pages. LC No. 68-14613.

The Urban Transportation Problem, by J.R. Meyer, J.F. Kain, and M. Wohl. Harvard University Press, 1966. 427 pages. (In hard and paper editions) LC No. 65-13848.

Supplementary References

The Future of American Transportation, edited by Ernest W. Williams, Jr. Prentice-Hall, Inc., 1971. 211 pages. LC No. 72-160529.

The Life and Decline of the American Railroad, by John F. Stover. Oxford University Press, 1970. 336 pages. LC No. 77-83054.

The Practice of (Transport) Law, by Colin Barrett. The Traffic Service Corp., 1971. 51 pages.

Research in Transportation: Legal/Legislative and Economic Sources and Procedures, by Kenneth U. Flood. Gale Research, 1970. 126 pages. LC No. 72-118792.

Transportation: Management, Economics, Policy, by John L. Hazard. Cornell Maritime Press, 1977. 608 pages.

Transportation: Principles and Perspectives, by Stanley J. Hille and Richard F. Poist. Interstate Printers and Publishers, 1974. 561 pages. LC No. 73-93578.

Transportation Research Forum Papers, published annually by The Transportation Research Forum.

Periodicals

Canadian Guide. Published monthly by International Railway Publishing Company. Limited. A complete shippers' guide and gazetteer for Canada. Canadian railway timetables are included.

Canadian Transportation and Distribution Management. Published monthly by Southam Business Publications, Ltd. Carries articles, statistics, and news stories on Canadian railway, highway, air and marine trasportation.

International Railway Journal. Published monthly by Simmons-Boardman Publishing Corporation. Subscription rates on request (Subscription Dept., P.O. Box 530, Bristol, Conn. 06010). Reports the latest developments and practices the world over. Articles are in English with resumes in French, German and Spanish.

The Official Intermodal Equipment Register. Published quarterly by National Railway Publication Company. Contains information on dimensions and capacities tariff for containers, trailers and chassis in intermodal use by U.S. and foreign companies. Lists ramp locations and port facilities and names of officials concerned with reports and payments.

The Official Railway Equipment Register. Published quarterly by National Railway Publication Company. Contains information on dimensions and capacities tariff for freight cars. Describes by reporting marks and series numbers of freight cars operated by railroads and private car companies of North America. Includes interchange points for railroads and home points for private car owners, with instructions regarding payments, movements and repairs. (LC A19-162)

The Official Railway Guide, Freight Service Edition. Published bimonthly by National Railway Publishing Company. Contains names and addresses of railroads operating freight service in North and Central America. Includes rail freight schedules, mileages, connections and other facilities of North American railroads, as well as system maps and personnel listings. Station index for 50,000 points, with line and schedule cross references.

The Official Railway Guide, Passenger Travel Edition. Published monthly, except February and August, by National Railway Publication Company. Complete Amtrak and other timetables for U.S., Canada and Mexico, with fares, equipment, ticket offices and station index cross references. Also, connecting bus and ferry, short-haul and commuter service tables.

Passenger Train Journal. Published monthly by PTJ Publishing, Inc. Contains news and features on Amtrak, Auto-Train and other intercity passenger operators, as well as transit, commuter and tourist railways. Also, latest industry developments and pre-Amtrak memorabilia.

The Pocket List of Railroad Officials. Published quarterly by National Railway Publication Company. Contains the names, titles, addresses and phone numbers of 20,000 officials of railroads, truck affiliates, transit systems and associated industry and governmental bodies. Covers railroads in North, Central and South America, Australia, the Philippines and Japan. Carries advertising of 400 supply companies, whose products and sales representatives are listed. (LC 7-41-41367)

Railway Age. Published semi-monthly by Simmons-Boardman Publishing Corporation. Subscription rates on application. Circulates extensively among railway officers and others interested in railway affairs. Discusses current railway problems, progress and developments, and carries general news and statistics of the railway industry. (LC CA8-3111;CA19-395)

Railway Gazette International. Published monthly by IPC Transport Press Limited. A journal of management, engineering and operation containing railroad news from all over the world. Frequently includes electric and diesel traction supplements.

Railway Line Clearances. Published annually, with interim change circulars, by National Railway Publication Company. Presents weight limitations and vertical and horizontal clearances for more than 250 railroads of North America.

Railway Track and Structures. Published monthly by Simmons-Boardman Publishing Corporation. Subscription rates on application (Subscription Dept., P.O. Box 530, Bristol, Conn. 06010). Published for railway employees who build and maintain tracks, bridges, buildings and other parts of the railway plant. (LC 14-435;54-31791)

The Short Line. Published bi-monthly by G.M. McDonald, editor and publisher. A journal of short line and industrial railroading. Covers news, operations, and motive power rosters and acquisiions. Every other issue features a location survey for a particular state or metropolitan area.

Traffic World. Published weekly by the Traffic Service Corporation. Publishes news concerning U.S. Interstate Commerce Commission decisions and hearings, legislation affecting rates and railway service, rate revisions and other transportation developments of special interest to shippers and industrial, commercial and railway traffic officers. (LC 42-22198)

Our thanks to the Association of American Railroads for the assistance provided in compiling this list.

INDEX

W

Y